NTK Publishing Company Limited
5/F AIA Plaza
18 Hysan Avenue
Causeway Bay
Hong Kong, SAR
e-mail: enquiry@ntk.edu.hk
Tel: +852 25777844

First published in 2006

ISBN
998-98831-0-4
978-988-98831-0-2

Acknowledgments

The authors would like to pass on their appreciation to their colleagues in the NTK mathematics department: Mr. Elton Chau, Mr. Ebenezer Dotser, Mr. Joshua Ho, Mr. Alex Lai and Mr. Desmond Wong, who generously gave of their time and experience in helping develop the test questions and for their very useful and constructive feedback. Finally, they would like to thank Mr. T.K. Ng, director of NTK Learning Center, for the opportunity to develop this book and bring it to fruition.

The Authors:

Alex Cheng has both a BSc and MSc in mathematics. He has over eight years math teaching experience at all levels, with students drawn from a wide variety of different countries and math systems. His main hobbies are playing basketball and swimming.

David Ollerearnshaw has a BSc in mathematics and a MEd in mathematical education. He is Head of Mathematics at NTK Learning Center and has been teaching SAT math for over ten years. His greatest interest is in math (naturally!) but he is also a keen runner and amateur astronomer.

Kenneth Weiner has a BS in physics from the Massachusetts Institute of Technology. With over 10 years of test prep teaching experience throughout Asia in cities like Tokyo, Singapore, Hong Kong and Seoul, Kenneth is a test prep specialist. He is also a keen musician and has a Bachelor of Music from the Eastman School of Music in Rochester.

Foreword

As an educator, I have had the good fortune of working with a wide range of great young people from diverse backgrounds over the last twenty years. Experience shows that hard work and a good learning attitude are the keys to academic success, but good guidance and instruction also play a key role.

It is therefore with great excitement that I introduce our first of many study-aids for standardized examinations. As many students know, one of the first steps of ensuring your acceptance to a first-rate university is to do well on standardized exams. We've now condensed and summarized NTK's years of experience and expertise in an easy-to-use book format.

Combining the experience of our teachers who have taught SAT Math over the last decade, we have pooled their expertise and knowledge to bring you SAT Math Level 2. This book contains detailed advice and tips on how to approach the exam, as well as exercises and study-aids that have been uniquely formulated by actual SAT test-prep teachers who have first-hand knowledge of what it takes to succeed on the SAT Math Level 2 exam.

NTK Learning Center is proud to have helped thousands of students who have studied at our center over the years. NTK prides itself in being your choice when it comes to quality teaching in Math, Science, English, Modern Languages, and of course, Exam Preparation.

With the publication of SAT Math Level 2, we hope that this is another step in our never ending quest to provide quality education services for our students. I invite you to join us on this journey and continue our shared goal for excellence.

T. K. Ng
The Director
NTK Learning Center Limited

C
O
N
T
E
N
T
S

Algebra

Functions

Coordinate Geometry

Solid Geometry

Trigonometry

Probability & Statistics

Miscellaneous Topics

Introduction

Welcome to the **NTK SAT MATH LEVEL 2 book**! This book is designed to give you the boost you need to confidently take the SAT Math Level 2 test. Our book offers you:

What You Need to Know;

The essential math information you need to get a high score.

Examples;

To highlight ideas and techniques.

Example Questions;

So you can see how the concepts work with SAT Math Level 2 multiple-choice questions.

Practice Tests;

At the end of the day, it's about doing the math, right? We have 4 tests to let you practice your skills.

Answers and Solutions;

Each question on every one of our tests has a full explanation. More than that, we provide multiple solutions so you can see how to approach the same problems from different angles: using algebra, plugging-in or a graphing calculator.

Flash Cards;

To get a top score, you need to remember lots of formulas and techniques. We provide over 100 flashcards that enable you to brush up your knowledge anywhere, anytime.

The SAT Math Level 2 Test

What is it?

The SAT Math Level 2 test is produced by the College Board, a non-profit association of colleges in the US. If you want to go to a US tertiary institution for engineering, mathematics, science or economics, then a good SAT Math Level 2 score is a MUST. Even if you intend to focus on the humanities, a fair SAT Math Level 2 score shows that you have challenged yourself with material that may not be in your area of expertise – just the kind of thing college admissions officers are looking for.

SAT II Math IIC Test

The SAT Math Level 2 test used to be called the "SAT II Math IIC" test. The name changed but the test didn't!

Do I have to use a calculator in the test?

Yes! Not every question requires one, and sometimes using a calculator is not the fastest way to go, but you definitely need one available to do many of the calculations quickly and handle things like square roots and trigonometry. Also, it's preferable to use a graphing calculator; this can REALLY speed you up.

What kind of calculator can I use?

What with the zillions of different models about nowadays we obviously can't give a complete list of which are acceptable or not. Generally though, if you have a scientific calculator or a graphing calculator you'll be okay. But be aware, **certain general types of calculating devices are banned**!

These are definitely **not** okay for the Math subject tests:
Writing pads, pocket organizers, mobile phone calculator options, laptops, QWERTY keyboard calculators or stylus/pen input devices.

These are not allowed on the test, so if you were thinking of using one of these then don't. Get a scientific or graphing model.

What's the test format?

Very straightforward. You have **one hour** to complete a maximum of **50 questions**. Each question is **multiple-choice** with five possible answers (A) → (E). You complete an answer sheet by shading in the appropriate bubble. You do not get points for your actual work.

How's it scored?

Simple:

$+1$ for every **correct** answer

$-\dfrac{1}{4}$ for every **wrong** answer

0 for an **omitted** question.

The $-\dfrac{1}{4}$ is designed to remove the benefit of random guessing.

What's the grading?

This is a bit strange. The lowest score is about 300 (it varies). To score a 300 you have to get nearly everything wrong. It's just about impossible to do this badly, even if you guess on everything! The highest score is **800**, but 800 is not necessarily 100%. You can still get 800 even if you get several questions wrong and omit a few. The actual number of questions right, wrong or omitted to get 800 varies slightly from test to test.

What's a good score?

A "good score" depends on what you want to achieve at college. If you want to go to MIT for science or engineering, then anything less than 750 is going to be considered weak. If you are applying to a good liberal arts college, then 600 might be considered an excellent score. Generally though, 700 is considered above average. To get this, you need to get 35-36 correct and none wrong.

If you don't think you can make a score of 550 – even after practice – you should think about taking the SAT Math Level 1 test (the easier cousin of the SAT Math Level 2 test) and aim for a higher score.

When should I take it?

If you are following a US system, you should take it after you have completed (or nearly completed) a **Pre-calculus honors** course. If you are taking classes in a British System or IB system, then take it toward the end or after your **first year** of math A levels or Diploma course. Of course, you may be confident and good enough to take it earlier, but the average student is unlikely to have sufficient skills or knowledge to get a decent score.

Should I guess answers?

Even if you have *no idea* about the answer for a particular question, it's okay to guess; overall, you will not lose out. However, in many questions you may be able to eliminate one or more choices by using logical thinking and knowledge of the situation. In these cases it is definitely to your benefit to make an <u>educated</u> guess.

How to use this book?

Read through all of the chapters – even if you think of yourself as a math genius. If you are familiar with a particular topic, then a quick skim through that section should do. On the other hand, if something is unfamiliar (which is common for topics in the miscellaneous section for example), then you need to read the materials thoroughly and go over the examples and example questions in detail. Make sure you understand each topic completely before moving on to the next one.

Have a pen and paper handy. If you have just read about a formula that is new to you, write it down a couple of times. Write it down with different variables. DO something; don't just read. When you come to an example question, cover up the answer first and think about how *you* would solve it. Even if you can't get the answer, it is important to set your mind thinking the right way. Reading a mathematics book is not the same as reading a novel or magazine – you have to think HARD!

Do the sample tests. After studying all the chapters, go on to the sample tests. There is advice on how to take them on pages 207 – 209.

Check the detailed solutions for both the questions you got wrong or omitted and even those you got correct but guessed. Follow the steps in the solutions and be sure that you know exactly what is discussed. Go back to the corresponding chapter to review if you are still unsure about a concept or technique, (the chapter corresponding to each question is given in the solutions too.) For questions with multiple answer methods, choose the one you feel most comfortable with. There is no definite best method in mathematics. The "best" technique is the one that enables you to get the correct answer in the shortest time; nobody cares how you get it!

Keep a record of questions you get wrong. Are there any patterns? For example, do you keep getting function questions wrong or do you have problems remembering certain formulas? Find your particular weaknesses and revise those topics in which you often make mistakes.

Use the FLASH CARDS. At the back of the book are over 100 tear-out flash cards covering all the main concepts, formulas and techniques you need to succeed in the SAT Math Level 2 test. Read them whenever you have a spare moment: on the bus, during lunch or even between classes. Get into the habit of doing some cards everyday. This will help you to memorize all the stuff necessary.

Be consistent in your learning. It's a lot better to spend just 20 minutes everyday reading the book, starting well before the actual test, rather than trying to cram everything into your head the night before. Pace your learning and draw up a review plan. In this way, you'll be confident of success.

What can do I do for extra help?

Although some people find they can work things out on their own, many students want a little extra help to achieve their potential. At **NTK Learning Center Ltd.**, we have years of experience helping students with the SAT Math Level 2 and other tests. We offer **intensive review courses** covering all the material for the SAT Math Level 2 test in both small classes (maximum of 6 students) and individual lessons. NTK's experienced, full-time instructors have the expertise and resources to help you reach your goals in math, the sciences and the humanities. Contact us for further information on how we at NTK can help you (details on back cover).

Algebra

Not surprisingly, algebra figures prominently on the SAT Math Level 2 test. You need to know quite a lot of formulas and techniques if you want to get a high score. Even if you have no problem with basic algebra techniques, e.g. how to factor quadratics, there are several useful techniques and formulas that you should review.

Key Ideas

Difference of Two Squares

This is based on the following identity:

$$x^2 - y^2 = (x+y)(x-y)$$

This is almost <u>guaranteed</u> to come up somewhere on the test!

Example:

$$4p^2 - 9q^2 = (2p)^2 - (3q)^2 = (2p - 3q)(2p + 3q)$$

Example question:

$\dfrac{z^4 - 16}{z - 2}$, where $z \neq 2$, is equivalent to

$(z^2 + 4)(z^2 - 4)$

$\dfrac{(z+2)(z-2)(z^2+4)}{(z-2)}$

$(z+2)(z^2 + 4)$

A. $z^3 + 8$

B. $z^3 - 8$

C. $(z-1)(z^2 + z + 1)$

D. $(z-1)(z^2 + z - 1)$

E. $z^3 + 2z^2 + 4z + 8$

Solution:

We first write the numerator as $(z^2)^2 - 4^2 = (z^2 - 4)(z^2 + 4)$.

There's nothing we can do to $z^2 + 4$, but $z^2 - 4 = (z - 2)(z + 2)$.

So, $\dfrac{z^4 - 16}{z - 2} = \dfrac{(z - 2)(z + 2)(z^2 + 4)}{z - 2} = (z + 2)(z^2 + 4)$.

If you expand these parentheses out, this would have +8 as the constant term.

Now we look at the choices. Only choices A and E have a constant +8 in them,

and the correct answer is clearly not choice A. The answer is E.

Quadratic Equations and Parabolas

The shape of a quadratic graph $y = ax^2 + bx + c$ is called a **parabola**. Its lowest or highest

point is called the **vertex**. The vertical line through the vertex is the **axis of symmetry** or

simply the **axis**.

Recall that if $a > 0$ the curve bends up: and if $a < 0$ the curve bends down:

Finding the Vertex

For the graph of the quadratic function $f(x) = ax^2 + bx + c$, we have the following fact:

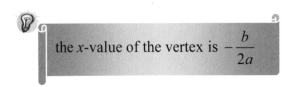

the x-value of the vertex is $-\dfrac{b}{2a}$

You can find the associated y-value by plugging this into the quadratic expression.

Example question:

What is the y-value of the vertex of the parabola given by the equation

$y = ax^2 + ax + 1$?

$$\frac{-a}{2(1)} \qquad -\frac{1}{2} = x$$

A. $\dfrac{4-a}{4}$

B. a

C. $2a$

D. $-\dfrac{a}{2}$

E. $\dfrac{a^2+a}{2}$

Solution:

The x-value of the vertex is given by $x = \text{"} - \dfrac{b}{2a} \text{"}$.

Here $b = a$, so $x = -\dfrac{a}{2a} = -\dfrac{1}{2}$. Now, plugging $x = -\dfrac{1}{2}$ into the given

equation gives $y = a\left(-\dfrac{1}{2}\right)^2 + a\left(-\dfrac{1}{2}\right) + 1 = -\dfrac{1}{4}a + 1 = \dfrac{4-a}{4}$.

The answer is A.

The Vertex Form of a Quadratic

If we complete the square of a quadratic function, we can read off its vertex immediately:

> If $y = a(x-h)^2 + k$, then the vertex of the parabola is the point (h, k).

Example:

By completing the square, $x^2 + 6x - 1 = (x+3)^2 - 10$.

This means that if we have a quadratic graph given by the equation

$y = x^2 + 6x - 1 = (x+3)^2 - 10$, then we can read off the vertex of

the parabola as $(-3, -10)$. Because the graph bends upwards, we

can sketch the graph like this:

Example question:

What is the vertex of the graph of the parabola $h = 4t^2 + 8kt + 2$, where k is a real number?

$$-\frac{b}{2a}$$

$$\frac{-8k}{2(4)} =$$

A. $(k, 2 - 4k^2)$

B. $(-k, 2 - 4k^2)$

C. $(4k, 2 + 4k^2)$

D. $(-4k, 8 - 16k^2)$

E. $(k, 8 - 16k^2)$

Solution:

We complete the square:

> When completing the square, look at the number in front of the square term. Factor this out of both the square and linear terms. (Leave the constant alone.)

$$4t^2 + 8kt + 2 = 4(t^2 + 2kt) + 2$$

$$= 4[(t+k)^2 - k^2] + 2$$

$$= 4(t+k)^2 - 4k^2 + 2$$

This is now in vertex form, so we recognize the x-coordinate (here the t-coordinate) as $-k$ and the y-coordinate (here the h-coordinate) as $-4k^2 + 2$. The answer is B.

Properties of Quadratic Roots

The roots (also called the zeros) of a quadratic equation have certain properties. You need to know about the <u>discriminant</u> and the <u>sum and product</u> of the roots.

The Discriminant

The **discriminant** of $ax^2 + bx + c$ is the number $b^2 - 4ac$.

This is a useful tool for deciding on the **types** of solution to the equation $ax^2 + bx + c = 0$.

$b^2 - 4ac < 0$

$\Rightarrow$ **no** real roots

$\Rightarrow$ curve does not cross the x-axis

$b^2 - 4ac = 0$

$\Rightarrow$ **one** real root

$\Rightarrow$ curve touches the x-axis

$b^2 - 4ac > 0$

$\Rightarrow$ **two** real roots

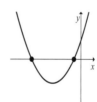

Example:

If $-3x^2 + x - 4 = 0$, then $b^2 - 4ac = (1^2) - 4(-3)(-4) = -47$. This is < 0 so <u>even without graphing</u> we know the curve $y = -3x^2 + x - 4$ <u>never</u> crosses the x-axis. In fact, because $a = -3$, we know the curve bends down. So this curve is **always below the x-axis**.

Example question:

Find the value(s) of p if the graph of $y = 2x^2 + px + 1$ is tangent to the x-axis.

$$-p \pm \sqrt{p^2 - 4(2)(1)}$$
$$p^2 - 8$$

A. $p > 0$

B. $-\sqrt{2} < p < 0$

C. $p = 1$

D. $p = \sqrt{8}$

E. $p = \pm 2\sqrt{2}$

Solution:

"Tangent to the x-axis" means the curve touches it, i.e. there is one real root, so we want $b^2 - 4ac$ to be **0**.

Therefore, $p^2 - 4(2)(1) = 0$

$$p^2 = 8$$

$$p = \pm\sqrt{8} \quad \text{(remember to take both square roots!)}$$

$$= \pm\sqrt{4 \times 2}$$

$$= \pm\sqrt{4} \times \sqrt{2}$$

$$= \pm 2\sqrt{2} \quad \Rightarrow \quad \text{The answer is E.}$$

Sums and Products of Roots

If you have a quadratic equation $ax^2 + bx + c = 0$, then there is an easy way to find the <u>sum</u> and <u>product</u> of the two roots **without solving the equation**! We use these two simple formulas:

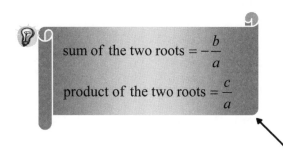

$$\text{sum of the two roots} = -\frac{b}{a}$$

$$\text{product of the two roots} = \frac{c}{a}$$

These formulas work even if the quadratic has complex roots. [See the Miscellaneous chapter for details on complex numbers.]

Example question:

If p is a prime number, and the product of the two roots of $2x^2 + 3x + p = 0$ is an integer, then p is equal to

$$\frac{p}{2} =$$

A.   1   not prime

B.   2

C.   3

D.   4   not prime

E.   5

Solution:

We are told the product of the roots, so we use the product of roots formula above:

$$\text{product of roots} = \frac{p}{2}$$

so $\qquad \dfrac{p}{2} = n \qquad$ (we are told that n is an integer)

$$p = 2n$$

This means p is an <u>even integer</u>; but p is also supposed to be <u>a prime</u>.

The only even prime is 2. The answer is B.

(Notice that we can eliminate choices A and D immediately because 1 and 4 are not primes. Remember that 1 is **not** a prime!)

Polynomials

A <u>polynomial</u> is a finite sum of positive integer powers of a variable, often x (we'll use x in most of our examples), with maybe a constant at the end of the expression. The **degree** is the highest power of x in the polynomial. The numbers in front of the various powers of x are the **coefficients**. The coefficient of the highest power of x is the **leading coefficient**.

Example:

$5x^6 + 3x^3 - 5x$, $x^3 + x^2 + 12x + 1$, $x - 5$ and $20x^2$ are all polynomials. Their degrees are 6, 3, 1 and 2, respectively. The coefficient of x in $5x^6 + 3x^3 - 5x$ is -5. The coefficient of x^2 in $5x^6 + 3x^3 - 5x$ is **0**. The leading coefficient of $x^3 + x^2 + 12x + 1$ is **1**.

Note that we usually write the powers of x in ascending or descending order, but that's just to make it easier to read and is not compulsory, so make sure you check out long polynomials carefully!

These are **not** polynomials: $\dfrac{1}{x}$, $x^2 + \sqrt{x}$ and $\sin x$.

Properties of Polynomials

Although the graphs of polynomials show a wide variety of shapes, they all share these common properties:

- Every polynomial is **continuous**: they have no gaps or holes.

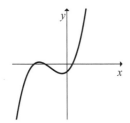

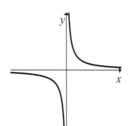

polynomial   not a polynomial

- They are **smooth** everywhere: polynomial graphs don't have sharp points or cusps.

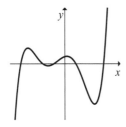

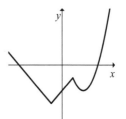

polynomial   not a polynomial

- A degree n polynomial has **at most n real roots**: it can cross the x-axis in at most n different places.

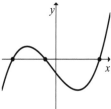

a degree 3 or greater ploynomial

- A degree n polynomial graph has **at most $(n-1)$ "bumps"** on it (technically called extrema).

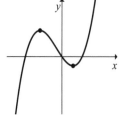

a degree 3 or greater ploynomial

Example:

A degree 5 polynomial could look like this:

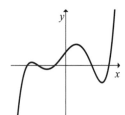   or this: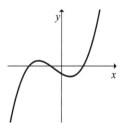

but <u>not</u> this:

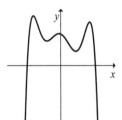

Example question:

If the polynomial $P(x)$ is of degree 3 and $Q(x)$ is a different polynomial of degree 3, then which of the following statements is/are true?

    I $P(x)Q(x)$ must be of degree 6

    II $P(x)+Q(x)$ must be of degree 3

    III $P(x)-Q(x)$ could be a constant

A.   I only

B.   III only

C.   I and II only

D.   I and III only

E.   I, II and III

Solution:

If you multiply $(ax^3+...)$ by $(bx^3+...)$, you'll <u>always</u> get something with an x^6 in it, so **statement I is true**. Statement II looks true, and certainly $P(x)+Q(x)$ is degree 3 <u>sometimes</u>; BUT $x^3+-x^3=0$, so **statement II is false**. Finally, we could use $x^3-(x^3+1)=-1$ to see that $P(x)-Q(x)$ could be a constant, so **statement III is true**. The answer is D.

End Behavior of Polynomials

Another property of all polynomials is that just by looking at the **degree** of the polynomial and the **sign of the leading coefficient**, we can tell in which quadrant the polynomial starts and finishes. Recall that the plane is divided into four <u>quadrants</u>:

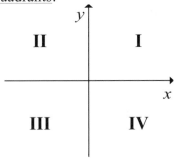

- **Even degree polynomials**

  Positive leading coefficient, graph looks like this:

  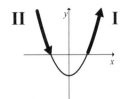

  Negative leading coefficient, graph looks like this:

  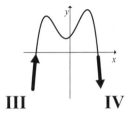

- **Odd degree polynomials**

  Positive leading coefficient, graph looks like this:

  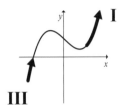

  Negative leading coefficient, graph looks like this:

  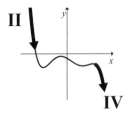

Although this is useful, remember, it only tells us where the polynomial graph will <u>eventually</u> go. It doesn't tell us what is happening in detail.

Example question:

Which of these graphs could be the graph of the equation $y = ax^5 + bx^3 + cx$, where $a \neq 0$?

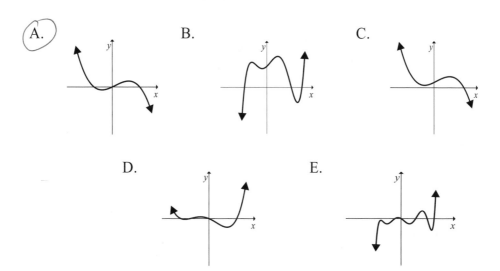

A.   B.   C.

D.   E.

Solution:

First, when $x = 0$, $y = 0$, so the graph must go through the origin; therefore, we can delete choices B and C. The original equation is degree 5, so it has at most four "bumps", so delete choice E. Finally, because it's an odd degree polynomial, it must start and finish in either quadrants III-I or IV-II. The answer has to be A.

The Remainder Theorem

If you divide one number by another, you get a quotient and remainder:

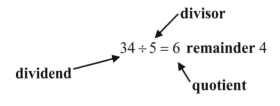

$$34 \div 5 = 6 \text{ remainder } 4$$

dividend, divisor, quotient

It's the same for polynomials: $(x^4 - 3x^2 + x) \div (x + 2) = (x^3 - 2x^2 + x - 1)$ remainder 2.

To find the **remainder** when you divide $P(x)$ by $(x - a)$, use the **remainder theorem**:

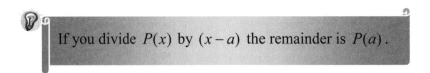

If you divide $P(x)$ by $(x - a)$ the remainder is $P(a)$.

The good news: this is FAST! Much better than long division.

The bad news: it won't give you the quotient. For that you need to divide.

Example:

If you divide $P(x) = 2x^4 - 3x^2 + x + 3$ by $x - 2$, you will get a remainder

of $P(2) = 2(2)^4 - 3(2)^2 + 2 + 3 = 25$.

Example question:

The polynomial $2x^3 - kx^2 + 1$ leaves a remainder of 2 when divided by $x + 1$. What is the value of k?

$x + 1 = 0$

$x = -1$

A. -3

B. -1

$-2 - k + 1$

C. 4

$-1 - k = 2$

D. 7

$\underline{+1} \qquad \underline{+1}$

E. 11

$-k = 3$

$k = -3$

Solution:

Just use the Remainder Theorem:

If we let $P(x) = 2x^3 - kx^2 + 1$

then, $P(-1) = 2(-1)^3 - k(-1)^2 + 1 = 2$

so, $-2 - k + 1 = 2$

$$k = -3 \quad \Rightarrow \quad \text{The answer is A.}$$

Example question:

When the polynomial $f(x) = x^n - a$ is divided by $x - 1$, the remainder is -26. In addition, $x - 3$ is a factor of $f(x)$. The value of n is equal to

A. -3

B.   3

C.   5

D.   6

E.   8

Handwritten:
$$X = 1$$
$$1^n - a = -26$$
$$a = 27$$
$$3^n - 27 = 0$$

Solution:

We can ignore choice A straight away because n has to be a <u>positive</u> integer (because $f(x)$ is a polynomial). Now let's use the remainder theorem:

$$f(1) = -26$$

$$1^n - a = -26$$

so $\qquad\qquad a = 27$

this means $\qquad f(x) = x^n - 27$

> If one number is a factor of another, that means the <u>remainder = 0</u>. It's the same for polynomials.

We now use the remainder theorem again to get

$$f(3) = 0 \quad \text{(remember: factor} \Rightarrow \text{remainder = 0)}$$

$$3^n - 27 = 0$$

$$3^n = 27$$

therefore, $\qquad n = 3 \Rightarrow$ The answer is B.

Logarithms

There are always several questions that test knowledge of logarithms, either directly or as part of another problem. There are <u>five key things</u> to remember about logarithms:

- You can only take the logarithm of a **positive number.**

- $\log_a(x) = k$ means <u>exactly</u> the same thing as $x = a^k$ where $a > 0$.

  For example, we can write $8 = 2^3$ as $\log_2(8) = 3$. They mean the same thing.

- **The 3 log laws**

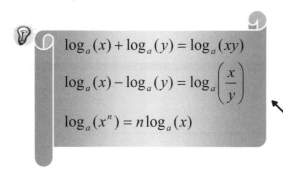

$$\log_a(x) + \log_a(y) = \log_a(xy)$$

$$\log_a(x) - \log_a(y) = \log_a\left(\frac{x}{y}\right)$$

$$\log_a(x^n) = n\log_a(x)$$

> Why the parentheses in $\log_a(x)$? Can't you just write $\log_a x$? The answer is, "Yes you can" as long as there's no confusion, e.g. you need them in $\log_a(x+1)$ because $\log_a(x+1)$ is <u>not the same</u> as $\log_a(x) + 1$.

- **Two important log values**

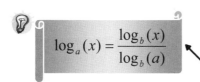

$$\log_a(a) = 1$$

$$\log_a(1) = 0$$

- **Change of base formula**

$$\log_a(x) = \frac{\log_b(x)}{\log_b(a)}$$

> In all cases here, a can be any real number as long as $a > 0$. But if $a = 10$, the convention is that we usually don't write it. So $\log_{10}(x) = \log(x)$. This means the change of base formula is:
> $$\log_a(x) = \frac{\log(x)}{\log(a)}.$$

Example:

To solve the equation $7(3.04^{2x}) = 10$, we *could* graph $y = 7(3.04^{2x})$ and $y = 10$ on a graphing calculator and find where they intersect. This is o.k., but it's a bit slow and every second counts in the SAT Math Level 2 test. Do it this way:

$$3.04^{2x} = \frac{10}{7}$$

Now take the log of both sides, we have $\quad 2x\log(3.04) = \log\left(\frac{10}{7}\right)$

$$x = \frac{\log\left(\frac{10}{7}\right)}{2\log(3.04)} = 0.160...$$

Example question:

If $\log_x(6) = x + 1$, what is the value of x?

A.   1.803

B.   1.837

C.   1.859

D.   1.861

E.   1.868

Solution:

The problem here is that we don't know what the base $(x+1)$ is; so **rewrite the equation** as an **exponential** equation: $6 = x^{x+1}$.

Now we have two ways to go: (1) plug in the answer values, or (2) graph $y = x^{x+1}$ and $y = 6$ and find where the graphs intersect:

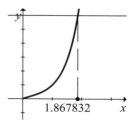

1.867832

The intersection x value is 1.867832, so the answer is E.

Example question:

If $\log_p(7) = r$ and $\log_p(q) = s$, what is $\log_q(49)$?

A. 7

B. $\dfrac{2r}{s}$

C. $2p$

D. $\dfrac{s}{r}$

E. rs

Solution:

We need to use the change of base formula:

$$\log_q(49) = \frac{\log_p(49)}{\log_p(q)}$$

$$= \frac{\log_p(7^2)}{s}$$

$$= \frac{2\log_p(7)}{s}$$

$$= \frac{2r}{s} \quad \Rightarrow \text{ The answer is B.}$$

Natural Logarithms

There are <u>two</u> logarithm keys on your calculator: "log" = $\log_{10}$ and "ln" = $\log_e$. "e" is a number that occurs often enough in math and science that it has its own symbol. Its value is 2.718 to 3 decimal places. The thing to remember is that if you see an exponential equation with "e" in it, it's faster to use the "ln" key.

Three Key Identities Using Natural Logs

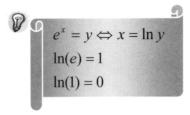

$$e^x = y \Leftrightarrow x = \ln y$$
$$\ln(e) = 1$$
$$\ln(1) = 0$$

Example:

To solve the equation $e^{2x} + e^x - 6 = 0$, we first factor:

$$(e^x - 2)(e^x + 3) = 0$$

so $\qquad e^x = 2$ or $e^x = -3$ (but it is rejected because you cannot take the log of a negative number)

$$x = \ln 2 = 0.693...$$

Radical Equations

Not every exponential equation is best solved by logarithms. If there is some <u>common base</u> to both sides, then it's often best to solve these equations as shown in the next example.

Example:

To solve the equation $\sqrt[3]{25} = 125^{x+1}$, we could graph it, but it's a bit faster if we use powers of five: $25 = 5^2$ and $125 = 5^3$ (so 5 is the <u>common base</u>).

The equation becomes $\qquad (5^2)^{\frac{1}{3}} = (5^3)^{x+1}$

so $\qquad\qquad 5^{\frac{2}{3}} = 5^{3x+3}$

Comparing powers, we have $\qquad \dfrac{2}{3} = 3x + 3$

so $\qquad\qquad\qquad x = -\dfrac{7}{9}$

"Funny Functions"

Sometimes a question will introduce you to a new operation and symbol that you've never seen before. It will give you the definition and you just work with that. Although they can look difficult, these questions are usually quite easy.

> **Example:**
>
> Suppose $\blacklozenge n \blacklozenge$ is defined on the positive integers by $\blacklozenge n \blacklozenge = 6n + n^2$. Then $\blacklozenge 5 \blacklozenge = 6(5) + 5^2 = 55$, $\blacklozenge 3 \blacklozenge = 6(3) + 3^2 = 27$ etc.

Example question:

An operation $\otimes$ is defined on number triplets as follows:

$(a, b, c) \otimes (x, y, z) = (ax, -by, cz)$

What is $[(1, 0, 2) \otimes (-1, 1, 2)] \otimes (2, 3, -1)$?

A. $(-2, 0, -4)$

B. $(2, -1, -4)$

C. $(0, 2, -1)$

D. $(0, 0, 0)$

E. $(1, -1, 1)$

Solution:

Just like "normal" algebra, we work out the square bracket first:

$$(1, 0, 2) \otimes (-1, 1, 2) = (-1, 0, 4)$$

$$[(1, 0, 2) \otimes (-1, 1, 2)] \otimes (2, 3, -1) = (-1, 0, 4) \otimes (2, 3, -1)$$

$$= (-2, 0, -4) \Rightarrow \text{The answer is A.}$$

Example question:

The symbol $\uparrow$ is defined on the set of all positive integers n as follows:

$n \uparrow$ = greatest odd factor of n

What is the smallest positive solution to the equation $(x^2) \uparrow = 11$?

A. 1

B. 3.317

C. 11

D. 121

E. There is no solution.

Solution:

Let's try to solve $(y) \uparrow = 11$ first. This says "the greatest odd factor of y is 11".

So we can see that $y = 11, 22, 44, 88, \ldots$ (Note that 33 is missing because the greatest odd factor of 33 is 33 itself.)

But we need to have $x^2 = y$, so the smallest solution is $x^2 = 11$. Therefore $x = 3.317$ (the question asks for the positive solution). The answer is B. (Notice that even though $x = 3.317$ is not a positive whole number, this doesn't matter as x^2 is.)

Absolute Value

The absolute value of a number is just the number "made positive", so $|6| = 6$, $|-7| = 7$, $|0| = 0$.

[Note: Students from a British system background often call this the "modulus" of a number. US schools and colleges don't use this term; they always use "absolute value".]

> **Useful Tip:**
> $|x|^2 = x^2 = |x^2|$ and $|x| = |-x|$

These are pretty obvious if you just try them with some numbers, but they are still very handy in simplifying questions.

Example:

To solve the inequality $|x|^2 - 2x < 0$, just rewrite it as $x^2 - 2x < 0$ and then factor: $x(x-2) < 0$. Using the technique for solving quadratic inequalities, we see that the solution is $0 < x < 2$.

Example question:

The symbol $\wedge$ is defined on pairs of real numbers by $x \wedge y = |x^2 - y^2|$. Which of the following statements is/are true?

I $x \wedge y = y \wedge x$ ✓

II $0 \wedge y = y^2$ ✓

III $x \wedge -y = x \wedge y$

A.   I only

B.   II only

C.   I and III only

D.   II and III only

E.   I, II and III

Solution:

This question uses a "funny function" along with the absolute value sign. First,

$x^2 - y^2 = -(y^2 - x^2)$, so $|x^2 - y^2| = |-(y^2 - x^2)| = |y^2 - x^2|$. So **statement**

I is true. Also, $0 \wedge y = |0 - y^2| = y^2$, so **statement II is true.** What about

statement III? Be careful with the "−" sign:

$x \wedge -y = |x^2 - (-y)^2| = |x^2 - y^2| = x \wedge y$. So **statement III is also true.**

The answer is E.

Direct Variation (or Proportion)

If we have two quantities which are always in the same ratio, we say they are **varying**

directly or they are **in direct proportion**. We often use the letter *k* to represent the **constant**

of proportionality.

Example:

If y varies directly as x, then $y = kx$. If y is directly proportional to x^2, then

$y = kx^2$. If h varies directly as $\sqrt{t}$, then $h = k\sqrt{t}$.

Example question:

The amount, M, in gallons, of water in a tank is directly proportional to $t^{\frac{2}{3}}$, where t is the time in seconds that the valve has been open. After 20 seconds there are 6 gallons of water in the tank. How many seconds will it take for the tank to fill with 20 gallons of water (to the nearest second)?

A.   33

B.   35

C.   122

D.   127

E.   203

Solution:

The question tells us that M is directly proportional to $t^{\frac{2}{3}}$, so we write this as $M = kt^{\frac{2}{3}}$, where k is the constant of proportionality.

To find out the value of k, we plug in the information given:

when $t = 20$, $M = 6$,

we get
$$6 = k(20^{\frac{2}{3}})$$

solution gives
$$k = 0.8143$$

Our equation is now
$$M = 0.8143t^{\frac{2}{3}}$$

To find the answer to the question, we now substitute $M = 20$ and solve

for t:

$$20 = 0.8143t^{\frac{2}{3}}$$

$$\frac{20}{0.8143} = t^{\frac{2}{3}}$$

$$\left(\frac{20}{0.8143}\right)^{\frac{3}{2}} = t$$

$$t = 121.7... \Rightarrow \text{ The answer is C. } $$

Indirect Variation (or Inverse Proportion)

Don't let the title put you off, this is quite a straightforward idea. If we have two quantities whose product is always the same, we say they are **varying indirectly** or they are in **indirect proportion**. We can also say they are **inversely proportional**. Just like the direct case outlined above, we often use the letter k to represent the **constant of proportionality**.

Example:

If y varies indirectly as x, then $y = \dfrac{k}{x}$. If y is indirectly proportional to x^2,

then $y = \dfrac{k}{x^2}$. If h varies indirectly as $\sqrt{t}$, then $h = \dfrac{k}{\sqrt{t}}$.

As before, just plug in the numbers they give you to find k then take it from there.

Example question:

p varies inversely as q^2, and when $q = 2$, $p = p_0$. What is the value of p when $q = 8$?

A. $\dfrac{p_0}{64}$

B. $\dfrac{p_0}{16}$

C. $4p_0$

D. $8p_0$

E. $16p_0$

Solution:

If p varies inversely as q^2, then we can write $p = \dfrac{k}{q^2}$, by using the definition of inverse variation.

We are also told that when $q = 2$, $p = p_0$, so we have $p_0 = \dfrac{k}{4} \Rightarrow k = 4p_0$.

We substitute $4p_0$ for k and the equation linking p and q becomes $p = \dfrac{4p_0}{q^2}$.

Finally, substitute $q = 8$ into this equation to get the answer we need:

$p = \dfrac{4p_0}{64} = \dfrac{p_0}{16} \Rightarrow$ The answer is B.

Factorials

Factorials make frequent appearances on the SAT Math Level 2 test, so it's worthwhile to know about them.

The symbol for factorial is "!" and it works like this:

$5! = 5 \times 4 \times 3 \times 2 \times 1$

$8! = 8 \times 7 \times 6 \times 5 \times 4 \times 3 \times 2 \times 1$

$2! = 2 \times 1$

Get the idea? It's an easy concept; just multiply all the positive whole numbers together less than or equal to the given number. In general,

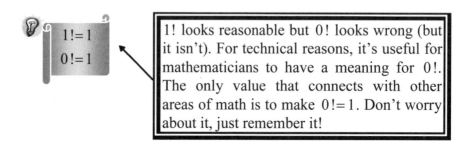

$$n! = n \times (n-1) \times (n-2) \times \ldots\ldots \times 3 \times 2 \times 1$$

There are two special ones to remember:

$1! = 1$
$0! = 1$

1! looks reasonable but $0!$ looks wrong (but it isn't). For technical reasons, it's useful for mathematicians to have a meaning for $0!$. The only value that connects with other areas of math is to make $0! = 1$. Don't worry about it, just remember it!

Note: There will be a "!" key on your calculator. Find out where it is now.

Example:

$$\frac{6!}{4!} = \frac{6 \times 5 \times 4 \times 3 \times 2 \times 1}{4 \times 3 \times 2 \times 1} = 30 \text{ and } \frac{100!}{99!} = 100.$$

Notice how in both examples many of the terms cancelled off. This is a very useful strategy to adopt with factorial questions.

Example question:

If p is an integer and $p > 2$, what is $\dfrac{(p!)^2}{((p-2)!)^2}$?

A. $p^2 - 2p$

B. p^2

C. $p^2 - p$

D. $p^4 + 2p^2$

E. $p^4 - 2p^3 + p^2$

Solution:

First, write out the first few terms of the numerator and denominator to see what's happening:

$$\frac{(p!)^2}{((p-2)!)^2} = \frac{(p \times (p-1) \times (p-2) \times (p-3) \times \ldots \times 3 \times 2 \times 1)^2}{((p-2) \times (p-3) \times \ldots \times 3 \times 2 \times 1)^2}$$

Everything down from (and including) $p-2$ is going to cancel out,

so we get $\dfrac{(p!)^2}{((p-2)!)^2} = \dfrac{(p \times (p-1))^2}{1} = (p^2 - p)^2$.

We don't see this in the answer choices directly, so we'll try multiplying out the parentheses:

$$\dfrac{(p!)^2}{((p-2)!)^2} = (p^2 - p)(p^2 - p) = p^4 - 2p^3 + p^2 \quad \Rightarrow \quad \text{The answer is E.}$$

Functions

Functions are extremely important on the SAT Math Level 2 test. About 25% of the test is based on this topic alone, so it's vital to learn this material well if you want a decent score.

Key Ideas

Vertical Line Test

Not every graph represents a function. To test <u>visually</u> if a graph represents a function, we use the <u>vertical line test</u> (VLT):

Pass a vertical line from left to right over the graph of $f(x)$. If the line intersects the curve in <u>two or more places at the same time</u>, then $f(x)$ is NOT a function.

Example:

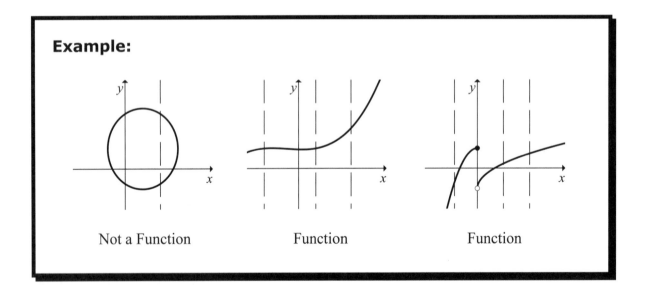

| Not a Function | Function | Function |

Function Domains

> The **domain** of a function is the set of *x*-values that we use as inputs.

Unless you are told otherwise, <u>we make the domain include every *x*-value possible.</u>

Example:

The domain of $f(x) = \dfrac{x}{x+3}$ is $x \neq -3$. You can NEVER divide by 0, so we have to remove –3 from the domain. Besides –3, any other real number will work in the formula and so would be in the domain of $f(x)$.

Example:

The domain of $g(t) = \sqrt{t}$ is $t \geq 0$. You can't take the square root of a negative number and get a real answer. (The answer is complex and ALL functions have real-value domains on the SAT Math Level 2 test unless a question says otherwise, which is very rare.)

Example question:

What is the domain of the function $f(t) = \log(t - 4)$?

A. All real t

B. $t < 4$

C. $t \leq 4$

D. $t > 4$

E. $t \geq 4$

Solution:

To answer this question you need to remember that <u>you cannot take the log of a negative number or zero</u>. This means $(t - 4)$ MUST be positive. Looking at the choices we see the answer is D.

Function Ranges

> The **range** of a function is the set of output values that the function takes as we input values from the domain.

If we are using the usual x and y variables, the range is the set of y-values for a given domain of x-values.

Finding ranges is often best done with the aid of a diagram, either by making a sketch or using a graphing calculator.

Example:

If we take the domain of $g(t) = t^2$ to be the largest possible, i.e. t is any real number, then the graph of $g(t)$ is:

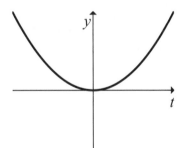

We see that the y-values of the output can be any positive real number or zero; hence, the range is $y \geq 0$.

Example question:

What is the range of the function $y = \dfrac{1}{x^2 - 1}$ where $|x| < 1$?

A. $y > 0$

B. $y \neq \pm 1$

C. $y \leq -1$ or $y > 0$

D. $y \neq 0$

E. $y \leq -1$

Solution:

The first thing to take care of is the domain: it's $|x| < 1$, so $-1 < x < 1$.

We now draw the graph between these x limits:

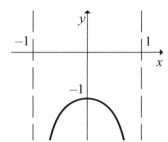

> Even though the function "works" for x-values outside -1 to 1, a function does not exist outside its domain, so we ignore anything outside in this question.

Because the curve is symmetrical about the y-axis, we see that the maximum must occur when $x = 0$ and that the corresponding y-value is -1. (You could also use a graphing calculator to find the maximum.) Because the function can also take any negative value *less* than its maximum, we see the answer is E.

Inverse Functions

If $f(x)$ is a function, then the **inverse** is written as $f^{-1}(x)$. There are <u>four key ideas</u> you need to know to confidently answer inverse function questions.

Be careful! $f^{-1}(x)$ is the <u>inverse</u> of $f(x)$. It does NOT mean the <u>reciprocal</u>: $\dfrac{1}{f(x)}$; you would write this as $[f(x)]^{-1}$.

1. Geometrical Inverses

To get the graph of inverse of a function, just REFLECT the graph of $f(x)$ in the line $\underline{y=x}$.

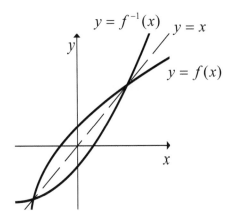

2. Algebraic Inverses

Swap the x's and y's. Make y the subject. That's the inverse function $f^{-1}(x)$.

Example:

Suppose $f(x) = \dfrac{\sqrt{x-5}}{4}$

First let $f(x) = y = \dfrac{\sqrt{x-5}}{4}$

Swap $x \leftrightarrow y$: $x = \dfrac{\sqrt{y-5}}{4}$

Now make y the subject using standard algebraic manipulations:

$$(4x)^2 + 5 = y$$

so $\qquad f^{-1}(x) = 16x^2 + 5$

3. $f^{-1}(f(x)) = f(f^{-1}(x)) = x$

Think of a number. Now add 2 to it. Now subtract 2 from your answer. You get the original number. Surprised? No, of course not! But that's all an inverse function does; it neutralizes the effect of the original function and brings you back to your starting point. So the key identity is:

$$f^{-1}(f(x)) = x$$

This is also true if you switch the two functions around:

$$f(f^{-1}(x)) = x$$

These are <u>always</u> true for a function and its inverse function. Remember them because they can save you a lot of time.

Example question:

If $g(x) = \dfrac{10 + x}{x - 4}$, find $g^{-1}(g(\sqrt[3]{127}))$.

A.   3.677

B.   5.027

C.   8.908

D.   8.998

E.   10.820

Solution:

This question could take a *lot* of time if you don't think first. The fast way is to use the fact that $g^{-1}(g(\sqrt[3]{127})) = \sqrt[3]{127} = 5.0265...$, so the answer is B.

4. Horizontal Line Test (HLT)

Every function has an inverse. You get its graph by reflecting in the line $y = x$. But not every inverse is an inverse <u>function</u>.

Example:

The graph of $y = x^2$ passes the VLT and is a function. When we reflect it in the line $y = x$ we get the inverse:

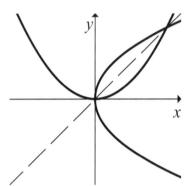

But we see the inverse <u>fails</u> the VLT and so is <u>not</u> a function.

There's an easy way to check if a function has an inverse that is itself a function. We use the <u>horizontal line test</u>:

> Pass a horizontal line from down to up over the graph of $f(x)$. If the line intersects the curve in <u>two or more places at the same time</u>, then $f(x)$ <u>doesn't</u> have an inverse that is also a function.

Example:

$h(t) = t^3 - 3t$ doesn't have an inverse which is also a function because its graph is

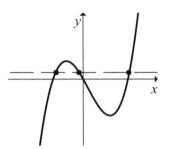

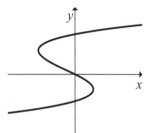

$h(t)$ fails HLT $\qquad \Rightarrow \qquad$ $h^{-1}(t)$ <u>not</u> a function

Odd and Even Functions

A function has <u>even symmetry</u> if you reflect it in the y-axis and it looks exactly the same as before. This means $f(x) = f(-x)$.

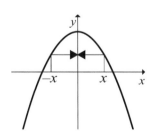

A function has <u>odd symmetry</u> if you rotate it 180° about the origin and it looks exactly the same as before. This means $f(x) = -f(-x)$.

If $f(x)$ is an odd function, then it MUST pass through the origin if it's defined at $x = 0$.

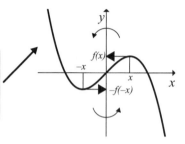

Example:

The function $y = \dfrac{|x| + \cos x}{x^3 + 1}$ cannot be odd because $y(0) = \dfrac{0+1}{0+1} = 1$.

Example question:

The function $f(x)$ is even and the function $g(x)$ is odd, and they are both defined for all real x. The function $h(x) = f(x)g(x)$

I.   must be an odd function

II. must be an even function

III. must pass through the origin

Which of the above statements is/are correct?

A.   I only

B.   II only

C.   I and III only

D.   II and III only

E.   None of the above

Solution:

Let's use the algebraic definition of odd and even functions:

$$h(-x) = f(-x)g(-x)$$
$$= f(x)(-g(x))$$
$$= -f(x)g(x)$$
$$= -h(x) \Rightarrow h(x) \text{ is an } \mathbf{odd} \text{ function. So statement I is correct.}$$

Also, $h(0) = 0$ because it is an odd function, which is defined everywhere. So statement III is also correct. There is a function which is both odd and even, it's $f(x) = 0$, so statement II *could* be correct. However the answer choice says it *must* be true, hence statement II is false. The answer is C.

Multivariable Functions

These are functions with **two or more input values**. These are usually quite easy, so don't be put off by the notation.

Example:

If $f(a,b,c) = \dfrac{a+b}{c}$, then $f(4,-2,2) = \dfrac{4+(-2)}{2} = 1$.

Example question:

If $h(w,x,y,z) = \ln(w^2 + x^2 + y^2 + z^2)$, what is z if $h(e,e,e,z) = \ln(4e^2)$?

A. 0

B. 1

C. 1 or -1

D. e

E. e or $-e$

Solution:

We just use the definition of $h(w,x,y,z)$ given:

If $\qquad\qquad h(e,e,e,z) = \ln(4e^2)$

then $\quad \ln(e^2 + e^2 + e^2 + z^2) = \ln(4e^2)$

so $\qquad\qquad 3e^2 + z^2 = 4e^2$

$$z^2 = e^2$$

$$z = e \text{ or } -e \Rightarrow \text{The answer is E.}$$

Subscripted Functions

Sometimes functions can have subscripts. These are not very common questions, but it's important to be confident if they do come up.

Example:

If $f_t(x) = tx^2 + 1$, then $f_4(1) + f_1(4) = 4(1)^2 + 1 + 1(4)^2 + 1 = 22$.

Example question:

If $g_t(x) = \begin{cases} x^2, & x < t \\ t^2 - tx, & x \geq t \end{cases}$, which of these graphs best represents $g_3(x)$?

A.
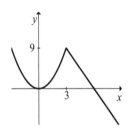

B
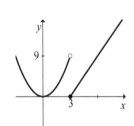

C.
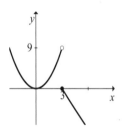

D.
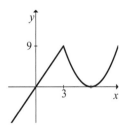

E.
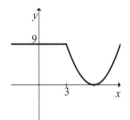

Solution:

Put $t = 3$ into the definition for $g_t(x)$ to get $g_3(x) = \begin{cases} x^2, & x < 3 \\ 9 - 3x, & x \geq 3 \end{cases}$

This is a quadratic stuck next to a downward sloping line. Since $3^2 = 9$,

but $9 - 9 = 0$, the two pieces *don't match up* at $x = 3$. Looking at the

choices, we see only one suitable choice: the answer is C.

Transformations

This is a favorite topic. You have to know how to translate (shift), dilate (squash and stretch) and reflect functions.

Shifts Parallel to the *x*-axis by a Distance *a*

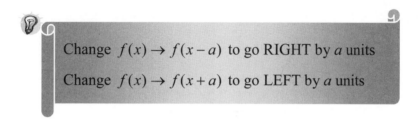

Change $f(x) \to f(x-a)$ to go RIGHT by a units

Change $f(x) \to f(x+a)$ to go LEFT by a units

Example:

If $f(x)$ looks like this:

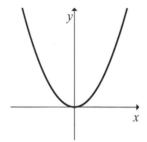

then $f(x-2)$ looks like this:

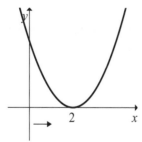

and $f(x+2)$ looks like this:

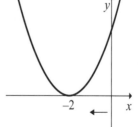

Shifts Parallel to the *y*-axis by a Distance *a*

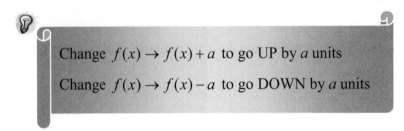

Change $f(x) \to f(x) + a$ to go UP by a units

Change $f(x) \to f(x) - a$ to go DOWN by a units

Example:

If $g(t)$ looks like this:

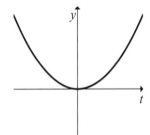

then $g(t) + 4$ looks like this:

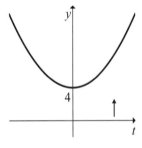

and $g(t) - 4$ looks like this:

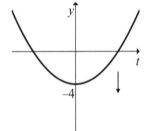

Dilations Parallel to the *x*-axis by a Factor *k* (*k* > 0)

Be careful here. Mathematicians often use the word "stretch" even if it's a squash! What they means is that a "squash is a "stretch" where the dilation factor, *k*, is between 0 and 1. It's better to use the more neutral word **dilation**.

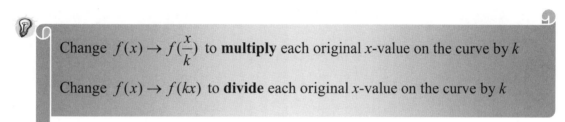

Change $f(x) \to f(\frac{x}{k})$ to **multiply** each original *x*-value on the curve by *k*

Change $f(x) \to f(kx)$ to **divide** each original *x*-value on the curve by *k*

This may seem the wrong way round, but it isn't!

Example:

If $f(x)$ looks like this:

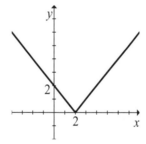

then $f(2x)$ looks like this:

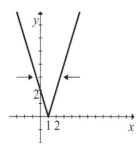

and $f(\frac{x}{2})$ looks like this:

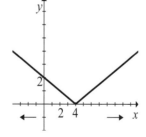

Dilations Parallel to the *y*-axis by a Factor *k* (*k* > 0)

This is much simpler than the *x*-dilations:

Change $f(x) \rightarrow kf(x)$ to **multiply** each original *y*-value on the curve by *k*

Change $f(x) \rightarrow \dfrac{f(x)}{k}$ to **divide** each original *y*-value on the curve by *k*

This seems logical!

Example:

If $h(x)$ looks like this:

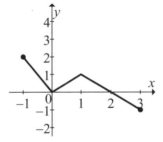

then $2h(x)$ looks like this:

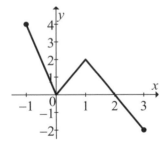

and $\dfrac{1}{2}h(x)$ looks like this:

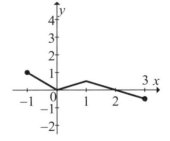

Reflection in the *x*-axis

Change $f(x) \rightarrow -f(x)$ to reflect in the *x*-axis

Example:

If $f(x)$ looks like this:

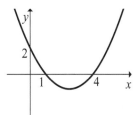

then $-f(x)$ looks like this:

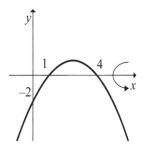

Reflection in the *y*-axis

Change $f(x) \rightarrow f(-x)$ to reflect in the *y*-axis

Example:

If $g(t)$ looks like this:

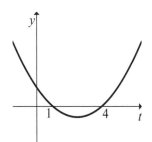

then $g(-t)$ looks like this:

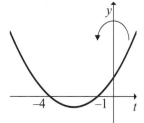

"In-to-out" Rule

If you have more than one transformation being used to move a function around, use the "In-to-out" rule. Start <u>inside</u> the function parentheses and work your way <u>outwards</u>:

Example:

If $f(x)$ has the graph:

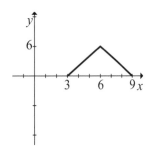

then $-2f(3x)$ has the graph:

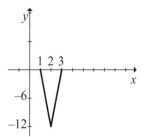

This is because the "3" on the inside means every x-value on the original curve is <u>divided by 3</u>, so the graph is <u>squashed</u> parallel to the x-axis. Secondly the "–2" on the outside is a vertical stretch by a factor of two **followed by** a reflection in the x-axis.

Example question:

The domain of a function $h(t)$ is $0 \leq t \leq 4$. What is the domain of the function $h(2-t)+2$?

A. $-6 \leq t \leq -2$

B. $-2 \leq t \leq 2$

C. $0 \leq t \leq 4$

D. $2 \leq t \leq 6$

E. $6 \leq t \leq 8$

Solution:

To start with, $h(2-t) = h(-[t-2])$. So you need to do two transformations:

First: $h(t) \rightarrow h(-t)$, this is a **reflection in the y-axis**.

Second: $h(-t) \rightarrow h(-[t-2])$, this is a **shift to the right by 2 units**.

Let's apply these two to the domain:

Start with the interval $0 \leq t \leq 4$.

Reflection in the y-axis: $-4 \leq t \leq 0$

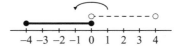

Then, shift to the right by 2 units: $-2 \leq t \leq 2$

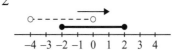

The answer is **B**.

If you're wondering what happened to the "+2" in the function $h(2-t)+2$, we **didn't need to bother about it** because this just shifts the graph up by two units. It doesn't affect the domain at all! (Though it does change the range.)

Two Special Reflections

Change $f(x) \to |f(x)|$ for a **partial reflection** in the x-axis. Only reflect parts of the graph **below the x-axis**. Keep the other parts fixed.

Example:

If $Q(x)$ looks like this: then $|Q(x)|$ looks like this:

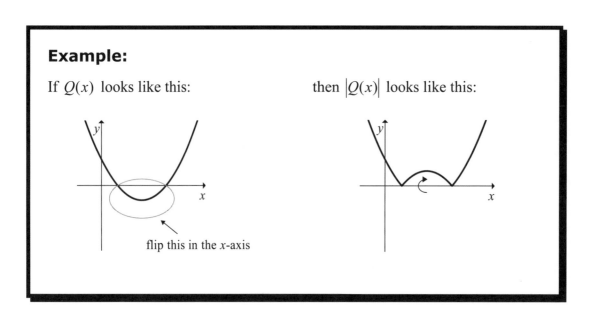

flip this in the x-axis

Change $f(x) \to f(|x|)$ for a **partial reflection** in the y-axis. This is a bit strange. DELETE ALL THE GRAPH for $x < 0$, keeping the right hand piece. KEEPING THIS FIXED, reflect it in the y-axis.

Example:

If $P(t)$ looks like this: then $P(|t|)$ looks like this:

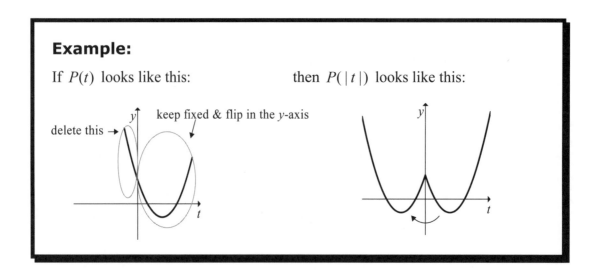

delete this →   keep fixed & flip in the y-axis

Coordinate Geometry

The geometry that's covered on the SAT Math Level 2 test can be divided into two parts: coordinate geometry and solid geometry. This chapter covers coordinate geometry, while the next chapter deals with solid geometry material. If you're taking the SAT Math Level 2 test, you will also need to know simple geometrical properties of triangles, parallel lines, etc., but you will not be tested on these topics directly, only as part of other questions.

Key Ideas

Straight Lines

If you're attempting the SAT Math Level 2 test, you should remember the two basic equations for a straight line with slope m:

 Slope-intercept form: $y = mx + b$ where b is the y-intercept

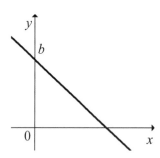

 Point-intercept form: $y - y_1 = m(x - x_1)$ where (x_1, y_1) is any particular point on the line

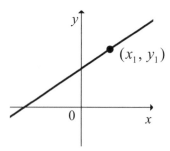

Slopes of Lines

To find the slope of a line or line segment through the two points (x_1, y_1) and (x_2, y_2), we use the formula

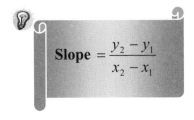

$$\textbf{Slope} = \frac{y_2 - y_1}{x_2 - x_1}$$

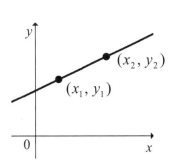

Here are two other basic, but important, points to note:

Two lines are **parallel** if they have the **same slope**.

Two lines are **perpendicular** if one slope is the **negative reciprocal** of the other.

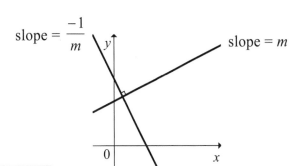

Remember that <u>vertical</u> lines, such as $x = 3$, don't have a slope (you can think of it as "infinite"). So what's perpendicular to a vertical line? A horizontal line (slope = 0), such as $y = 6$.

Example question:

Line L goes through $(0, 2)$ and $(8, 0)$. Line M is parallel to line L and passes though the origin. Line N is perpendicular to line L and passes through $(0, 2)$. Where do lines M and N intersect?

A. $(-0.47, 0.12)$

B. $(-0.50, 0.50)$

C. $(-0.53, -0.32)$

D. $(-1.00, 1.00)$

E. $(-1.88, 0.27)$

> If you can, make a <u>diagram</u> with geometry questions. A sketch for this question only takes a few seconds. Remember you only need a very rough sketch, as your work is not marked.

Solution:

The slope of line L is $\dfrac{2-0}{0-8} = -\dfrac{1}{4}$.

This means the slope of line M is

also $-\dfrac{1}{4}$ and the slope of line N is

therefore 4.

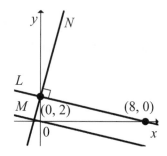

Line M goes through $(0, 0)$, so its equation is $y = -\dfrac{1}{4}x.$

Line N goes through $(0, 2)$, so the y-intercept is 2, and its equation is

$y = 4x + 2$.

We now need to find where lines M and N intersect.

Method 1: Equate the two expressions and solve for x:

$$-\frac{1}{4}x = 4x + 2$$

$$-x = 16x + 8$$

$$-17x = 8$$

$$x = -0.4705...$$

Looking at the choices, we see the answer has to be **A.** There was no point finding the corresponding y-value because all the answer choices have different x-values.

Method 2: Graph on the calculator and find where they intersect:

$x = -.470588$, $y = .11764706$

The answer is A.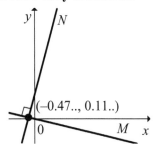

Line Segments

You need to be able to find the midpoint of a line segment and its length given its endpoints (x_1, y_1) and (x_2, y_2).

Midpoint of a Line Segment

To find the coordinates of the midpoint of a line segment between two points, just find the averages of the x-values and y-values separately:

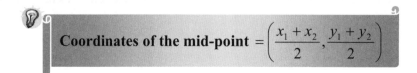

$$\text{Coordinates of the mid-point} = \left(\frac{x_1 + x_2}{2}, \frac{y_1 + y_2}{2} \right)$$

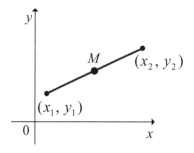

Length of a Line Segment

Just use the Pythagorean Theorem applied to the coordinates:

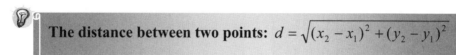

The distance between two points: $d = \sqrt{(x_2 - x_1)^2 + (y_2 - y_1)^2}$

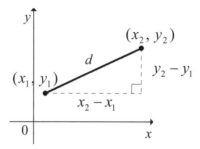

Example:

For the two points $(4, -3)$ and $(6, 5)$, the midpoint is $\left(\dfrac{4+6}{2}, \dfrac{-3+5}{2}\right) = (5, 1)$ and the distance between them is

$$d = \sqrt{(4-6)^2 + (-3-5)^2} = \sqrt{68}.$$

Dividing a Line Segment in a Given Ratio

Very occasionally we need to divide the line segment between two points (x_1, y_1) and (x_2, y_2) in a given ratio like 2 : 3 or 1 : 2.

The coordinates of the point that divides the line segment in the ratio $m : n$ is given by the following formula:

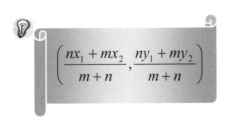

$$\left(\frac{nx_1 + mx_2}{m+n}, \frac{ny_1 + my_2}{m+n} \right)$$

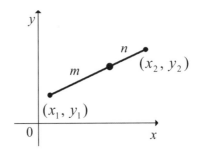

The expression given above for the midpoint of a line segment is, in fact, a special case when $m = n$.

Example:

If you divide the line segment with end points (4, 6) and (10, 8) in the ratio 3 : 2, you get the point $\left(\dfrac{3(10) + 2(4)}{3+2}, \dfrac{3(8) + 2(6)}{3+2} \right) = \left(\dfrac{38}{5}, \dfrac{36}{5} \right)$

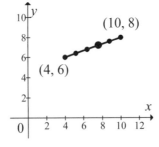

Conic Sections

There are four conic sections that you could meet on the SAT Math Level 2 test: circles, ellipses, hyperbolas and parabolas. We've already covered parabolas in the algebra section. Fortunately, the conic section questions on the SAT Math Level 2 test are generally pretty straightforward. Just make sure you know the formulas and how they relate to their graphs.

Circles

The general equation of a circle of radius r, center (0, 0) is

$$x^2 + y^2 = r^2$$

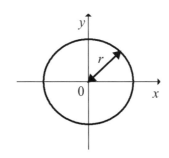

Example:

In the equation $2x^2 + 2y^2 = 10$, we divide both sides by 2 to get $x^2 + y^2 = 5 = (\sqrt{5})^2$. So the equation represents a circle of radius $\sqrt{5}$ and center (0, 0).

Changing the Center

Of course, not every circle has its center at the origin (0, 0). If the center is at the point (h, k), then the formula changes slightly:

The general equation of a circle of radius r and center (h, k) is

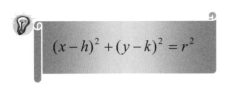

$$(x-h)^2 + (y-k)^2 = r^2$$

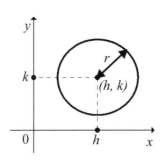

Example question:

What is the center of the circle $x^2 + 4x + y^2 - 8y = 0$?

A.   (4, 8)

B.   (0, 0)

C.   (−2, 4)

D.   (−4, 8)

E.   (16, 64)

Solution:

At first sight this doesn't even look like the equation for a circle! We need to **complete the square** for the x's and y's:

$$x^2 + 4x = (x+2)^2 - 4$$
$$y^2 - 8y = (y-4)^2 - 16$$

So $x^2 + 4x + y^2 - 8y = 0$ becomes $(x+2)^2 - 4 + (y-4)^2 - 16 = 0$.

Rearranging, we get $(x+2)^2 + (y-4)^2 = 20 = \left(\sqrt{20}\right)^2$.

Now we can see that the center is (–2, 4). The answer is C.

Ellipses

An ellipse is basically a squashed circle, something like this:

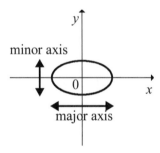

so there isn't a constant "radius" or "diameter". The long and short "diameters" (the **major** and **minor axes**) are all we need to get its equation.

The general equation of an ellipse with x-intercepts at a and $-a$, y-intercepts at b and $-b$, center $(0, 0)$ is

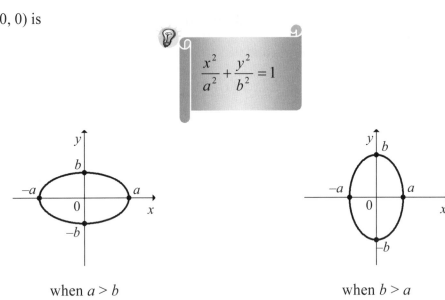

$$\frac{x^2}{a^2} + \frac{y^2}{b^2} = 1$$

when $a > b$ when $b > a$

Example:

In the equation $\dfrac{4x^2}{9} + y^2 = 4$, we can see it's not in the right form: the

right-hand side <u>must be 1</u>. So divide by 4 to get $\dfrac{x^2}{9} + \dfrac{y^2}{4} = 1$ or

$\dfrac{x^2}{3^2} + \dfrac{y^2}{2^2} = 1$. Now everything is o.k., and our ellipse looks like this:

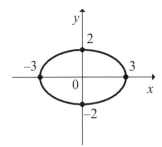

Example question:

How many intersection points are there between the graphs of $y = |x| - 3$ and

$$1 = \frac{x^2}{16} + \frac{y^2}{9}?$$

A.   0

B.   1

C.   2

D.   3

E.   more than 3

Solution:

This question is solved by graphing the two curves. Unfortunately, most graphing calculators are not very effective at graphing conic sections, so we'll do it by hand. (It's also faster!)

$1 = \frac{x^2}{16} + \frac{y^2}{9}$ is an ellipse, center (0, 0), with $a = 4$ and $b = 3$. The graph of $y = |x| - 3$ is an absolute value graph shifted down by 3 units:

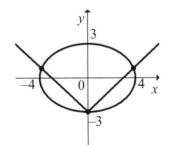

> Remember that "intersect" doesn't necessarily mean "cross". Even though the two graphs only <u>touch</u> at (0, −3), this <u>does</u> count as an <u>intersection point</u>.

We can see that there are three points of intersection, so the answer is D.

If you wanted to use a calculator, you would need to rewrite $1 = \dfrac{x^2}{16} + \dfrac{y^2}{9}$ so

that y is the subject: $y = \pm 3\sqrt{1 - \dfrac{x^2}{16}}$.

Now graph

$$Y_1 = 3\sqrt{1 - \dfrac{x^2}{16}}$$

$$Y_2 = -3\sqrt{1 - \dfrac{x^2}{16}}$$

$Y_3 = |\,x\,| - 3 \ \ [= \text{ABS}(X) - 3 \text{ on most calculators}].$

Then you find there are 3 intersection points as before.

Changing the Center of an Ellipse

Just like the circle, an ellipse might have its center at another point (h, k).

Its equation is

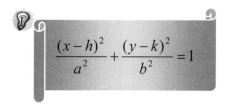

$$\frac{(x-h)^2}{a^2} + \frac{(y-k)^2}{b^2} = 1$$

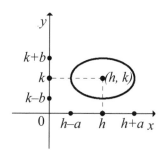

Hyperbolas

Hyperbolas on the SAT Math Level 2 test will look like:

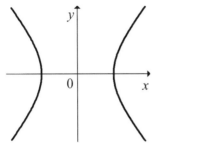   or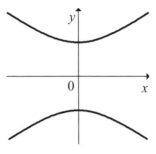

The general equation of a hyperbola looks like this:

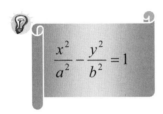

$$\frac{x^2}{a^2} - \frac{y^2}{b^2} = 1$$

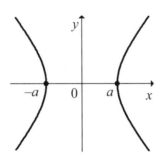

Don't confuse this equation with the ellipse: ellipses have a "+" sign and hyperbolas have a "−" sign.

This has the center at $(0, 0)$. If we want to change the center to (h, k) we get

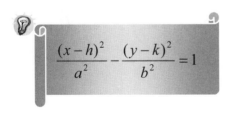

$$\frac{(x-h)^2}{a^2} - \frac{(y-k)^2}{b^2} = 1$$

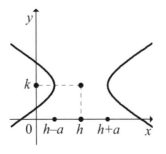

How to Sketch a Hyperbola

There's a four-stage procedure for graphing a hyperbola in standard form:

1. **Draw a box** with center (h, k), width $2a$ and height $2b$.

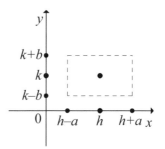

2. **Draw two lines** through the corners and center of the box. These are the (sloping) **asymptotes.** The hyperbola will get closer to these but never cross them.

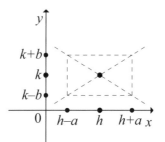

3. **Plot the two vertices** to the left and right of the center on the sides of the box.

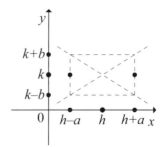

4. **Draw the two branches** of the hyperbola getting closer to the asymptotes.

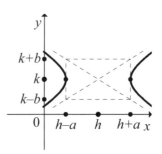

Example:

To get a sketch of $\dfrac{x^2}{5^2} - \dfrac{y^2}{3^2} = 1$, we first draw a box, center (0, 0), with width $10 = 2 \times 5$ and height $6 = 2 \times 3$. Then we draw two lines through the corners:

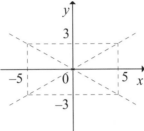

Now plot the two vertices, and then draw in the hyperbola:

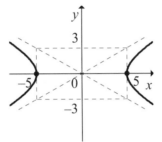

y-axis Hyperbolas

If you have $\dfrac{y^2}{a^2} - \dfrac{x^2}{b^2} = 1$, (so the **y is before the x**); then the parabola will open **up-down**, not left-right.

Example:

The graph of $\dfrac{y^2}{5^2} - \dfrac{x^2}{3^2} = 1$ looks like this.

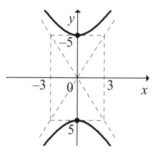

3D Coordinates

You might be asked questions on 3D coordinates. These are points (x, y, z) in space like this: (2, 3, 8) or (0, 0, 7). The origin is (0, 0, 0). It is a bit difficult to visualize 3D points by drawing diagrams on paper. We usually draw the coordinate axes like this:

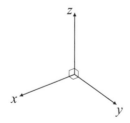

We can now plot some points:

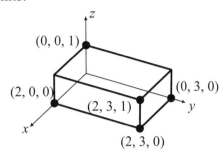

Planes in Space

There are three **planes** (flat surfaces) that you need to know about:

The *xy*-plane is where $z = 0$.

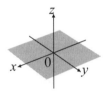

The *xz*-plane is where $y = 0$.

The *yz*-plane is where $x = 0$.

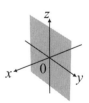

Example:

Suppose we have the point (4, 2, 3) and we reflect it in the *xz*-plane. This means the *y*-coordinate changes sign:

so $(4, 2, 3) \rightarrow (4, -2, 3)$

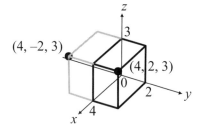

Example question:

Point *P* has coordinates (5, 0, 0). It is rotated 90° counter-clockwise around the *z*-axis to point *Q*. Point *Q* is then rotated 90° counter-clockwise about the *x*-axis to point *R*. The coordinates of *R* are

A.   (0, 5, 0)

B.   (0, 0, 5)

C.   (0, –5, 0)

D.   (5, 0, 0)

E.   (–5, 0, 0)

Solution:

First sketch a set of axes, and plot point P:

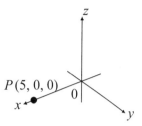

Now rotate it to get point Q. We see that the coordinates of it are $(0, 5, 0)$.

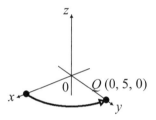

Finally, rotate point Q about the x–axis to get point R:

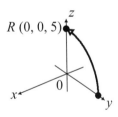

We see that its coordinates are $(0, 0, 5)$. The answer is B.

3D Distance Formula

Recall the distance formula for 2 dimensions $d = \sqrt{(x_2 - x_1)^2 + (y_2 - y_1)^2}$

The 3D version is almost as simple, just add an extra bit for the z-coordinate:

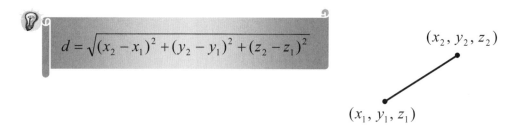

$$d = \sqrt{(x_2 - x_1)^2 + (y_2 - y_1)^2 + (z_2 - z_1)^2}$$

(x_2, y_2, z_2)

(x_1, y_1, z_1)

Example question:

What is/are the value(s) of k if the distance between $(2, 0, -3)$ and $(k, 5, -4)$ is 17?

A. -6.7 or 6.7

B. -14.2

C. -14.9 or 17.0

D. -14.9

E. -14.2 or 18.2

Solution:

We just plug the information into the 3D distance formula:

$$d = \sqrt{(2-k)^2 + (0-5)^2 + (-3-(-4))^2} = 17$$

$$(2-k)^2 + 25 + 1 = 289$$

$$(2-k)^2 = 263$$

$$2 - k = \pm\sqrt{263} \quad \text{(Don't forget both roots!)}$$

$$k = 2 - \sqrt{263} = -14.21.... = -14.2 \text{ (correct to 3 significant figures) or}$$

$$= 2 + \sqrt{263} = 18.21.... = 18.2 \text{ (correct to 3 significant figures)}$$

The answer is E.

Polar Coordinates

Polar coordinates are another way of indicating the position of a point in the plane. Instead of the origin, we talk about the **pole**. The positive x-axis is now called the **initial line.**

pole   initial line

The **polar coordinates** of a point are its <u>distance, r,</u> from the pole and its <u>angle, θ,</u> a counter-clockwise rotation about the pole from the initial line. We write these as a pair (r, θ). We can measure θ in degrees or radians. Look at these diagrams to see you how it works:

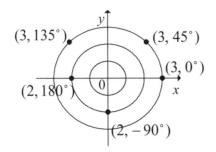

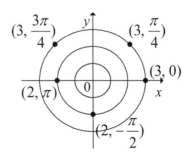

Important! Unlike "normal" **Cartesian** coordinates (also called **rectangular** coordinates), the polar coordinates for a given point are not unique, e.g. $(4, 30°)$, $(4, 390°)$ and $(4, -330°)$ all represent the same point:

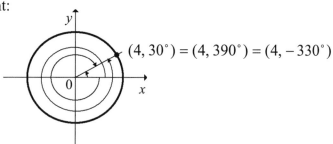

Often a question will give you a range for the angle, say $0° \leq \theta < 360°$. In this case, the polar coordinate *will* be unique for a given positive r value.

Negative *r* Values

Although it can seem a bit strange, it is possible to give a meaning to *negative r* values. We define the polar coordinates of a point with a negative value of r to be the same as the positive value of r, but we **add 180° to the angle**. Look at the diagrams to see what is happening.

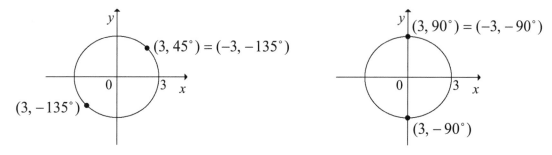

Example question:

The point Q has Cartesian coordinates $(4, -7)$. Possible polar coordinates of Q are

I $(8.06, -60.3°)$

II $(-8.06, 119.7°)$

III $(-8.06, -60.3°)$

A.   I only

B.   II only

C.   III only

D.   I and III only

E.   None of the aobve

Solution:

First we need to find a possible polar coordinate representation for Q. A quick sketch will do, along with the distance formula and basic right-angled trigonometry:

$$r = \sqrt{4^2 + (-7)^2} = 8.06 \text{ and } \theta = \tan^{-1}(\frac{7}{4}) = -60.3°$$

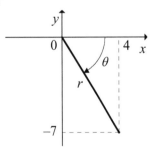

So $(8.06, -60.3°)$ is one possibility – in fact, it's statement I. The points in statements II and III have the correct r value, so we need to check their angles. Because it's easier to visualize positive r values, we'll add $180°$ to each of their angles.

Then expressions in statements II and III are now $(8.06, 299.7°)$ and $(8.06, 119.7°)$, respectively. Plotting these:

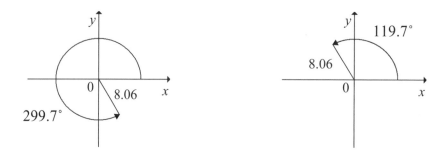

We see that statement II is right but statement III is wrong. Overall, statements I and II are correct. This means the answer is E.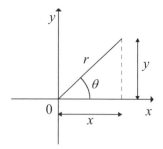

Converting between Polar and Cartesian Coordinates

There are formulas that enable us to convert between polar and Cartesian coordinates. If we draw a diagram showing both the Cartesian and polar coordinates of a point:

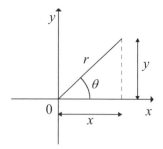

We can see that

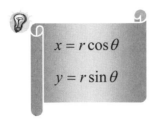

$$x = r\cos\theta$$

$$y = r\sin\theta$$

These formulas work even if $r < 0$ and $\theta < 0$.

To go the other way use:

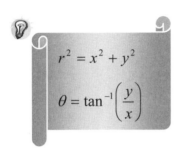

$$r^2 = x^2 + y^2$$

$$\theta = \tan^{-1}\left(\frac{y}{x}\right)$$

Be careful with these two formulas. Remember r can be positive or negative, and we need to take account of the quadrant. **Always draw a diagram**.

Example question:

A curve has a polar equation $r = 4\sin\theta$. The equation of the curve in rectangular coordinates is

A. $x + 4y = 1$

B. $(x+2)^2 = 4$

C. $(x-2)^2 = 16$

D. $x^2 + (y-2)^2 = 4$

E. $x^2 + y^2 = 4$

Solution:

We first replace $\sin \theta$ by $\dfrac{y}{r}$.

Then, we get $r = 4\dfrac{y}{r}$

so $r^2 = 4y$

Change the r^2 on the left by using $r^2 = x^2 + y^2$ (because we use r^2, there's no need to worry if r is positive or negative):

This gives us $x^2 + y^2 = 4y$.

Now move the $4y$ over and complete the square: $x^2 + (y-2)^2 - 4 = 0$.

The answer is D.

Solid Geometry

This chapter deals with the surface areas and volumes of various 3D shapes such as cones, spheres and prisms. We also analyze the relationships between the surface areas and volumes of similar shapes.

Key Ideas

Formulas

Volume Formulas

You need to remember these fundamental formulas from basic geometry:

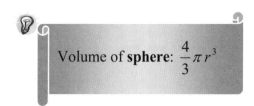

Volume of **sphere**: $\dfrac{4}{3}\pi r^3$

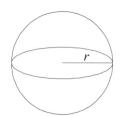

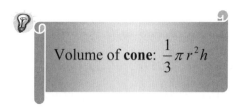

Volume of **cone**: $\dfrac{1}{3}\pi r^2 h$

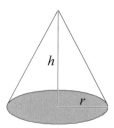

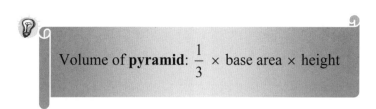

Volume of **pyramid**: $\dfrac{1}{3} \times$ base area $\times$ height

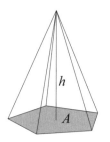

> This means that a circular-based pyramid, i.e. <u>a cone</u>, has volume $\dfrac{1}{3}\pi r^2 h$.

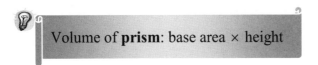

Volume of **prism**: base area × height

Surface Area Formulas

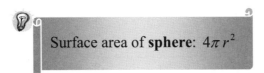

Surface area of **sphere**: $4\pi r^2$

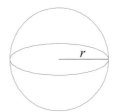

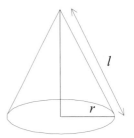

Surface area of **cone (not including base)**: $\pi r l$

where l is (confusingly!) called the **slant height**

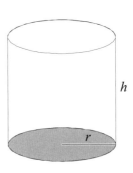

Surface area of **cylinder**: $2\pi r(r + h)$

Inscribed and Circumscribed Shapes

To **inscribe** a shape is to put one shape inside another so that all the vertices are on the faces of the second shape. We can also say the shape around the outside is **circumscribed** around the inside shape. These are common questions and often involve a cube inscribed within a sphere or a sphere in a cube.

Example question:

A cube is inscribed within a sphere of radius 6. What is the volume of the cube?

A.   48.0

B.   134.7

C.   257.9

D.   332.6

E.   414.1

Solution:

First draw a diagram:

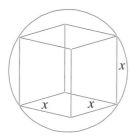

To find the volume of the cube, we need to find the length, x, of a side. We don't know that length, but we *do* know the length of the *diagonal* of the cube: it's just the diameter of the sphere, which is $2 \times 6 = 12$.

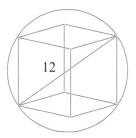

Now we use the 3D distance formula:

$$\sqrt{x^2 + x^2 + x^2} = 12$$

$$3x^2 = 144$$

$$x^2 = 48 \Rightarrow x = \sqrt{48}$$

Therefore, the volume of the cube is

$$x^3 = (\sqrt{48})^3 = 332.553... = 332.6 \text{ (correct to 1 decimal place)}$$

The answer is D.

Sometimes we may have to use other basic geometrical ideas:

Example question:

A hollow right cone has a height of 13 cm. A cube of volume 64 cm³ has been placed inside the cone so that four corners are touching the curved surface of the cone and four corners are touching the base of the cone. What is the volume outside the cube but inside the cone?

A.   47.2 cm³

B.   49.6 cm³

C.   50.1 cm³

D.   53.1 cm³

E.   58.3 cm³

Solution:

We know the volume of the cube is <u>64 cm³</u>, so the length of a side must be <u>4 cm³</u>.

Draw a diagram showing the side-on view of the cone and cube and add this information to your sketch: (all units are in cm)

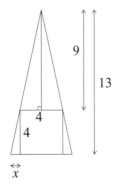

x is the unknown distance from the cube to the bottom of the cone.

Now we can see two similar triangles, one of them involving x:

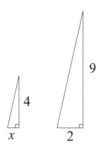

so $\dfrac{2}{9} = \dfrac{x}{4}$

Solving for x gives $x = \dfrac{8}{9}$

This means the base radius of the cone $= 2 + \dfrac{8}{9} = \dfrac{26}{9}$ cm.

Therefore, the volume of the cone is

$$\frac{1}{3}\pi r^2 h = \frac{1}{3}\pi \left(\frac{26}{9}\right)^2 13 = 113.61... = 113.6\,\text{cm}^3 \text{ (correct to 1 decimal place)}$$

The answer we want is the difference between the cone and the cube:

$(113.61 - 64)\text{cm}^3 = 49.61\ \text{cm}^3 \Rightarrow$ The answer is B.

Solids of Revolution

If you take a curve in the plane and rotate it (usually) 360° about a line, often the *x*- or *y*-axis, you will get a solid 3D shape called a **solid of revolution**.

Example:

If you rotate this line segment:

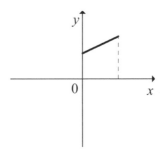

about the *x*-axis, you'll get a frustrum of a cone:

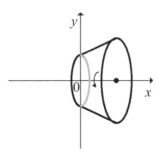

If you rotate the line segment about the *y*-axis, you'll get a cone:

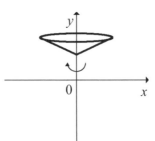

Example question:

The line segment formed from the line $2x - y = 0$, where $-2 \leq x \leq 2$, is rotated $360°$ about the x-axis. What is the volume of the solid formed?

A. 64.2

B. 65.1

C. 66.2

D. 66.8

E. 67.0

Solution:

Draw the line segment $2x - y = 0$ with $-2 \leq x \leq 2$, and then rotate it about the x-axis:

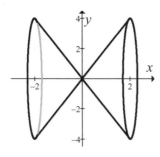

We can see that we have formed a **double cone**. As both cones are the same, we can just find the volume of the right-hand one and then double our answer. For this cone, the "height" is 2 and the base radius is $2 \times 2 = 4$.

So, the volume of cone $= \dfrac{1}{3}\pi r^2 h = \dfrac{1}{3}\pi (4)^2 2 = \dfrac{32}{3}\pi$.

Therefore, the total volume of the shape is

$2 \times \dfrac{32}{3}\pi = 67.02... = 67.0$ (correct to 1 decimal place) $\Rightarrow$ The answer is E.

Areas and Volumes of Similar Shapes

Remember that "similar" in geometry means something very specific:

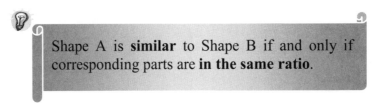

> Shape A is **similar** to Shape B if and only if corresponding parts are **in the same ratio**.

This 2D shape: is similar to this:

This 3D shape: is similar to this:

But this 2D shape: is not similar to this:

The key point about similar shapes is that their areas and volumes are in a precise ratio as well:

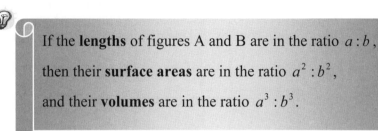

If the **lengths** of figures A and B are in the ratio $a:b$,

then their **surface areas** are in the ratio $a^2:b^2$,

and their **volumes** are in the ratio $a^3:b^3$.

Example:

A cylinder has a base radius of 6 and a height of 4. Another cylinder has a base radius of 9 and a height of 6. We see that the cylinders' corresponding lengths are in the ratio $1:1.5 = 2:3$ so the surface areas will be in the ratio $2^2:3^2 = 4:9$ and the volumes will be in the ratio $2^3:3^3 = 8:27$.

Example question:

A cone has a height of $4h$ cm and a base radius of r cm. A smaller cone is formed by slicing the original cone by a plane parallel to the base. The height of the new cone is h cm. What is the ratio of the curved surface area of the small cone to the curved part of the frustrum of the original cone?

A. $1 : \sqrt{8}$

B. $1 : 4$

C. $1 : 15$

D. $3 : 64$

E.   It cannot be determined.

Solution:

Draw a side-on view of the situation:

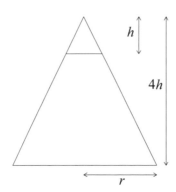

We see that the two triangles, and so cones, are similar, so we can use the ratio formulas.

We have the ratio of lengths = 1 : 4

So the ratio of curved surface areas of the cones = 1 : 16

This means that the small cone has $\dfrac{1}{16}$ of the curved surface area of the big

cone, and hence the frustrum must have $1 - \dfrac{1}{16} = \dfrac{15}{16}$ of the curved surface area

of the big cone.

The ratio required is therefore $\dfrac{1}{16} : \dfrac{15}{16} = 1:15 \Rightarrow$ The answer is C.

Notice that we didn't need to use the radius, r, at all!

Trigonometry

Trigonometry is another key area. There's a lot of emphasis on triangles and trigonometric graphs on the SAT Math Level 2 test. You are expected to know the basic concepts of trigonometry, such as the definitions of sine, cosine and tangent in terms of a right triangle.

Key Ideas

Basic Trigonometric Ratios of a Right Triangle

If you're thinking of taking the SAT Math Level 2 test, then you should know these already!

Consider this right triangle with sides a, b and c:

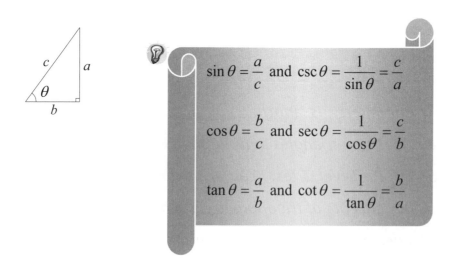

$$\sin \theta = \frac{a}{c} \text{ and } \csc \theta = \frac{1}{\sin \theta} = \frac{c}{a}$$

$$\cos \theta = \frac{b}{c} \text{ and } \sec \theta = \frac{1}{\cos \theta} = \frac{c}{b}$$

$$\tan \theta = \frac{a}{b} \text{ and } \cot \theta = \frac{1}{\tan \theta} = \frac{b}{a}$$

[Note: Sometimes (but not on the SAT Math Level 2 test) you will see "**csc**" written as "**cosec**". It means exactly the same thing.]

Trigonometric Ratios of Special Angles

You should remember the two "special triangles", $45° - 45° - 90°$ and $30° - 60° - 90°$, and their associated trigonometric ratios:

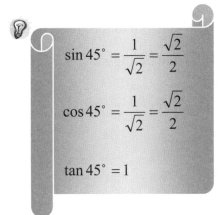

$$\sin 45° = \frac{1}{\sqrt{2}} = \frac{\sqrt{2}}{2}$$

$$\cos 45° = \frac{1}{\sqrt{2}} = \frac{\sqrt{2}}{2}$$

$$\tan 45° = 1$$

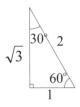

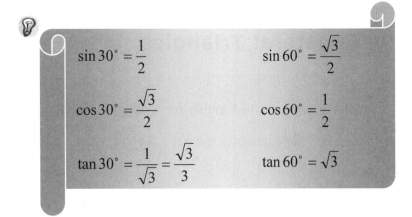

$$\sin 30° = \frac{1}{2} \qquad\qquad \sin 60° = \frac{\sqrt{3}}{2}$$

$$\cos 30° = \frac{\sqrt{3}}{2} \qquad\qquad \cos 60° = \frac{1}{2}$$

$$\tan 30° = \frac{1}{\sqrt{3}} = \frac{\sqrt{3}}{3} \qquad\qquad \tan 60° = \sqrt{3}$$

Area of a Triangle

Of course, the area of a triangle is "half base times height", but there are three other useful formulas to know that will save you a lot of time in certain situations.

Two Sides and Included Angle

You need to know how to find the area if you have <u>two sides</u> given and the <u>angle between</u> them (called the **included angle**):

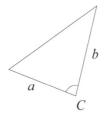

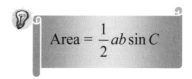

$$\text{Area} = \frac{1}{2}ab\sin C$$

Equilateral Triangles

Here's another useful formula for working out the area of an equilateral triangle of side length a. This eliminates the need for the Pythagorean Theorem and saves you valuable time.

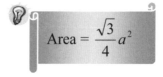

$$\text{Area} = \frac{\sqrt{3}}{4}a^2$$

Heron's Formula

This is a quick way of working out the area of a triangle if you have the **three sides** and **no angles**.

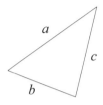

First, work out the **semiperimeter** $= s = \dfrac{a+b+c}{2}$.

Then use the formula:

$$\text{Area} = \sqrt{s(s-a)(s-b)(s-c)}$$

Example question:

$\triangle ABC$ has sides of length 13, 14 and 15. Its area is equal to

A. 84

B. 86

C. 88

D. 90

E. 92

Solution:

This is easy using Heron's formula! Draw a sketch anyway:

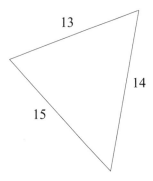

Now find the semiperimeter, $s = \dfrac{13 + 14 + 15}{2} = 21$.

So the area $= \sqrt{21(21-13)(21-14)(21-15)} = \sqrt{21(8)(7)(6)} = 84$. The

answer is A.

Another way would be to use the cosine rule to find out an angle then use

area $= \dfrac{1}{2}ab\sin C$, but this is quite a bit slower than Heron's formula.

Cosine Rule

We can use the cosine rule if we have <u>three sides</u> or <u>two sides and the included angle</u> and we want to find the other side or angles:

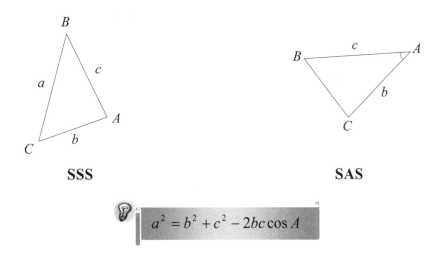

SSS　　　　　　　　　　　　　　　　　　**SAS**

$$a^2 = b^2 + c^2 - 2bc \cos A$$

Sine Rule

We use this if we have two angles and the included side and we want the other sides or angles:

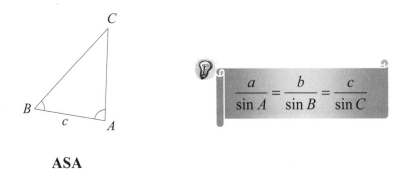

ASA

$$\frac{a}{\sin A} = \frac{b}{\sin B} = \frac{c}{\sin C}$$

The Ambiguous Case of the Sine Rule

If you have the SSA case, then you have a problem: there may be one or two solutions.

Example:

You could draw a triangle with one side of length 3 cm, another side of length 6 cm, and an angle of 20° opposite to the 3 cm side like this:

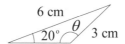

However, there is another, totally different, triangle you could draw with the <u>same measurements</u>:

There are two possible triangles we can draw: the situation is **ambiguous**. See how this is different from the SAS case. There we also had two sides and an angle, but the angle was <u>between</u> the two sides and this resulted in a unique triangle and so only one possible solution (using the cosine rule).

The procedure for dealing with the ambiguous, SSA, case is as follows:

- Solve using the sine rule, as usual.

- When you get your angle answer, θ, find another possible answer, $180° - \theta$.

- Check to see whether you could draw another triangle with the second possibility. If you can, then this is a second answer. If you can't, then there's only one answer.

Example question:

What is the measure of $\angle QPR$ in $\triangle PQR$ if $\angle PQR = 20°$, $PQ = 8$ cm and $PR = 7$ cm?

A.   26.9°

B.   28.9°

C.   137.0° or 3.0°

D.   134.3° or 5.8°

E.   137.0°

Solution:

As usual, sketch a diagram before doing anything:

Using the sine rule we have $\dfrac{\sin \alpha}{8} = \dfrac{\sin 20°}{7}$

so $\alpha = 23.009...° = 23.0°$ (correct to 1 decimal place)

Now, because it's an SSA case, we try $180° - 23.0° = 157.0°$ (correct to 1 decimal place) as well.

Now, is it possible to have triangles with angles $20°$, $23.0°$, x; or $20°$, $157.0°$, x? Yes, it is. The two possibilities for the third angle are $x = 137.0°$ or $x = 3.0°$:

The answer is C.

However, be careful. Don't assume a triangle must have 2 solutions just because it's an SSA case; <u>it might have only one solution</u>. You need to check each case.

Radians

To convert radians to degrees or vice versa, we use the following conversion formula:

$$180° = \pi \text{ rad}$$

> What's the "official" symbol for radian? There isn't one! Some people use a little "c": 6 rad = 6^c. But the convention is that when doing trigonometry, if you <u>don't</u> see any angle symbol, then assume the angle is in <u>radians</u>.
> So cos 0.6 = cos (0.6 rad) = 0.8253.

Example:

$$1 \text{ rad} = \left(\frac{180}{\pi}\right)^° = 57.296...°$$

$$\frac{3\pi}{5} \text{ rad} = \frac{3 \times 180°}{5} = 108°$$

$$30° = \frac{\pi}{6} \text{ rad}$$

$$315° = \frac{7\pi}{4} \text{ rad}$$

Areas of Sectors

A sector of a circle is a "pizza slice". If θ (in radians) is the central angle of a circle, then

Area of sector $= \dfrac{1}{2}r^2\theta$

Lengths of Arcs of a Circle

An arc is the length of a piece of a curve. If θ (in radians) is the central angle of a circle, then

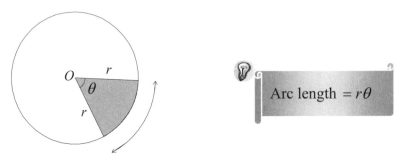

Arc length $= r\theta$

Example question:

A 10 cm length of thin wire is bent to form the shape of a sector of a circle. If the radius of the sector is 4 cm, then the measure of the included angle is

A.   28.6°

B.   29.1°

C.   29.8°

D.   30.2°

E.   30.3°

Solution:

Draw a diagram and use θ for the included angle:

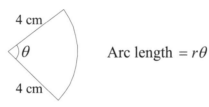

Arc length $= r\theta$

The length of the wire is 10 cm,

so $4 + 4 + 4\theta = 10$

$\theta = 0.5$ radians

Now convert to degrees using $180° = \pi$ rad:

0.5 radians $= \left(\dfrac{180}{\pi}\right)° \times 0.5 = 28.64°...$

The answer is A.

Trigonometric Graphs

You need to know the three basic trigonometric graphs of sine and cosine (called sinusoidals) and tangent.

Basic Graphs of Sine and Cosine

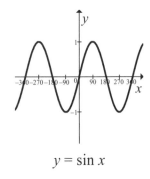

$$y = \sin x$$

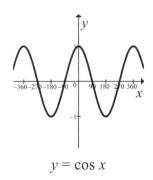

$$y = \cos x$$

Note: the scales on the x-axis are in degrees.

For both sine and cosine graphs:

Domain: the set of all real numbers

Range: $-1 \le y \le 1$

Period: $360° = 2\pi$ radians

Sinusoidal Graphs

The graphs of sin or cos can be transformed with stretches and translations. The basic general formula is as follows:

$$y = A\cos[B(x+C)] + D$$

You can read off the values of A, B, C and D from the graph

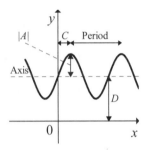

$|A|$ is the "**height**" of the curve above the axis.

C is the **translation left or right** parallel to the x-axis (negative when it's to the right and positive when it's to the left).

D is the **translation up or down** parallel to the y-axis (negative when it's down and positive when it's up).

B is the **stretch or squash parallel to the x-axis**. To find it, it's usually easier to use this identity

$$B = \frac{360°}{period} = \frac{2\pi}{period}$$

Example:

Consider this diagram of a sinusoid:

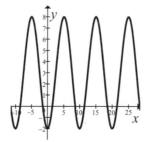

Note: the scales on the x-axis are in degrees.

The axis is the half-way line, so this is $y = 3$, which implies that $D = 3$. Now we can easily find the amplitude: $A = 5$. To find C, notice the "first" peak of our basic $y = \cos x$ graph has moved to the right by $5°$, so $C = -5°$. Finally we see the period (peak to peak) is $10°$, so

$$B = \frac{360°}{10°} = 36.$$

Putting this altogether gives the sinusoid $y = 5\cos[36(x - 5°)] + 3$.

Tangent Graphs

The basic graph of tan x looks like this:

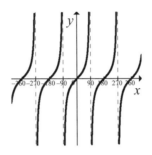

> **Domain:** the set of all real numbers except odd multiples of $90°$ ($\pm 90°, \pm 270°, \pm 450° \ldots$)
>
> **Range:** the set of all real numbers
>
> **Period:** $180° = \pi$ radians

Notice that the **period** of tan x is $180° = \pi$ radians, and that there are **vertical asymptotes** at odd multiples of $90°$ ($\pm 90°, \pm 270°, \pm 450° \ldots$)

The "CAST" Diagram

This is a useful tool for remembering in which of the four quadrants of the plane the trigonometric ratios are positive or negative:

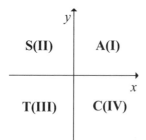

The letter tells you which of the ratios is **positive**. Otherwise you assume the ratio is **negative** in that quadrant. For instance, in the "T" quadrant, tan (and $\dfrac{1}{\tan x} = \cot x$) is positive. The other four ratios (sin, cos, sec and csc) are <u>all</u> <u>negative</u> here. Note that "A" stands for "All".

Example question:

Find the solution to $(\sec^2 y)(\sin y)(\tan y) > 0$ for $0 < y < 2\pi$.

A. $0 < y < \dfrac{\pi}{2}, \dfrac{3\pi}{2} < y < 2\pi$

B. $\dfrac{\pi}{2} < y < \dfrac{3\pi}{2}$

C. $0 < y < \pi$

D. $0 < y < \dfrac{\pi}{2}, \pi < y < \dfrac{3\pi}{2}$

E.   Inequality is true for all y in the interval $0 < y < 2\pi$.

Solution:

Notice that $\sec^2 y > 0$ for every y (except at $\dfrac{\pi}{2}$ and $\dfrac{3\pi}{2}$ where it's <u>not defined</u>), so we can forget about it; it doesn't affect the inequality. Now we want $(\sin y)(\tan y) > 0$, so either $\sin y > 0$ and $\tan y > 0$ <u>OR</u> $\sin y < 0$ and $\tan y < 0$.

Now look at the "CAST" diagram:

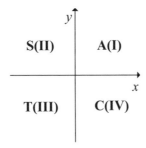

It's easy to see that quadrants I and IV fit the bill, so the answer is A.

Reference Angles

When you have a rotation angle of greater than $90°$, the acute angle between the rotation line and the x-axis is the **reference angle**.

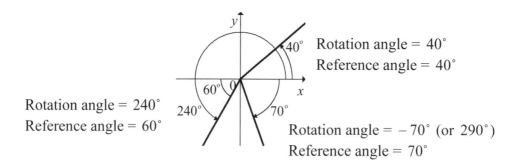

Rotation angle = $40°$
Reference angle = $40°$

Rotation angle = $240°$
Reference angle = $60°$

Rotation angle = $-70°$ (or $290°$)
Reference angle = $70°$

The reference angle can be used with the special triangles and the "CAST" diagram to find the exact values of trigonometric ratios.

Example:

We can find $\cos 135°$ by drawing a quick diagram and realizing that the reference angle $180° - 135° = 45°$.

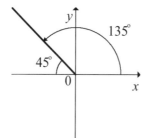

Now $\cos 45° = \dfrac{1}{\sqrt{2}}$, but in <u>quadrant II cosine is negative</u>, hence

$\cos 135° = -\dfrac{1}{\sqrt{2}}$.

Trigonometric Identities

For the SAT Math Level 2 test, there are a few trigonometric identities to know:

Definitions of $\csc\theta$, $\sec\theta$ and $\cot\theta$:

$$\csc\theta = \frac{1}{\sin\theta}, \ \sec\theta = \frac{1}{\cos\theta}, \ \cot\theta = \frac{1}{\tan\theta}$$

Students from a British-based system usually use "cosec" for "csc". The SAT Math Level 2 test will <u>always</u> use "csc".

Pythagorean identities:

$$\sin^2\theta + \cos^2\theta = 1$$

$$1 + \tan^2\theta = \sec^2\theta$$

$$1 + \cot^2\theta = \csc^2\theta$$

Double angle formulas:

$$\cos 2\theta = \cos^2\theta - \sin^2\theta$$

$$\sin 2\theta = 2\sin\theta\cos\theta$$

Others:

$$\sin\theta = \cos(90° - \theta)$$

$$\cos\theta = \sin(90° - \theta)$$

$$\cot\theta = \tan(90° - \theta)$$

Example question:

$$\sin^3 y + \sin y \cos^2 y =$$

A. $\sin^2 y$

B. $\cos y$

C. $\cos y + \sin y$

D. $\cos y - \sin y$

E. $\sin y$

Solution:

Look for a common factor; we can see it's $\sin y$. Factor this out:

$$\sin^3 y + \sin y \cos^2 y = \sin y(\sin^2 y + \cos^2 y)$$
$$= \sin y(1) \quad \{\text{use the identity } \sin^2 y + \cos^2 y = 1\}$$
$$= \sin y \Rightarrow \text{ The answer is E.}$$

Example question:

$(\sin 2t + \cos t)\sec t$ is equivalent to which of the following?

A. $\sin t$

B. $2\sin t + 1$

C. $\cos t$

D.   1

E. $\sin t + \cos t$

Solution:

First, we see $\sin 2t$. There's only one identity with $\sin 2t$, so let's use it. Then

we see $\sec t$. If it was, $\sec^2 t$, we could use one of the Pythagorean identities,

but what about $\sec t$? The only thing is to replace $\sec t$ by its definition: $\dfrac{1}{\cos t}$.

So $(\sin 2t + \cos t)\sec t = (2\sin t \cos t + \cos t)\dfrac{1}{\cos t}$

$$= 2\sin t + 1 \Rightarrow \text{The answer is B.}$$

Trigonometric Equations

To solve a trigonometric equation, you can use either a mixture of algebra and a
calculator, or just use a graphing calculator directly.

Using Algebra

Example question:

Find all the solutions to the equation $4\sin^2 t = 1$ in the interval $0° \le t \le 360°$.

    A. $30°$

    B. $30°$ or $150°$

    C. $30°$, $150°$, $210°$ or $330°$

    D. $330°$

    E. $30°$, $150°$, $270°$ or $300°$

Solution:

Move the 4 over and take the square root:

$$\sin t = \pm \frac{1}{2}$$

We solve each possibility separately:

If $\sin t = \frac{1}{2}$, then the calculator gives $t = 30°$. Using either a graph or the

"CAST" diagram, we find the other solution to be $150°$.

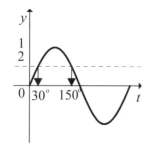 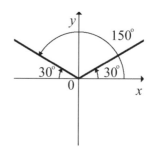

If $\sin t = -\frac{1}{2}$, then we can use either the sketched graph or the "CAST"

diagram to find the other solutions to be $210°$ or $330°$.

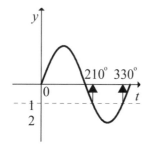 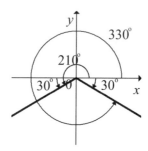

In summary, we have four different solutions: $30°$, $150°$, $210°$ or $330°$. The

answer is C.

Solving Using a Graphing Calculator

With this approach, we solve the equation by graphing both sides and finding their intersection points. Let's look at the previous question from this viewpoint:

Example question:

Find all the solutions to the equation $4\sin^2 t = 1$ in the interval $0° \leq t \leq 360°$.

A. $30°$

B. $30°$ or $150°$

C. $30°$, $150°$, $210°$ or $330°$

D. $330°$

E. $30°$, $150°$, $270°$ or $300°$

Solution:

If we draw the graphs of $y = 4\sin^2 t$ and $y = 1$ we get:

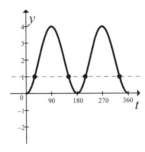

Using the graphing calculator to get the intersection point gives $t = 30°$, $150°$, $210°$ or $330°$. The answer is C.

Note: you don't have to find all four points. From the calculator we can see <u>four intersection points</u>, so it must be choices C or E. Now, once we get 30° as one answer we can see from the graph that the largest solution looks to be about the same distance back from 360°. There's no way it's 300°, it must be 330°, and that means we can confidently go for choice C. We've saved ourselves some time, and although it might not seem like much to save 10 seconds on each question, it adds up to nearly 5 minutes by the end of the test!

Probability and Statistics

There are usually a couple of probability and statistics questions on the SAT Math Level 2 test. Except for permutations and combinations, these are usually pretty straightforward. However, the amount of arithmetic required in some problems can be quite large, so be careful with your accuracy.

Key Ideas

Probability

The probability that something will happen is defined as

$$\text{Probability of a success} = P(\text{success}) = \frac{\text{number of possible successes}}{\text{total number of possible outcomes}}$$

Example:

If you throw a single normal die, then $P(\text{a prime number}) = \dfrac{3}{6}$

because there are 3 possible successes: 2, 3 or 5, and there are 6

possible outcomes: 1, 2, 3, 4, 5 or 6.

Events

The word "event" is generally used for a particular outcome. For example, if E is the event "throw an even number with one die", then the probability of event $E = P(E) = 0.5$.

The Complement

The **complement** of an event refers to all outcomes in which the event <u>doesn't</u> happen.

If A is any event, A' ("A not") is the complement event.

In some books you might see a different notation for A' such as A^c or $\bar{A}$.

Example:

You throw two normal dice. The event you want is X: "throw at least one prime". The complement would be the event X': "you <u>don't</u> throw any prime (with two dice)".

A very useful formula to remember is

$$P(A') = 1 - P(A)$$

In other words, this says the probability of A **not** happening is 1 minus the probability that **does** happen.

Addition Rule

If you have two events A, B, then the probability that A or B happens is

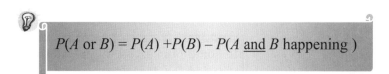

$$P(A \text{ or } B) = P(A) + P(B) - P(A \underline{\text{ and }} B \text{ happening })$$

> In math, "or" usually means A or B **or both together**. Be careful, as this is not the way we usually use this word in everyday English!

Example:

Suppose you throw a single die and A is the event "throw an even number"

and B is the event "throw a prime".

Then, $P(A \text{ or } B) = P(A) + P(B) - P(A \,\&\, B)$

$$= \frac{3}{6} + \frac{3}{6} - \frac{1}{6}$$ [there are 3 evens out of 6 numbers, 3 primes out of 6 numbers, and two is the number which is even <u>and</u> prime]

$$= \frac{5}{6}$$

Multiplication Rule

If you have two independent events A, B, then the probability that A and B happen is

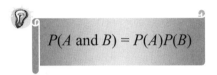

$$P(A \text{ and } B) = P(A)P(B)$$

Example question:

Two 12-sided dice are thrown. Each die is numbered 1, 2,…, 12. If A is the event "throw at least one multiple of 3", find $P(A)$.

A. 0.23

B. 0.32

C. 0.50

D. 0.56

E. 0.68

Solution:

The clue is the words "at least". This means we'll go for the complementary event A'.

Now, A' = "Don't throw at least one multiple of 3 with the two dice"

   = "Don't throw **any** multiples of 3 with the two dice"

So A' = "Don't throw a multiple of 3 with the first die **and** then don't throw a multiple of 3 with the second die"

But P(don't throw a multiple of 3 with a single die) $= \dfrac{8}{12}$ because there are 8

non-multiples of 3: 1, 2, 4, 5, 7, 8,10 and 11.

Using the multiplication rule: $P(A') = \dfrac{8}{12} \times \dfrac{8}{12}$

So $P(A) = 1 - P(A') = 1 - \dfrac{8}{12} \times \dfrac{8}{12} = 0.555\ldots = 0.56$ (correct to 2 decimal

places) $\Rightarrow$ The answer is D.

Notice in this question that the denominators are the same each time because you don't use up the numbers just because you've thrown them once! But in the next question the denominators are different.

Example question:

In a bag there are 6 red and 4 blue balls. Find the probability of picking 2 blue balls, if the first ball is **not** replaced in the bag.

A.   0.13

B.   0.25

C.   0.33

D.   0.41

E.   0.60

Solution:

P(picking a blue ball on the first pick) $= \dfrac{4}{10}$

But we now have only **9 balls left**, of which **3 are blue**.

So P(picking a blue ball on the second pick) $= \dfrac{3}{9}$

Using the multiplication rule:

P(success) $= P$(blue on the first **and** blue on the second picks)

$$= \frac{4}{10} \times \frac{3}{9}$$

$$= 0.13 \text{ (correct to 2 decimal places)} \Rightarrow \text{The answer is A.}$$

Tree Diagrams

When we have multi-stage probability problems, **a tree diagram** can be useful.

Example question:

A woman takes a driving test. The probability she will pass on her first attempt

is 0.7. If she fails, then the probability she will pass on any successive attempt is

0.8. What is the probability she will pass in less than 4 attempts?

A.   0.008

B.   0.06

C.   0.56

D.   0.68

E.   0.988

Solution:

Draw a tree diagram with 3 stages. Of course, when she passes she will not take any further tests!

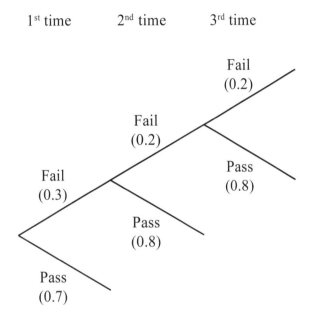

1st time   2nd time   3rd time

Fail (0.2)

Fail (0.2)

Pass (0.8)

Fail (0.3)

Pass (0.8)

Pass (0.7)

Now we want P(pass with less than 4 attempts). But this is the same as

P(pass on 1st attempt) + P(pass on 2nd attempt **and fail on 1st attempt**) +

P(pass on 3rd attempt **and fail on both 1st and 2nd attempts**)

$= 0.7 + (0.3)(0.8) + (0.3)(0.2)(0.8)$

$= 0.988 \Rightarrow$ The answer is E.

Can you see a faster method? We could have used the complementary event technique:

P(pass in 3 or fewer attempts) $= 1 - P$(fail all 3 attempts)

$$= 1 - (0.3)(0.2)(0.2)$$

$$= 0.988$$

We have the same result!

Conditional Probability

Suppose you throw a fair die. It's pretty clear that $P(\text{odd number}) = 0.5$ because there are 6 equally likely possible outcomes, all from the set $\{1, 2, 3, 4, 5, 6\}$, and we want 3 of them: $\{1, 3, 5\}$. But now suppose we ask this question:

What is $P(\text{odd number } \textbf{given that it is a prime number})$?

This is more tricky. First, we are given the new information that <u>we are dealing with only primes</u>, so our set of possible outcomes is down to $\{2, 3, 5\}$. Now, how many of these are odd ? Clearly there are two: 3 and 5. So we can now answer our question:

$$P(\text{odd number given it is a prime number}) = \frac{2}{3}$$

We often use the symbol '$|$' instead of the word 'given', so we'd usually write the above as

$$P(\text{odd number } | \text{ it is a prime number}) = \frac{2}{3}$$

Sometimes you can do these **conditional probability** questions like this, from first principles; however, there is also a formula which can be handy.

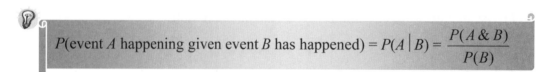

$$P(\text{event } A \text{ happening given event } B \text{ has happened}) = P(A \,|\, B) = \frac{P(A \,\&\, B)}{P(B)}$$

Don't confuse the "$|$" symbol with the "$/$" sign, meaning division. $P(A \,|\, B)$ does NOT mean $P(A \div B)$!

Example:

If you draw a card from a pack of 52 playing cards, then the above formula tells us

$P(\text{ Ace } | \text{ Black }) = \dfrac{P(\text{Ace \& Black})}{P(\text{Black})}$. Now, there are 2 aces which are also black

(the ace of spades and the ace of clubs), so $P(\text{Ace \& Black}) = \dfrac{2}{52}$. In addition, there

are 26 black cards, so $P(\text{Black}) = \dfrac{26}{52}$. Putting these two together we get

$$P(\text{Ace } | \text{ Black}) = \dfrac{P(\text{Ace \& Black})}{P(\text{Black})} = \dfrac{\dfrac{2}{52}}{\dfrac{26}{52}} = \dfrac{1}{13}.$$

Example question:

S and T are two random events. If $P(S) = 0.3$, $P(T \text{ or } S) = 0.9$ and $P(T | S) = 0.6$, what is $P(T)$?

A.   0.78

B.   0.70

C.   0.58

D.   0.54

E.   0.18

Solution:

We will start with the conditional probability formula, $P(T \mid S) = \dfrac{P(T \& S)}{P(S)}$

So we have $0.6 = \dfrac{P(T \& S)}{0.3}$

$$0.18 = P(T \& S)$$

Now we use the general addition formula:

$P(T \text{ or } S) = P(T) + P(S) - P(T \& S)$

Plugging in the numbers gives us: $0.9 = P(T) + 0.3 - 0.18$

$$0.78 = P(T) \implies \text{The answer is A.}$$

Permutations

Some questions are about the number of ways you can <u>arrange</u> a set of things. If the order is important, then we call it a **permutation**.

Example:

There are **6** permutations of the letters A, B and C if two different letters are chosen:

$$AB \leftrightarrow BA$$
$$AC \leftrightarrow CA$$
$$BC \leftrightarrow CB$$

The Multiplication Principle

If a restaurant has 4 choices for a starter, 5 for a main course and 3 for desert (this is a pretty poor restaurant!), how many possible dinners could you select?

The answer is 4 choices × 5 choices 3 choices = 60 choices.

The above is an example of the **multiplication principle**:

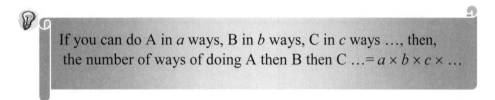

If you can do A in a ways, B in b ways, C in c ways ..., then, the number of ways of doing A then B then C ...= $a \times b \times c \times ...$

Example question:

How many ways can the letters P, Q, R, S, T, U be arranged if 4 of the letters are used each time and each letter cannot be used more than once per arrangement?

A. 360

B. 420

C. 426

D. 892

E. 1296

Solution:

We have 4 spaces to fill: _____ _____ _____ _____

We can fill the first space in 6 ways, the 2nd in 5 ways (because we can't use a letter once it's been used), the 3rd space in 4 ways and the last space in 3 ways.

Altogether the total number of ways = (6)(5)(4)(3) = 360 ways.

The answer is A.

Example:

If we *were* allowed to repeat letters in the previous example, then the total number of arrangements would have been (6)(6)(6)(6) = 1296 ways.

Formula for Permutations

There is a formula for working out some permutations. Be careful! It is only used if you are trying to find the number of permutations of r objects taken from n objects. This is the same as your $_nP_r$ or P_r^n key on your calculator. A very few questions may need you to use this formula:

$$_nP_r \text{ or } P_r^n = \frac{n!}{(n-r)!}$$

Combinations

A **combination** is like a permutation but the <u>order of the things is not important</u>, i.e., the combination AB is the same as the combination BA.

> ### Example:
>
> There are only 3 possible combinations of the letters A, B, C taken 2 at a time and with no letter repeated:
>
> AB
> AC
> BC

Key words to look out for are **choice** or **choose**. If you see these words, the question probably has something to do with combinations.

Using the Calculator

Unless you have a small number of items, it takes too long to list all the possible combinations. There could be millions of them! There <u>is</u> a formula for combinations (we'll see it a bit later) but it's <u>much</u> faster just to use your calculator's combination key: it will look something like $_nC_r$ or C_r^n. n is the total number of things you are choosing from, and r is the number of things you want to select. Find out what your combination key looks like and how it works now!

Example question:

There are 8 male students and 13 female students in a class. In how many ways can the teacher choose a committee of 2 male and 4 female students?

A.   14404

B.   16996

C.   18518

D.   20020

E.   22580

Solution:

First, this is not a straight permutation or combination question. It's a bit of both! We have two spaces to fill:

number of male students and **number of female students**

This is the permutation part. But the number of students in each group is a *choose* problem; we don't care in what order the students are selected *within each group*.

Now, number of male student choices = choose 2 things from 8 things

$$= C_2^8$$

$$= 28 \text{ (using calculator)}$$

Number of female student choices = choose 4 things from 13 things

$$= C_4^{13}$$

$$= 715 \text{ (using calculator again!)}$$

So the number ways = $28 \times 715 = 20020 \Rightarrow$ The answer is D.

Formula for Combinations

Just like the permutation case, there is a formula for working out the combination of

r things taken from n things:

$$_nC_r \text{ or } C_r^n = \frac{n!}{(n-r)!r!}$$

The Three Averages:
Mean, Median and Mode

Although this is basic stuff, don't get these three **averages** mixed up.

$$\text{Mean} = \frac{\text{sum of values}}{\text{number of items}}$$

Median = value of the $\left(\dfrac{n+1}{2}\right)^{th}$ item when the items are arranged in order of increasing value. If n is odd, you just take the middle value of the items. If n is even, then you take the mean of the two numbers on either side.

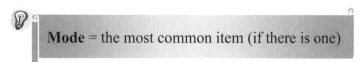

Mode = the most common item (if there is one)

Example:

If we have the items 5, 7, 7, 3, 8, 10, 8 and 6, we calculate the three averages as follows:

$$\text{Mean} = \frac{5+7+7+3+8+10+8+6}{8} = \textbf{6.75}$$

To find the median, we first arrange the items in order: 3, 5, 6, 7, 7, 8, 8, 10

$$\text{Median} = \left(\frac{8+1}{2}\right)^{th} \text{item} = 4.5^{th} \text{item. This implies we take the mean of the}$$

4th and 5th items, which is $\frac{7+7}{2} = \textbf{7}$.

Mode: there is no **unique** mode as there are two 7s and two 8s.

Two Useful Properties of the Mean

You can sometimes speed yourself up by using one or both of these properties of the mean:

1. If you **add or subtract** the same number from <u>all</u> the data items, then the mean changes by the **same amount**.

2. If you **multiply or divide** <u>each</u> data item by the same number, then the mean is **multiplied or divided** by the same amount.

Example question:

A teacher marks 7 test papers with the following marks: 6, 8, 8, 4, 5, 9 and 5.

She then realizes that she should have given each paper an extra mark. What

is the difference between the new mean and the old mean mark?

A.   0

B.   0.135

C.   0.5

D.   1

E.   3

Solution:

We could find the mean of all 7 numbers, add one to each number and then find

the mean again. This is not difficult but it takes a bit of time. A much faster way

is to use property 1 above. If you add one to each item, then the mean will also

increase by one. That implies the difference between the old and new means is 1.

The answer is D.

Standard Deviation

Although you may well get a question on means, medians or modes on the SAT Math Level 2 test, it's rare to get a question on standard deviations; it might just happen, however, so read on if you've never met them before.

Remember than the **mean** (sometimes called the **arithmetic mean**) of a set of numbers is a kind of 'best guess' for a number that represents a given set of numbers. The standard deviation is a measure which tells you how <u>spread out</u> the data is about this "best guess". The rough idea you want to have about the standard deviation is that:

small standard deviation → data is mostly clustered around the mean

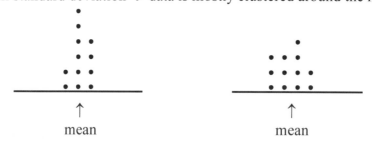

large standard deviation → data is mostly spread out, far from the mean

Calculating the Standard Deviation

There is a formula for this, but it's unnecessary to use it, as any serious calculator will be able to calculate the standard deviation after you have entered the data. Look on your calculator for a "σ_n" key. In fact, it's very unusual ever to have to do even this, but there are a couple of properties of the standard deviation that you should know about:

1. If you **add or subtract** the same number from <u>all</u> the data items, then the standard deviation is **unchanged**. (This is different from the mean.)

2. If you **multiply or divide** each data item by the same number, then the standard deviation is **multiplied or divided** the same way. (This is the same as with the mean.)

Example:

Using a calculator, we find the standard deviation of the numbers 5, 6, 8, 10, 10, 11 and 14 is **2.85**. The standard deviation of 10, 11, 13, 15, 15, 16 and 19 is also **2.85** because we've just added 5 to each number. The standard deviation of 10, 12, 16, 20, 20, 22 and 28 is **2** × 2.85 = **5.7** because we multiplied each number in the data set by 2.

Example question:

If σ is the standard deviation of a set of numbers, then the variance is defined as σ^2. For a group of 10 numbers, the variance is calculated as 5.76. If each of the 10 numbers were multiplied by 3, the new value of the variance would be

A.   2.4

B.   7.2

C.   17.28

D.   33.18

E.   51.84

Solution:

We are told $\sigma^2 = 5.76$ so $\sigma = 2.4$

> σ is always > 0 so we don't need to bother with the negative square root.

Now if we multiply each of the ten numbers by 3, then the new standard deviation will be three times the old one.

So the new standard deviation $= 3 \times 2.4 = 7.2$

To get the new variance we just square this: $7.2^2 = 51.84$

The answer is E.

Miscellaneous Topics

*"Miscellaneous" covers all the bits and pieces left over: limits, sequences and series, vectors, logic and proofs, and complex numbers. This doesn't mean that these topics are unimportant in any way, but if you're **really** short of time then you should skip this chapter and focus on the **big three**: algebra, trigonometry and functions.*

Key Ideas

Limits

These are easy to spot: they're the algebraic expressions with something like " $\lim_{x \to}$ "stuck in front of them. There are two types: <u>finite</u> and <u>infinite</u>. In each case we want to see what the expression to the right of the lim sign gets close to as the variable gets closer to a particular value.

Finite Limits

These are where x gets closer to a particular number, e.g. $\lim_{x \to 2}$ or $\lim_{x \to \frac{1}{2}}$.

Finite limits are usually solved by a <u>three stage process</u>:

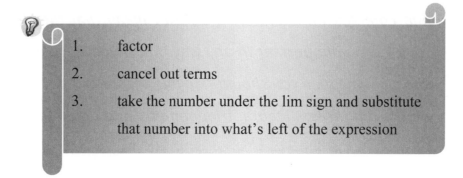

1. factor
2. cancel out terms
3. take the number under the lim sign and substitute that number into what's left of the expression

Example question:

What is the value of $\displaystyle\lim_{x \to 4} \frac{x^2 - 3x - 4}{x - 4}$?

A. -3

B. 0

C. 5

D. 8

E.   Undefined

> Note you can't just substitute $x = 4$ into this because you'll get $\dfrac{0}{0}$.

Solution:

First, factor (in this case, just the numerator) to get $\displaystyle\lim_{x \to 4} \frac{(x - 4)(x + 1)}{x - 4}$.

Now cancel the term $(x - 4)$ off the top and bottom:

$$\lim_{x \to 4} \frac{(x - 4)(x + 1)}{x - 4} = \lim_{x \to 4}(x + 1)$$

Finally plug the 4, under the lim sign, into what's left: $4 + 1 = 5$.

The answer is C.

Infinite Limits

These start with a "$\lim\limits_{x\to\infty}$" sign, so we're trying to see what happens to the expression as x gets very, very large. The key "equation" to remember here is that "$\dfrac{1}{\infty} = 0$".

Example question:

Find $\lim\limits_{x\to\infty} \dfrac{2x}{x-10}$.

A. -10

B. $-\dfrac{1}{5}$

C. 0

D. 2

E.   Undefined

Solution:

First, to get "$\dfrac{1}{\infty}$" in the expression, divide the numerator and denominator by x:

$$\lim_{x\to\infty} \frac{2x}{x-10} = \lim_{x\to\infty} \frac{2}{1-\dfrac{10}{x}}$$

Now as $x \to \infty$, $\dfrac{10}{x} \to 0$, so the fraction gets closer and closer to $\dfrac{2}{1} = 2$. The answer is D.

Sequences

There are usually a couple of questions on the test which deal with arithmetic or geometric sequences.

Arithmetic Sequences

These have a **constant difference** between successive terms.

Example:

7, 10, 13, 16, … is an arithmetic sequence with first term 7 and constant difference 3.

4, 6, 9, 13, … is **not** an arithmetic sequence because the difference between 4 and 6 is 2, but between 6 and 9 it's 3.

To find the nth term of an arithmetic sequence we use the following formula:

$$a_n = a + (n-1)d$$

where a_n is the nth term,

a is the value of the 1st term and

d is the common difference between any two successive terms

Example question:

What is the 100th term of the sequence 7, 6.8, 6.6, 6.4, ...?

A.   −12.8

B.   −10

C.   0

D.   1.6

E.   3.6

Solution:

First, we see it is an arithmetic sequence with $a = 7$ and $d = -0.2$. Use the arithmetic sequence formula:

$$a_{100} = 7 + (100 - 1)(-0.2) = -12.8 \Rightarrow \text{The answer is A.}$$

Geometric Sequences

These have a **constant ratio** between successive terms.

Example:

36, 18, 9, 4.5, … is a geometric sequence with first term 36 and constant ratio $\frac{1}{2}$.

1, 4, 9, 16, … is **not** a geometric sequence because the ratio is $\frac{4}{1}$ between the first two terms but it's $\frac{9}{4}$ between the 3rd and 2nd terms.

To find the nth term of a geometric sequence we use the formula

$$a_n = ar^{n-1}$$

where a_n is the nth term,

a is the value of the 1st term and

r is the constant ratio between any two successive terms.

Example question:

What is the value of the first term of the geometric sequence 8, 12, ... which is greater than 2000?

A.   2027.8

B.   2135.0

C.   2335.4

D.   2401.9

E.   2411.7

Solution:

We are told the sequence is geometric so we only need the first two terms to find a and r. So we have $a = 8$ and $r = \dfrac{12}{8} = 1.5$.

We need to solve the inequality $8(1.5)^{n-1} > 2000$.

Divide both sides by 8 to get $(1.5)^{n-1} > 250$.

The key step is to <u>take logs</u> of both sides, so the term $(n-1)$ will drop down:

$(n-1)\log 1.5 > \log 250$

$$n - 1 > \frac{\log 250}{\log 1.5}$$

$$n > \frac{\log 250}{\log 1.5} + 1$$

$$n > 14.61....$$

> **Be careful when dividing by logs!** For example, log 0.5 is negative, so you'd need to flip any inequality sign over if dividing by it. (Here, log 1.5 is positive so we're o.k.)

But n is an **integer**, and the smallest integer greater than 14.61… is 15.

To find the value of the 15th term, put $n = 15$ into the expression $8(1.5)^{n-1}$

giving 2335.43… = 2335.4 (correct to 1 decimal place).

The answer is C.

Series

Series are what you get when you replace the commas of a sequence by "+" signs:

Example:

4, 7, 10, 13, … is a <u>sequence</u>.

4 + 7 + 10 + 13 + … is a <u>series</u>.

There are two formulas you should remember for finding finite arithmetic and geometric series and one for infinite geometric series:

Arithmetic Series

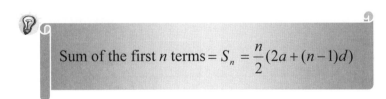

$$\text{Sum of the first } n \text{ terms} = S_n = \frac{n}{2}(2a + (n-1)d)$$

> **Example:**
>
> The sum of the first 50 terms of the arithmetic series
>
> $0.2 + 0.5 + 0.8 + 1.1 + ...$ is $\frac{50}{2}(2 \times 0.2 + (50-1) \times 0.3) = 377.5$,
>
> where we just use the formula directly.

Here's a more difficult example:

Example question:

In an arithmetic sequence 100, 93, 86, 79, … , what is the least number of terms that need to be added together to make a sum less than 0?

A.   24

B.   26

C.   28

D.   30

E.   32

Solution:

In the sequence we have $a = 100$, $d = -7$. We need to find n so that $S_n < 0$, but we don't know the value of n. We have to solve this inequality:

$$\frac{n}{2}(2 \times 100 + (n-1) \times -7) < 0$$

$$\frac{n}{2}(207 - 7n) < 0$$

$$n(207 - 7n) < 0$$

Now this is a quadratic inequality. We could solve it by graphing it, but because we're given choices, it's just as fast to plug them into the inequality and see what works:

$24(207 - 7 \times 24) = 936 > 0$

$26(207 - 7 \times 26) = 650 > 0$

$28(207 - 7 \times 28) = 308 > 0$

$30(207 - 7 \times 30) = -90 < 0$

There's no need to check the last choice because we're looking for the smallest such n, so the answer is D.

Geometric Series

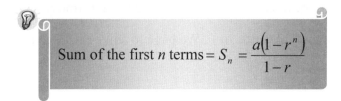

$$\text{Sum of the first } n \text{ terms} = S_n = \frac{a(1-r^n)}{1-r}$$

Example:

The sum of the first 12 terms of the series $2 + 6 + 18 + 54 + \ldots$ is given by the geometric series sum formula with $a = 2$, $r = 3$ and $n = 12$:

$$S_{12} = \frac{2(1-3^{12})}{1-3} = 531440$$

Example question:

What is the sum of the first 19 terms of the sum $ab - ab^3 + ab^5 - ab^7 + \ldots$, where $b \neq 1$?

A. $\dfrac{a(1-b^{19})}{1-b}$

B. $\dfrac{a(1+b^{19})}{1+b^2}$

C. $\dfrac{ab(1+b^{38})}{1+b^2}$

D. $\dfrac{ab(1-b^{38})}{1-b}$

E. $\dfrac{a(1-b^{38})}{1-b}$

Solution:

First, we notice that this is a geometric series, the common ratio is $r = -b^2$.

We now use the geometric sum formula:

$$S_{19} = \frac{ab(1 - (-b^2)^{19})}{1 + b^2}$$

$$= \frac{ab(1 + b^{38})}{1 + b^2} \Rightarrow \text{The answer is C.}$$

Infinite Geometric Series

In certain circumstances, it may be possible to add up an **infinite** set of numbers and still get a finite answer. On the SAT Math Level 2 test, they will only ask you about **infinite geometric series**. There is a simple formula for this:

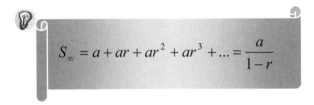

$$S_\infty = a + ar + ar^2 + ar^3 + \ldots = \frac{a}{1 - r}$$

This formula only works **provided that $-1 < r < 1$**.

> A lot of students forget that the common ratio **must** lie in this range for the formula to work.

> **Example:**
>
> To find $4 - 2 + 1 - \dfrac{1}{2} + ...$, we use the infinite sum formula
>
> with $a = 4$ and $r = -\dfrac{1}{2}$.
>
> This gives $S_\infty = \dfrac{4}{1-(-\dfrac{1}{2})} = \dfrac{8}{3}$.

Example question:

The first term of a geometric sequence consisting of positive terms is 3. If the third term of the sequence is 1, what is the sum to infinity?

A.   6.084

B.   7.098

C.   7.006

D.   8.256

E.   8.845

Solution:

First, we know that the third term of *any* geometric sequence is ar^2. The

question also tells us that the first term, a, is 3. So we get $3r^2 = 1$.

Therefore, $r = \pm\sqrt{\dfrac{1}{3}}$. But the sequence consists of **positive terms**, so we

reject the $-\sqrt{\dfrac{1}{3}}$ as a possibility, and we choose $r = \sqrt{\dfrac{1}{3}}$.

Now we use the infinite sum formula (which will work, as $r = \sqrt{\dfrac{1}{3}}$ is in the

necessary range) to get

$$S_\infty = \frac{3}{1 - \sqrt{\dfrac{1}{3}}} = 7.0980... = 7.098 \text{ (correct to 3 decimal places)}$$

The answer is B.

Logic and Proofs

Occasionally you'll see a logic or proof question on the SAT Math Level 2 test. Usually you can solve these just by thinking logically(!). There is some terminology that may be unfamiliar, however, so look through the following material to see if there is anything that's new to you.

Converse

Math is full of theorems and proofs. They can all be written in the following form:

IF X is true, **THEN** Y is true.

where X and Y are things like " n is a prime", " $\triangle ABC$ is a right-angled triangle", " $a^2 + b^2 = c^2$ " etc. These are called conditional sentences.

> To get the **converse** of a conditional statement, you change the places of the X and Y.

Contrapositive

Suppose we have a conditional sentence of the form

IF X, **THEN** Y.

To get the **contrapositive** of the conditional statement, you make this conditional:

IF not Y,   **THEN** not X.

Although they appear different, they are actually saying the same thing. Look at this:

Example:

Suppose you have the conditional statement

If n is positive, then $2n$ is positive.

      X   Y

which is true, of course.

The contrapositive statement would be

If $2n$ is **not** positive, then n is **not** positive.

    not Y   not X

Although it sounds slightly weird, if you think about it the contrapositive *is* saying the same thing as the original statement.

Don't confuse the contrapositive with the converse. A conditional statement and its associated contrapositive say the same thing, just in different ways. The converse of a conditional statement is making a *new* claim, one that may or may not be true, even if the original statement is true.

Example:

If *n* is a prime number bigger than 2, then *n* is an odd integer.

X Y

If we flip the two statements X and Y around, we get the **converse**:

If *n* is an odd integer, then *n* is a prime number bigger than 2.

But this is **not true**! There are lots of odd integers that aren't prime. So this tells us that just because a conditional statement is true, that doesn't mean the converse is. It may or may not be.

Counterexample

A **counterexample** is an example which proves that a particular claim is **wrong**.

Example:

If someone says that "All primes are odd," you can provide a **counterexample** by saying, "You're wrong; two is prime but it's even."

Example question:

What value of n provides a counterexample to the statement "$2^n + 3^n$ is a prime number for all non-negative integers n." ?

A. -1

B. 0

C. 1

D. 2

E. 3

Solution:

The simplest strategy is sometimes the best; we will check the options one-by-one to see which one does <u>not</u> give a prime as the answer. That will be a counterexample.

$n = -1 \Rightarrow 2^{-1} + 3^{-1} = \dfrac{1}{2} + \dfrac{1}{3} = \dfrac{5}{6}$, not a prime. BUT this is NOT a counterexample! If we check the statement carefully, it says "$2^n + 3^n$ is a prime number for all **non-negative** integers n." Because -1 is a negative integer it's actually irrelevant as a test of the statement; it neither confirms nor disproves it. We could have just skipped this answer choice straightaway.

$n = 0 \Rightarrow 2^n + 3^n = 2^0 + 3^0 = 1 + 1 = 2$, a prime.

$n = 1 \Rightarrow 2^n + 3^n = 2^1 + 3^1 = 2 + 3 = 5$, a prime.

$n = 2 \Rightarrow 2^n + 3^n = 2^2 + 3^2 = 4 + 9 = 13$, a prime.

$n = 3 \Rightarrow 2^n + 3^n = 2^3 + 3^3 = 8 + 27 = 35$, *not* a prime, so the case $n = 3$ provides a counterexample.

The answer is E.

Direct and Indirect Proofs

To prove things in mathematics, we are really proving conditional statements:

IF X is true, **THEN** Y is true.

For instance, **IF** you inscribe a quadrilateral in a circle, **THEN** the opposite angles of the quadrilateral are supplementary.

There are two main ways to prove "If X is true, then Y is true" statements.

1.   **Assume X is true** and then try to show that Y must follow. This is the obvious way of proving things and is called a **direct proof**.

2.   **Assume Y is false** and then show that **X is false**. This is not so obvious and is called an **indirect proof**.

You can see that it makes sense, though, by thinking about the following non-mathematical situation. Suppose I want to show that this statement is true:

If it rains, then Karl always takes an umbrella.

I could prove it in two ways:

1.   Assume it is raining and then show Karl always takes his umbrella (direct proof).

or

2.   Assume Karl <u>doesn't</u> take his umbrella and then show it's <u>never</u> raining (indirect proof).

Example question:

In order to prove that the statement "If $ax^2 + bx + c = 0$ has two distinct real roots, then $b^2 - 4ac > 0$", an indirect proof would start with the assumption that

A. $ax^2 + bx + c = 0$

B. $b^2 - 4ac > 0$

C. $b^2 - 4ac \leq 0$

D. $ax^2 + bx + c < 0$

E. $ax^2 + bx + c > 0$

Solution:

To prove "**IF** X is true, **THEN** Y is true" using an indirect proof, we start by assuming Y is <u>false</u>. In this question, Y is "$b^2 - 4ac > 0$". If we assume this is false, we're assuming that $b^2 - 4ac \leq 0$. The answer is C.

Vectors

The vector questions on the SAT Math Level 2 test are fairly straightforward. If you've done some physics, then you should not have many problems. If you've never done vectors, you'll need to read this carefully.

Component Vectors

We represent a vector by giving the x, y and z (if it's a 3D vector) components. These tell you how far to move in the various directions from the initial point of the vector. The initial point **does not have to be the origin**. The end of a vector is the **terminal point**, and has an arrow.

Example:

The vector $\begin{pmatrix} 5 \\ -2 \end{pmatrix}$ is represented by arrows like this:

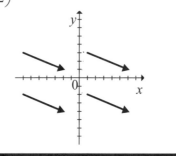

There are two other notations:

1.   row notation: $(5, -2)$

2. ij notation: $5i - 2j$

> Don't worry about what the i and j mean. Just think of them as markers telling you which is the x direction component (i), and y direction component (j) [or z direction (k) if it's 3D]

Be careful with the row notation. Don't confuse it with the coordinates of a point.

Example:

The 3D vector $\begin{pmatrix} 0 \\ 6 \\ 2 \end{pmatrix}$ could also be written as $(0, 6, 2)$ or $6\boldsymbol{j} + 2\boldsymbol{k}$.

We often use capital letters to represent the initial and terminal points and bold lower case letters to represent vectors:

Vector $\overrightarrow{AB}$ Vector $\boldsymbol{u}$

Example:

If A is the point $(5, 7)$ and B is the point $(8, 9)$, then the vector $\overrightarrow{AB} = \begin{pmatrix} 3 \\ 2 \end{pmatrix}$

looks like this:

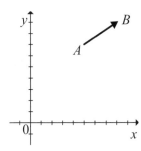

The vector $\overrightarrow{BA} = \begin{pmatrix} -3 \\ -2 \end{pmatrix}$, so it's important to watch which way you're going.

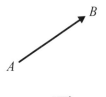

$\overrightarrow{AB}$

$\overrightarrow{BA}$

Magnitude of a Vector

The <u>magnitude</u> of a vector is its <u>length</u>. Just use the Pythagorean Theorem (2D or 3D version as necessary).

Example:

If $a = \begin{pmatrix} 4 \\ -1 \end{pmatrix}$, then the magnitude of $a = |a| = \sqrt{4^2 + (-1)^2} = \sqrt{17}$.

Don't confuse this symbol with the absolute value of a number.

Adding and Subtracting Vectors

This is straightforward. Just add or subtract the components as appropriate.

Example:

$(3, 6, -5) + (2, 0, 7) = (5, 6, 2)$.

$5i + k - (2i + 3j - 5k) = 3i - 3j + 6k$

Multiplication by a Scalar

On the SAT Math Level 2 test, "scalar" is just a fancy word for a real number. When we multiply a vector by a scalar, we just <u>multiply each component</u> by the same number:

> **Example:**
>
> If $a = -3i + 5j + k$, then $5a = -15i + 25j + 5k$.

> There are, in fact, several ways to **multiply two vectors** together that are taught in more advanced courses. But you will not be expected to know about these for the SAT Math Level 2 test.

Example question:

If $u = \begin{pmatrix} -3 \\ 2 \end{pmatrix}$ and $v = \begin{pmatrix} x \\ -1 \end{pmatrix}$, what is x if $|u + 2v| = 10$?

A. 5

B. −3.5 or 6.5

C. 6.5

D. −5

E. −5 or 8.5

Solution:

First, $\quad \mathbf{u} + 2\mathbf{v} = \begin{pmatrix} -3 \\ 2 \end{pmatrix} + 2 \begin{pmatrix} x \\ -1 \end{pmatrix} = \begin{pmatrix} -3+2x \\ 0 \end{pmatrix}$

So, $\quad \left| \mathbf{u} + 2\mathbf{v} \right| = \sqrt{(-3+2x)^2 + 0^2} \quad$ (Pythagorean Theomrem)

We want to solve $\left| \mathbf{u} + 2\mathbf{v} \right| = 10$

$$\sqrt{(-3+2x)^2} = 10$$

So we have $\quad (-3+2x)^2 = 100$

$$-3 + 2x = \pm 10$$

$$x = -3.5 \text{ or } 6.5 \implies \text{The answer is B.}$$

Parallel Vectors

Two vectors are called **parallel** if one is a **scalar multiple** of another.

Example:

$(-6, 8, 10)$ is parallel to $(-3, 4, 5)$ because $(-6, 8, 10) = 2(-3, 4, 5)$.

$2\mathbf{i} + 2\mathbf{j} + 2\mathbf{k}$ is <u>not</u> parallel to $6\mathbf{i} - 6\mathbf{j} + 6\mathbf{k}$ because you'd need to multiply the first vector by 3 to get the x components to match up, but by -3 to get the y components the same.

Unit Vectors

A **unit vector** has magnitude (length) 1.

Example question:

If vector **a** is a unit vector parallel to (3, 0, –4), then **a** =

A.   (0.3, 0, –0.4)

B.   (1, 1, 1) or (–1, –1, –1)

C.   (0.6, 0, –0.8) or (–0.6, 0, 0.8)

D.   (1, 0, –1)

E.   (0.6, 0, –0.8)

Solution:

The magnitude of vector (3, 0, –4) = $\sqrt{3^2 + 0^2 + (-4)^2} = 5$.

If we divide each component of (3, 0, –4) by 5, we get a new, **unit** vector:

$\left(\dfrac{3}{5}, 0, -\dfrac{4}{5}\right)$. (You can check that the magnitude is actually 1.)

Now the question says **a** is parallel to this vector, but if we multiply a non-zero

vector by any number **other than 1 or –1**, we will change its magnitude.

So $\boldsymbol{a} = \left(\dfrac{3}{5}, 0, -\dfrac{4}{5}\right)$ or $-\left(\dfrac{3}{5}, 0, -\dfrac{4}{5}\right)$ ⇒ The answer is C.

Non-component Vectors

These are vectors which are drawn as line segments, without any coordinate system or components.

Adding

There are two equivalent ways of adding non-component vectors: the **parallelogram method** or the **head-to-tail method**. Look at the following example to see how they work.

Example:

Find $p + q$ if p and q are two vectors as in the following diagram:

To use the **parallelogram method**, we slide the vectors so they have the same initial point and then form a parallelogram. $p + q$ is the vector represented by the <u>diagonal</u> from the initial point:

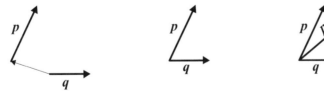

To use the **head-to-tail method**, we slide the head of one vector to the tail (initial point) of the other. *p* + *q* is the vector represented by the line segment making the third side of a triangle:

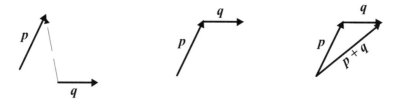

Subtracting

In ordinary arithmetic it's obvious that $a - b = a + (-b)$. So we define the **subtraction** of two vectors, *a* and *b*, $a - b$, to be $a + (-b)$.

Example:

If *p* and *q* are as in the following diagram: *p* − *q* looks like this:

Here we used the parallelogram method to add together *p* and −*q*, but you could also use the head-to-tail method.

Multiplication by a Scalar

To multiply a vector by a scalar (remember which is just a number), we just stretch it by the scalar factor. If the scalar is negative, we stretch it and <u>change its direction</u> the other way round.

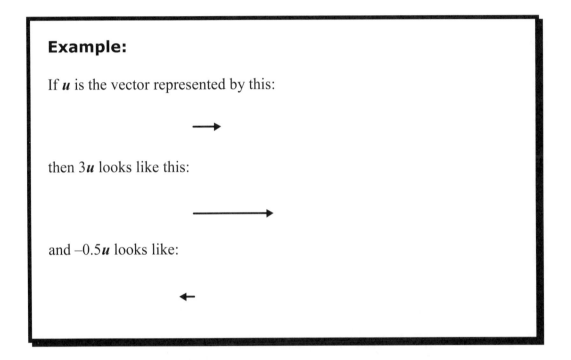

Example:

If *u* is the vector represented by this:

then 3*u* looks like this:

and –0.5*u* looks like:

Example question:

In $\triangle ABC$, $\overrightarrow{AB}$ represents vector a and side $\overrightarrow{AC}$ represents vector b. M is the midpoint of $\overline{BC}$. $\overrightarrow{AM} =$

A. $\dfrac{1}{2}(b - a)$

B. $\dfrac{3}{2}(a - b)$

C. $\dfrac{1}{2}(a - b)$

D. $\dfrac{3}{2}(a + b)$

E. $\dfrac{1}{2}(a + b)$

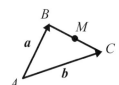

Solution:

If we use the head-to-tail method to add vectors, we see that

$\overrightarrow{AM} = \overrightarrow{AB} + \overrightarrow{BM} = a + \overrightarrow{BM}$. But vector $\overrightarrow{BM} = \dfrac{1}{2}\overrightarrow{BC}$ (because M is the midpoint).

Now, $\overrightarrow{BC} = \overrightarrow{BA} + \overrightarrow{AC} = -\overrightarrow{AB} + \overrightarrow{AC} = -a + b$

If we put this altogether, we get $\overrightarrow{AM} = a + \dfrac{1}{2}(-a + b) = \dfrac{1}{2}(a + b)$.

The answer is E.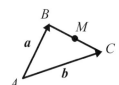

Complex Numbers

If you try to find $\sqrt{-1}$ on a calculator, you will get an error message. There's no real number x with the property that $x^2 = -1$. Mathematicians get around this difficulty by using the symbol i to represent a new kind of number called an <u>imaginary number</u> with the following property:

$$i^2 = -1$$

The name "imaginary" is an unfortunate historical accident. It implies they are somehow less real than "real" numbers. But think about it, how "real" is something like π, an infinite, non-repeating sequence of digits?

Square Roots of Negatives

Once we have i, we can take the square root of negatives very easily.

Example:

$\sqrt{-4} = 2i$ because $\sqrt{-4} = \sqrt{4}\sqrt{-1} = 2i$

$\sqrt{-25} = \sqrt{25}\sqrt{-1} = 5i$

In general, if x is a positive real number, then

$\sqrt{-x} = (\sqrt{x})i$

Complex Numbers

These are all complex numbers: $4 + 3i$, $-6 + 2i$, $-0.67 - 2.69i$, $\dfrac{3}{4} + \dfrac{2}{3}i$

So a complex number looks like this:

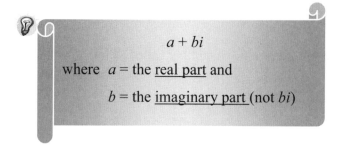

$$a + bi$$

where a = the <u>real part</u> and

b = the <u>imaginary part</u> (not bi)

Don't get confused by the terminology here: both a and b are real numbers, but the number in front of the i is called the imaginary part.

We usually don't bother writing such things as $0 + 2i$ or $-6 + 0i$. Instead, we generally omit the 0 and just write $2i$ or -6 instead.

The Complex Plane

There's an easy way to visualize complex numbers by thinking of the a and b as Cartesian coordinates (a, b) and plotting in the plane. The only difference is we now call it the **complex plane**. Look at this diagram for some examples:

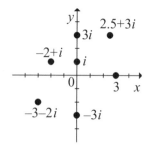

Modulus of a Complex Number

The **modulus** of a complex number, $z = a + bi$, is its distance from the origin. Just use the Pythagorean Theorem:

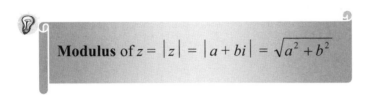

$$\text{Modulus of } z = |z| = |a + bi| = \sqrt{a^2 + b^2}$$

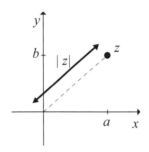

Example question:

If z is the complex number $4 + xi$, where x is a real number, find the largest possible value for $|z|$ if x also satisfies the equation $x^2 + 2x - 3 = 0$.

A. 3.16

B. 3.32

C. 7.14

D. 7.20

E. 14.22

Solution:

We must use the formula for the modulus of a complex number, $|z| = \sqrt{16 + x^2}$, and we need to make this as large as possible. Now, without any other conditions on x we could obviously make this as big as we like. But the question tells us that x must also satisfy the equation $x^2 + 2x - 3 = 0$. Then,

$$x^2 + 2x - 3 = 0$$

$$(x + 3)(x - 1) = 0$$

$$x = -3 \text{ or } 1$$

Although $-3 < 1$ we are going to choose $x = -3$ because we want to find the biggest value for x^2. Therefore the maximum value of $|z| = \sqrt{1 + (-3)^2} = \sqrt{10}$ and this tells us that the answer is A.

Adding and Subtracting Complex Numbers

This is very easy, just deal with the real and imaginary parts separately:

> ### Example:
>
> $(4 + 6i) + (3 + 10i) = 7 + 16i$, $(3 - 5i) - 2i = 3 - 7i$

Example question:

z and w are two complex numbers such that $z = 2p + pi$ and $w = q + pi$, where p and q are real numbers. If $z + w = 1 + i$, then $p + q =$

A. -2

B. $-\dfrac{1}{2}$

C. 0

D. $\dfrac{1}{2}$

E. 2

Solution:

We first work out $z + w$:

$$(2p + pi) + (q + pi) = (2p + q) + 2pi$$

But $$z + w = 1 + i$$

So $$(2p + q) + 2pi = 1 + i$$

Now, **two complex numbers can be equal if and only if their real and imaginary parts are equal.**

Equating gives $2p + q = 1$ and $2p = 1$.

Solving these two equations gives $p = \dfrac{1}{2}$ and $q = 0$, hence $p + q = \dfrac{1}{2}$. The answer is D.

Multiplying Complex Numbers

Multiplying complex numbers is just like multiplying out binomials in normal algebra except that we replace i^2 by -1.

Example:

$$(-2+3i)(5+2i) = -10+15i-4i+6i^2 = -10+11i+6(-1) = -16+11i$$

Dividing Complex Numbers

This is a bit more difficult.

First we need to define the **conjugate** of $a + bi$:

Conjugate of $a + bi = a - bi$

Example:

The conjugate of $7 + 2i = 7 - 2i$. The conjugate of $-6i = 6i$

This is the important thing to remember about conjugates:

If you **multiply** a complex number by **its conjugate**, you get a **real number**.

Example:

$$(7 + 2i)(7 - 2i) = 49 - 4i^2 = 49 - 4(-1) = 53$$

$$(4 - i)(4 + i) = 16 - i^2 = 16 - (-1) = 17$$

So in order to divide by a complex number, we multiply both the top and bottom of the original fraction by the <u>conjugate of the denominator</u>.

Example:

$$\frac{3 + 5i}{-1 + 2i} = \frac{3 + 5i}{-1 + 2i} \times \frac{-1 - 2i}{-1 - 2i} = \frac{7 - 11i}{5} = \frac{7}{5} - \frac{11}{5}i$$

Example question:

If m, n and p are real numbers and $np \neq 0$ then $\dfrac{mi}{n+pi} =$

A. $\dfrac{-m}{n-pi}$

B. $\dfrac{m}{n} - \dfrac{mi}{p}$

C. $\dfrac{m}{n^2} + \dfrac{mi}{p^2}$

D. $\dfrac{mp}{n^2+p^2} + \dfrac{mn}{n^2+p^2}i$

E. $\dfrac{m}{p^2} - \dfrac{m}{n^2}i$

Solution:

The condition $np \neq 0$ is just there to ensure that the denominator isn't 0 and we can be sure an answer exists.

We now follow the procedure for working out a complex division:

$$\frac{mi}{n+pi} = \frac{mi}{(n+pi)} \times \frac{(n-pi)}{(n-pi)} \quad \text{[multiply by the conjugate of the denominator]}$$

$$= \frac{mni - mpi^2}{n^2 - p^2i^2}$$

$$= \frac{mni + mp}{n^2 + p^2} \qquad [i^2 = -1]$$

$$= \frac{mp}{n^2+p^2} + \frac{mni}{n^2+p^2} \quad \text{[we usually write the real part first]}$$

We see that this result is the same as choice D.

Sample Test Introduction

Here are **four sample tests** each similar in difficulty to the actual test you will take. The questions are graded in difficulty. Generally, the easier questions are at the start and the harder ones at the end; however, just like on the actual test, you will sometimes find a tricky question early on and a relatively easy question near question 50.

How to Do the Tests

Each test is **one hour**. If you are doing this on your own,

1. Find a quiet place where you are not going to be disturbed. Get your calculator. Turn off your mobile (it's only an hour, you can do it!). Don't have any music on (you can't in the actual test, right?).

2. Use the answer sheet provided with each test. (Why not just circle your answer on the question paper? Because it takes longer to actually shade in the bubble! Over the course of the test this will result in a loss of 1 – 2 minutes in actual problem solving time, and this is what will happen in the real test so you need to factor that in.)

3. See how far you get after one hour.

4. If you didn't finish all 50 questions, was it because you ran out of time or because the questions became too difficult?

If you ran out of time, draw a line across your paper so you will know where to score up to but **keep going** and see which questions you could do if you had more time. If you find you could do most of them correctly, then obviously you need to improve your time management. If you find the questions got too difficult, first, don't worry! Mark your answers, but you **must** check through all the answer explanations to see where you went wrong or how to do them if you didn't attempt them at all.

Plugging-in Strategy

Sometimes you can choose values for the variables in a question and see if your answer matches any of the choices. For example, suppose you have this question:

Question:

When simplified $\dfrac{x+1}{x} - \dfrac{x}{x+1} =$

A. $\dfrac{1}{x(x+1)}$

B. $\dfrac{x-1}{x(x+1)}$

C. $\dfrac{1-x}{x(x+1)}$

D. $\dfrac{2x+1}{x(x+1)}$

E. $\dfrac{x^2-1}{x(x+1)}$

If you couldn't work this out algebraically, you could try a plugging-in strategy. Choose

$x = 3$, say, and plug this into the given expression. We get $\dfrac{3+1}{3} - \dfrac{3}{3+1} = 0.583$.

Now we plug $x = 3$ into the choices:

A. $\dfrac{1}{3(3+1)} = 0.0833$. This doesn't equate.

B. $\dfrac{3-1}{3(3+1)} = 0.167$. This doesn't equate.

C. $\dfrac{1-3}{3(3+1)} = -0.167$. This is negative so this certainly doesn't equate.

D. $\dfrac{2(3)+1}{3(4)} = 0.583$. This equates and so choice D **could** be the answer.

Do you now check choice E? Well, sometimes we can be unlucky when we plug in and we can get *two or more choices that equate*. In this case you'd need to try **another value** to distinguish between the answer choices that gave you the same answer.

You can also plug-in values given in the answer choices themselves into a given formula to see what works. Look at this very simple question:

Question:

If $(x+2)^2 = 16$, then the complete solution is

A. 0
B. 2
C. 2 or –2
D. 4
D. 2 or –6

If you plug-in $x = 0$ into the equation it doesn't work, so choice (A) is definitely out. If you plug in $x = 2$ then it does work BUT there is another x value that will also work: it's the value $x = –6$. So the answer choice is actually (E).

Now, in the SAT math Level 2 Test, it's *usually* the case that the first plug-in choice that works from the answers given *is* the one you want. Just be aware that you could be wrong occasionally. So if you have time, you should check them all.

However, if each answer choice has only *one* value given, the first answer choice that works *must* be the unique answer and you can confidently write this down as the answer.

Of course, you can't plug-in to *every* question because (a) not every question is suitable for it (e.g. graphical questions) and (b) this would just take too much time. But as a problem-solving strategy you should keep it in mind, especially if you just can't work a question out any other way.

Sample Test 1

Time: **One hour**

Write your answers on the sheet overleaf by **shading in** the appropriate oval like this:

Use a pencil and if you wish to correct an answer, ensure that you erase the original answer completely.

Mark Scheme: Each answer is worth +1 mark if correct, $-\dfrac{1}{4}$ mark if incorrect and 0 mark if omitted.

Calculator Use: A calculator is necessary to answer some of the questions on the test although not all questions require calculator use. You will need a calculator that can at least perform roots, logarithms and trigonometric ratios. You may use a graphing calculator.

Diagrams: Diagrams are drawn to scale unless stated otherwise.

Function Domains: All functions have real number domains unless stated otherwise.

Formulas: The following is a list of formulas which may be used for reference:

Volume of a sphere of radius *r*: $\dfrac{4}{3}\pi r^{3}$

Surface area of a sphere of radius *r*: $4\pi r^{2}$

Volume of a pyramid of height *h* and base area *A*: $\dfrac{1}{3}Ah$

Volume of a right circular come of height *h* and base radius *r*: $\dfrac{1}{3}\pi r^{2}h$

Curved surface of a right circular cone of height *h* and slant height *l*: πrl

for calculation use

1. The expression $\dfrac{3}{x-1} - 6$ will be equal to 0 when x equals which of the following?

    A. -3

    B. $-\dfrac{2}{3}$

    C. $\dfrac{1}{2}$

    D. $\dfrac{3}{2}$

    E. 3

$\dfrac{3}{x-1} - 6 =$

$= 6$

$3 = 6x - 1$

$+1 \qquad +1$

$4 = 6x$

2. If $x^2 - 8x = 5$, then $x =$

    A. -19 or 23

    B. -17 or 25

    C. -13 or 29

    D. $4-\sqrt{21}$ or $4+\sqrt{21}$

    E. $8-\sqrt{21}$ or $8+\sqrt{21}$

$x^2 - 8x - 5 = 0$

$\dfrac{8 \pm \sqrt{64 - 4(1)(-5)}}{2(1)}$

$\dfrac{8 \pm \sqrt{84}}{2}$

$\dfrac{8 \pm 2\sqrt{21}}{2(1)} = \dfrac{8 \pm 2\sqrt{21}}{2}$

3. Given that $90° \geq x \geq 0°$ and $\sqrt{3}\sin x - \cos x = 0$, then $x =$

    A. $0°$

    B. $30°$

    C. $45°$

    D. $60°$

    E. $90°$

$\sqrt{3}\ \sin x = \cos x$

for calculation use

4.   The dimensions of a rectangular box are 3 cm by 4 cm by 5 cm. What is the sum of the lengths of all the edges?

   A.   24 cm

   B.   36 cm

   C.   38 cm

   D.   48 cm

   E.   60 cm

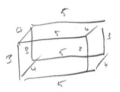

$3 \times 4 = 12$
$4 \times 4 = 16$
$5 \times 4 = 20$

5.   Solving $2^x = 7^{x+3}$ for x gives $x =$

   A.   4.66

   B.   3.99

   C. -4.66

   D. -3.99

   E.   0

$2^x = 7^{x+3}$

6.   If $\arctan(\tan x) = \dfrac{\pi}{3}$, then x could be which of the following?

   A. $\dfrac{2\pi}{3}$

   B. π

   C. $\dfrac{4\pi}{3}$

   D. $\dfrac{5\pi}{3}$

   E. 2π

for calculation use

7. If $h(x) = x^2 + 2x$, then $h(2x) =$

    A. $2x^3$
    B. $2x^2 + 2x$
    C. $2x^2 + 4x$
    D. $4x^2 + 2x$
    E. $4x^2 + 4x$

$(2x)^2 + 2(2x)$

$4x^2 + 4x$

8. Solve for x in the following equation:

    $$\frac{1}{x+2} - \frac{2}{x-3} = \frac{-3}{2-3x}$$

    A. $x = 4$ or $x = -\dfrac{4}{3}$

    B. $x = 4$ or $x = \dfrac{2}{3}$

    C. $x = -4$ or $x = \dfrac{4}{3}$

    D. $x = -4$ or $x = \dfrac{2}{3}$

    E. $x = -4$ or $x = \dfrac{16}{3}$

$\dfrac{x-3}{x-3}\cdot\dfrac{1}{x+2} - \dfrac{2}{x-3}\cdot\dfrac{x+2}{x+2} = \dfrac{-3}{2-3x}$

$+2x-3x$

$\dfrac{x-3}{x^2-x-6} - \dfrac{2x+4}{x^2-x-6} = \dfrac{-3}{2-3x}$

$\dfrac{-x-7}{x^2-x-6} = \dfrac{-3}{2-3x} \cdot \dfrac{2-3x}{1}$

$2-3x(-x-7)$

$-2x-14+3x^2+21x$

$3x^2+21x-14 = \neq 3$

$3x^2+21x-14 = 3x^2-3x-18$

$-3x + 3x +18 \quad -3x \quad +3x +18$

$24 \qquad = 0$

for calculation use

9. The line segment joining the points $A\,(6,\,-2\,)$ and $B\,(-3\,,\,9)$ crosses the x-axis at point C. Find the ratio $AC:CB$.

$\dfrac{9-(-2)}{-3-6} \Rightarrow \dfrac{11}{-9} = x\dfrac{11}{9}$

$\dfrac{11}{4x} - 9.333$

$\dfrac{11}{9x} - \dfrac{28}{3}$

A. $2:9$

B. $9:2$

C. $3:1$

D. $1:3$

E. $4:3$

10. The three sides of a triangle are 8, 9 and 9. The degree measure of the smallest angle in this triangle is

A. 42.61°

B. 47.53°

C. 52.78°

D. 58.12°

E. 63.61°

11. If $f(x) = 2x+3$ and $g(x) = x-3$, then $f(g(x))$ is

$2(x-3)+3$

$2x-6+3$

$2x-3$

A. $2x$

B. $2x-6$

C. $2x-3$

D. $5x-15$

E. $2x^2 - 3x - 9$

for calculation use

12. Make p the subject in the following equation:

$$\frac{2p + m - n}{4a - p} = \frac{c}{d}$$

   A. $p = 4md - na - cd$

   B. $p = \dfrac{4ac + nd - md}{c + 2d}$

   C. $p = \dfrac{2cd}{4md - ad + cn}$

   D. $p = \dfrac{4nd - ad - 2ac}{ad + 2c}$

   E. $p = \dfrac{ac + 4md - nd}{cd + 2ad}$

13. Given that $\pi < x < 2\pi$ and $\tan x = 1.234$, then

$$\sin\left(\frac{x}{2}\right) =$$

   A. -0.78

   B. -0.43

   C. 0.43

   D. 0.78

   E. 0.90

Handwritten working (for calculation use):

$$\frac{2p + m - n}{4a - p} = \frac{c}{d} \cdot 4a - p$$

$$4a - p$$

$$\frac{4ac - pc}{d} \cdot d$$

$$2pd + md - nd = 4ac + pc$$
$$-2pd \qquad\qquad -4ac$$
$$md - nd - 4ac = pc - 2pd$$
$$\frac{p(c - 2d)}{c - 2d}$$

for calculation use

$C = 3$

14. Given that $f(x) = ax^2 + bx + c$ for all real numbers x, if $f(0) = 3$ and $f(1) = 2$, then $a + b =$

    A. -2

    B. -1

    C.   0

    D.   1

    E.   2

15. A cube is circumscribed about a sphere. If the radius of the sphere is 3, what is the volume of the cube?

$3\sqrt{2}$

    A.   5.2

    B.   27

    C.   41.6

    D.   113

    E.   216

16. If the equations $x^2 + y^2 = 25$ and $y = x^2 - 6$ are graphed on the same set of axes, how many points of intersection are there?

$(0,0)$

    A.   0

    B.   1

    C.   2

    D.   3

    E.   4

for calculation use

17. There are 6 red balls and 4 white balls in a bag. Two balls are drawn out without replacement. What is the probability of getting 2 red balls?

$\dfrac{6}{10} \cdot \dfrac{5}{9}$

   A.   0.13

   B.   0.16

   C.   0.20

   D.   0.33

   E.   0.36

18. What is the value of $\tan^2 \theta - \sec^2 \theta$?

$\dfrac{\sin^2 x}{\cos^2 x} - \dfrac{1}{\cos^2 x}$

$\dfrac{\sin^2 x - 1}{\cos^2 x} =$

   A. -1

   B.   0

   C.   1

   D. $\csc^2 \theta$

   E. $\cot^2 \theta$

19. Given that $ab = 6$, $bc = 12$, $ac = 32$ and all of a, b and c are positive, then $(abc)^3 =$

$ab = 6$

$bc = 12$ 3 4

$ac = 32$ 8,4

   A.   2304

   B.   6912

   C.   110,592

   D.   331,776

   E.   5,308,416

for calculation use

20. If $a \otimes b = a^2 + 2ab + b^2$ and $-2 \otimes x = 36$, what is/are the value(s) of x?

    A. -8

    B. -4

    C. -8 and 8

    D. -4 and 8

    E. 8

$-2 \otimes x = 36$

$4 + 2(-2)(x) + x^2 = 36$
$ -36 \qquad -4x + x^2 \quad -36$
$\overline{-32}$

$x^2 - 4x - 32$
$(x+4)(x-8)$

21. If the 4th term and the 9th term of a geometric sequence are -24 and 768, respectively, what is the common ratio of the sequence?

    A. -3

    B. -2

    C. 0

    D. 2

    E. 3

-24

$-24, x, y\, 768$

22. Given that $f(x) = \begin{cases} \sqrt{x} + 2 & x \geq 0 \\ -x + 2 & x < 0 \end{cases}$ if . Find $f(9) - f(-3)$.

    3

    A. -10

    B. -8

    C. -4

    D. -2

    E. 0

$\sqrt{9}$

$3+2$

$5 - 5$

for calculation use

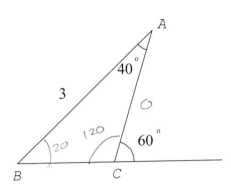

Note: Figure not drawn to scale.

23. In the figure above, what is the length of AC?

   A. $2\sqrt{3}\sin 40°$

   B. $3\sqrt{2}\sin 20°$

   C. $2\sqrt{3}\sin 20°$

   D. $3\sin 40°$

   E. $\sqrt{3}$

$\sin 20 \qquad \dfrac{O}{3}$

24. If $f(x) = 3x^3 + 4x^2 - 5$, what is the remainder if $f(x)$ is divided by $(x+1)$?

   A. -4

   B. -1

   C. 1

   D. 2

   E. 7

$x = -1$

$3(-1)$

$-3 + 4 - 5$

$1 - 5$

-4

for calculation use

25. Given that $\sin x + \cos x = \sqrt{2}$, then the value of $\sin x \cos x$ is

   A. -1
   B. -0.5
   C. 0
   D. 0.5
   E. 1

26. If $g(f(x)) = x$ and $g(x) = 5e^x - 4$, then $f(x) =$

   A. $5x - 4$

   B. $0.2e^x + 4$

   C. $\ln(\dfrac{x+4}{5})$

   D. $\ln(\dfrac{x}{5} + 4)$

   E. $\ln(x + \dfrac{4}{5})$

$f(5e^x - 4)$

$5e^x - 4 = 0$

$\dfrac{4}{5}$

27. For every pair (x, y) in the coordinate plane, if $f : (x, y) \to (xy, x^2 + y^2)$ and $g : (x, y) \to (2x, 2y)$, then for which point(s) is/are $f(x, y) = g(x, y)$?

   A. All the points (x, y) such that $x = 0$
   B. All the points (x, y) such that $y = 2$
   C. $(0, 0)$ only
   D. $(0, 2)$ only
   E. $(0, 0)$ and $(0, 2)$ only

$6, 9+4$
$6, 13$
$3, 2$
$6, 4$

2

for calculation use

28. For what value(s) of K will the equation $2x^2 - 4x - K = 0$ have no real root?

$-4^2 - 4(2)(-K) = 0$

$16 - 4(2)(-K)$

$16 - (-8K)$

    A. $K = -2$

    B. $K < -2$

    C. $K > -2$

    D. $K < 2$

    E. $K > 2$

29. If $f(x) = e^x$ and $f(g(\pi)) = 1$, which of the following could be $g(x)$?

e^{π}

    A. $\sin x + \cos x$

    B. $\sin x - \cos x$

    C. $\tan x$

    D. $\tan x + \cos x$

    E. $\tan x - \cos x$

30. The coordinates of the points A and B are $(-2, 3)$ and $(4, 7)$, respectively. What is the equation of the perpendicular bisector of the line segment AB?

$\dfrac{3-7}{4-(-2)} = \dfrac{-4}{6}$

$\dfrac{2}{3}x + b = 7$

$1.55 \quad = 2.625$

    A. $2x - 3y + 13 = 0$

    B. $2x + 3y - 13 = 0$

    C. $3x + 2y - 13 = 0$ $\dfrac{-3x}{2} + \dfrac{13}{2}$

    D. $3x + 2y + 13 = 0$

    E. $2x - 3y - 13 = 0$

$\dfrac{2}{3x} + \dfrac{13}{3}$

$-\dfrac{3x}{2}$

for calculation use

31. All students in a group take Mathematics, Physics and English tests. The following statements are true:

Some students fail Mathematics.
Those who fail mathematics also fail Physics.
Those who pass Physics all fail English.
Some students fail English and Mathematics.

Which of the following statements must also be true?

A. Some students pass physics but fail Mathematics.

B. Those who pass mathematics all pass Physics.

C. No student passes English and fails Physics.

D. No student fails both Physics and Mathematics.

E. Some students fail all three subjects.

32. If $\log_2 x = \log_2 (x+8) - \log_2 5$, then $x =$

A. 1
B. 2
C. 3
D. 4
E. 5

for calculation use

33. Given that $i = \sqrt{-1}$, $|i - 2| =$

A. 1

B. $\sqrt{3}$

C. 2

D. $\sqrt{5}$

E. 3

34. Let $f(x) = \dfrac{x^2 - 9}{x - 3}$. If x approaches 3, then $f(x)$ approaches

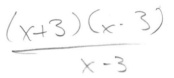

$\dfrac{(x+3)(x-3)}{x-3}$

A. 0

B. 3

C. 6

D. Infinity

E. None of the above

35. If $\tan^2\theta - 3 = 0$ and $180° \le \theta \le 270°$, then the value of θ is

A. 60°

B. 71.6°

C. 210°

D. 240°

E. 251.6°

for calculation use

36. If the two numbers 2 and 8 are added to a set of 8 positive integers with mode 2, mean 5 and median 5, which of the following will not be changed?

      I   Mean

      II   Mode

      III   Median

A. I only

B. II only

C. III only

D. I and II

E. I, II, and III

2 5 5 5 5 5 5 8

5, 5, 5, 5, 5

5, 5

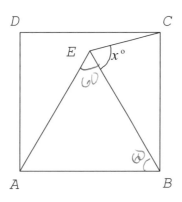

Note: Figure not drawn to scale.

37. In the figure above, *ABCD* is a square and *ABE* is an equilateral triangle. What is the value of *x*?

A. 30

B. 45

C. 60

D. 75

E. It cannot be determined from the given information.

38. For any non-zero whole numbers p and r, $\dfrac{p}{r}$ is a whole number. Which of the following is/are also always whole number(s)?

   I $\dfrac{p^2 - 2pr + r^2}{r^2}$

   II $\dfrac{p^4 - r^4}{r^2}$

   III $\dfrac{p^3 - r^3}{p^3}$

   A.   I only

   B.   I and II only

   C.   I and III only

   D.   II and III only

   E.   I, II and III

$$\frac{4}{2}$$

39. If $\sin \alpha \cos \alpha > 0$, then which of the following must be true?

   A. $\tan \alpha > 0$

   B. $\sin \alpha > 0$

   C. $\cos \alpha > 0$

   D. $\cos \alpha < 0$

   E. $\tan \alpha < 0$

for calculation use

40　For an arithmetic sequence, the ath term is b and the bth term is a where $a \neq b$. What is the common difference of this arithmetic sequence?

   A.　$2a$

   B.　$b - a$

   C.　$a - b$

   D.　-1

   E.　It cannot be determined from the given information.

41.　In xyz-space, a triangle is formed by connecting the points $(0, 0, 1)$, $(0, 1, 0)$, and $(1, 0, 0)$. What is the area of the triangle?

   A.　$\dfrac{1}{2}$

   B.　$\dfrac{\sqrt{3}}{2}$

   C.　1

   D.　2

   E.　$3\sqrt{2}$

42.　In $\triangle ABC$, $AB = 14$, $AC = 13$ and $\tan \angle A = 2.4$. Find the length of BC.

   A.　15

   B.　17

   C.　19.1

   D.　24

   E.　25.2

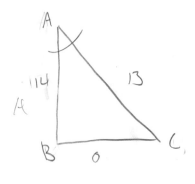

for calculation use

43. Sample A contains x light bulbs, 10% of which are defective. Sample B contains $2x$ light bulbs, 25% of which are defective. The light bulbs of the two samples are mixed together and a light bulb is randomly picked. Given that the picked light bulb is non-defective, what is the probability that the light bulb is from sample A?

A. $\dfrac{3}{8}$

B. $\dfrac{11}{24}$

C. $\dfrac{13}{24}$

D. $\dfrac{5}{8}$

E. $\dfrac{19}{20}$

44. Which of the following cannot be formed by the intersection of a cylinder and a plane?

A. Triangle

B. Rectangle

C. Circle

D. Line segment

E. Point

for calculation use

45. The equation $ax^2 + bx + c = 0$ has two real roots p and q. In addition, the following conditions hold:

$$p + q = -1$$
$$pq = -6$$
$$a + b + c = -4$$

Find $a^2 + b^2 - c^2$.

A. -136

B. -64

C. -34

D. 34

E. 64

46. If a and b are different positive integers and $\sqrt{ab} = 6$, which of the following could not be a value of $a + b$?

A.   12

B.   13

C.   15

D.   20

E.   37

$(x-3)$

$2, -3, -3$

$-1 -3$

$4 + 9 - 9$

$(x-2)(x+3)$
$x^2 + 3x - 2x - 6$
$x^2 + x + 6$

$6 \cdot 6$
$9 \cdot 4$
$12 \cdot 3$
$18 \cdot 2$

47.

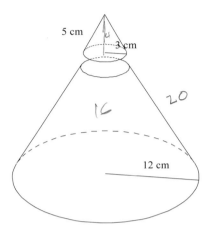

5 cm

3 cm

20

16

12 cm

Note: Figure not drawn to scale.

A cone with radius 3 cm and slant height 5 cm is cut from a bigger cone with radius 12 cm. What is the volume of the remaining part?

A. 752π

B. 756π

C. 758π

D. 760π

E. 764π

for calculation use

48. For an arithmetic sequence, the 2nd term is $-x$ and the 5th term is x. Find the yth term in terms of x and y.

A. $\dfrac{-xy + 2x}{2}$

B. $\dfrac{4xy - 5x}{2}$

C. $\dfrac{2xy - 7x}{3}$

D. $\dfrac{4xy - 3x}{2}$

E. $\dfrac{2xy + 3x}{2}$

49. Find the center of the ellipse given by the equation $16x^2 + 64x + 9y^2 + 54y + 1 = 0$.

A. $(-2, -3)$

B. $(-4, -6)$

C. $(-8, -9)$

D. $(2, 3)$

E. $(4, 6)$

50. Given that $x + \dfrac{1}{x} = 5$, find the value of $x^2 + \dfrac{1}{x^2}$.

A. 20

B. 21

C. 22

D. 23

E. 25

$5 - x = \dfrac{1}{x} \cdot x$

$-x^2 + 5x = 1$

-1

$-x^2 + 5x - 1$

$-x$

Finding Your Test Score

Step 1: Count the number of correct answers and record it here:

Step 2: Count the number of wrong answers, divide it by 4 and record it here:

Step 3: Subtract the number in the second box from that in the first box and round it to the

nearest integer. This is you raw score:

Step 4: By using the conversion table below, you can find your test score.

Raw Score	Probable scaled SAT Math Level 2 score	Raw Score	Probable scaled SAT Math Level 2 score	Raw Score	Probable scaled SAT Math Level 2 score
42 - 50	800	26	650	10	510
41	790	25	640	9	500
40	780	24	630	8	480
39	770	23	620	7	460
38	760	22	610	6	450
37	750	21	600	5	430
36	740	20	600	4	400
35	730	19	590	3	390
34	720	18	580	2	370
33	720	17	570	1	360
32	710	16	570	0	350
31	700	15	560	−1	320
30	690	14	550	−2	300
29	680	13	540	−3	280
28	670	12	530	−4	260
27	660	11	520	−5	250

The College Board will convert your raw score to a **scaled score**. The highest score you can get is **800**. The lowest is **200**.

In the actual SAT Math Level 2 test, there is always some slight variation from test to test for the score boundaries. It's possible to get somewhat lower than our scores by getting very few correct and many wrong. But, to be honest, if you are getting scores this low it would be a lot better for you to try the easier SAT Math Level 1 test.

Sample Test 2

Time: <u>One hour</u>

Write your answers on the sheet overleaf by **shading in** the appropriate oval like this:

Use a pencil and if you wish to correct an answer, ensure that you erase the original answer completely.

<u>Mark Scheme</u>: Each answer is worth +1 mark if correct, $-\dfrac{1}{4}$ mark if incorrect and 0 mark if omitted.

<u>Calculator Use</u>: A calculator is necessary to answer some of the questions on the test although not all questions require calculator use. You will need a calculator that can at least perform roots, logarithms and trigonometric ratios. You may use a graphing calculator.

<u>Diagrams</u>: Diagrams are drawn to scale unless stated otherwise.

<u>Function Domains</u>: All functions have real number domains unless stated otherwise.

<u>Formulas</u>: The following is a list of formulas which may be used for reference:

Volume of a sphere of radius *r*: $\dfrac{4}{3}\pi r^3$

Surface area of a sphere of radius *r*: $4\pi r^2$

Volume of a pyramid of height *h* and base area *A*: $\dfrac{1}{3}Ah$

Volume of a right circular come of height *h* and base radius *r*: $\dfrac{1}{3}\pi r^2 h$

Curved surface of a right circular cone of height *h* and slant height *l*: πrl

1. Ⓐ Ⓑ Ⓒ Ⓓ Ⓔ
2. Ⓐ Ⓑ Ⓒ Ⓓ Ⓔ
3. Ⓐ Ⓑ Ⓒ Ⓓ Ⓔ
4. Ⓐ Ⓑ Ⓒ Ⓓ Ⓔ
5. Ⓐ Ⓑ Ⓒ Ⓓ Ⓔ
6. Ⓐ Ⓑ Ⓒ Ⓓ Ⓔ
7. Ⓐ Ⓑ Ⓒ Ⓓ Ⓔ
8. Ⓐ Ⓑ Ⓒ Ⓓ Ⓔ
9. Ⓐ Ⓑ Ⓒ Ⓓ Ⓔ
10. Ⓐ Ⓑ Ⓒ Ⓓ Ⓔ
11. Ⓐ Ⓑ Ⓒ Ⓓ Ⓔ
12. Ⓐ Ⓑ Ⓒ Ⓓ Ⓔ
13. Ⓐ Ⓑ Ⓒ Ⓓ Ⓔ
14. Ⓐ Ⓑ Ⓒ Ⓓ Ⓔ
15. Ⓐ Ⓑ Ⓒ Ⓓ Ⓔ
16. Ⓐ Ⓑ Ⓒ Ⓓ Ⓔ
17. Ⓐ Ⓑ Ⓒ Ⓓ Ⓔ
18. Ⓐ Ⓑ Ⓒ Ⓓ Ⓔ
19. Ⓐ Ⓑ Ⓒ Ⓓ Ⓔ
20. Ⓐ Ⓑ Ⓒ Ⓓ Ⓔ
21. Ⓐ Ⓑ Ⓒ Ⓓ Ⓔ
22. Ⓐ Ⓑ Ⓒ Ⓓ Ⓔ
23. Ⓐ Ⓑ Ⓒ Ⓓ Ⓔ
24. Ⓐ Ⓑ Ⓒ Ⓓ Ⓔ
25. Ⓐ Ⓑ Ⓒ Ⓓ Ⓔ

26. Ⓐ Ⓑ Ⓒ Ⓓ Ⓔ
27. Ⓐ Ⓑ Ⓒ Ⓓ Ⓔ
28. Ⓐ Ⓑ Ⓒ Ⓓ Ⓔ
29. Ⓐ Ⓑ Ⓒ Ⓓ Ⓔ
30. Ⓐ Ⓑ Ⓒ Ⓓ Ⓔ
31. Ⓐ Ⓑ Ⓒ Ⓓ Ⓔ
32. Ⓐ Ⓑ Ⓒ Ⓓ Ⓔ
33. Ⓐ Ⓑ Ⓒ Ⓓ Ⓔ
34. Ⓐ Ⓑ Ⓒ Ⓓ Ⓔ
35. Ⓐ Ⓑ Ⓒ Ⓓ Ⓔ
36. Ⓐ Ⓑ Ⓒ Ⓓ Ⓔ
37. Ⓐ Ⓑ Ⓒ Ⓓ Ⓔ
38. Ⓐ Ⓑ Ⓒ Ⓓ Ⓔ
39. Ⓐ Ⓑ Ⓒ Ⓓ Ⓔ
40. Ⓐ Ⓑ Ⓒ Ⓓ Ⓔ
41. Ⓐ Ⓑ Ⓒ Ⓓ Ⓔ
42. Ⓐ Ⓑ Ⓒ Ⓓ Ⓔ
43. Ⓐ Ⓑ Ⓒ Ⓓ Ⓔ
44. Ⓐ Ⓑ Ⓒ Ⓓ Ⓔ
45. Ⓐ Ⓑ Ⓒ Ⓓ Ⓔ
46. Ⓐ Ⓑ Ⓒ Ⓓ Ⓔ
47. Ⓐ Ⓑ Ⓒ Ⓓ Ⓔ
48. Ⓐ Ⓑ Ⓒ Ⓓ Ⓔ
49. Ⓐ Ⓑ Ⓒ Ⓓ Ⓔ
50. Ⓐ Ⓑ Ⓒ Ⓓ Ⓔ

for calculation use

1.	Given that $g(x) = x^2 - 3$ and $f(x) = 1 - x$, write a simplified expression for $g(f(x))$.

	A.	$x^2 + 3x + 2$

	B.	$x^2 - 3x + 2$

	C.	$x^2 - 2x - 2$

	D.	$x^2 - 2x - 4$

	E.	$2x^2 - x + 1$

2.	If $a = 2b$, $3b = 4c$, $5c = 6d$, $de = a$ and $a \neq 0$, find the value of e.

	A.	0.3125

	B.	3.2

	C.	12.4

	D.	96

	E.	120

3.	The angle of elevation from a ship to the top of a 40-meter high lighthouse on the shore is $3°$. How far is the ship from the shore? (Correct to the nearest m)

	A.	40 m

	B.	120 m

	C.	763 m

	D.	764 m

	E.	943 m

4. A cylinder has a volume of 72π cubic inches and a height of 8 inches. If the height is increased by 4 inches, what will be the new volume of the cylinder in cubic inches?

    A. 84π

    B. 96π

    C. 108π

    D. 120π

    E. 144π

5. If $g(a,b) = 2^{a+b}$, what is the solution to the equation $g(3,x) = \dfrac{1}{4}$?

    A. -5

    B. -0.372

    C. 1.372

    D. 2

    E. 4

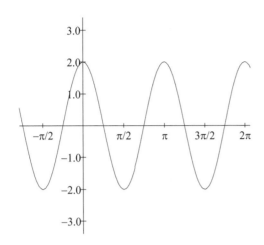

6.   The figure above shows the graph of $y = a\cos kx$.
     What are the values of a and k?

   A. $a = \dfrac{1}{2}$, $k = \dfrac{1}{2}$

   B. $a = 1$, $k = \dfrac{1}{2}$

   C. $a = \dfrac{1}{2}$, $k = 2$

   D. $a = 2$, $k = \dfrac{1}{2}$

   E. $a = 2$, $k = 2$

7.   Given that $f(x) = x^2 - 8x + 12$. Which of the
     following has only one root?

   A. $f(-x)$

   B. $f(x-4)$

   C. $-f(x)$

   D. $f(x)+4$

   E. $f(x)-4$

for calculation use

8. Simplifying $\dfrac{\sqrt{a}+\sqrt{b}}{\sqrt{a}-\sqrt{b}} - \dfrac{\sqrt{a}-\sqrt{b}}{\sqrt{a}+\sqrt{b}}$ where $a > 0$,

    $b > 0$ and $a \neq b$ gives

    A. $\dfrac{2\sqrt{b}}{a-b}$

    B. $\dfrac{a+b}{a-b}$

    C. $\dfrac{2(a+b)}{a-b}$

    D. $\dfrac{2\sqrt{ab}}{a-b}$

    E. $\dfrac{4\sqrt{ab}}{a-b}$

9. What is the perimeter of a triangle with vertices at $(1, 4)$, $(1, 7)$ and $(4, 4)$?

    A. $3 + \sqrt{2}$

    B. $3\sqrt{2}$

    C. 6

    D. $6 + 3\sqrt{2}$

    E. $9 + 3\sqrt{2}$

10. Solve $2 \sin 2\theta = \sqrt{3}$ for $0° \leq \theta \leq 90°$.

    A. $0°$

    B. $25.7°$

    C. $30°$

    D. $45°$

    E. $90°$

11. In a factory, the average cost per computer, C, is given by $C = 5x^2 - 400x + 12{,}000$, where x is the number of computers produced per day. What is the minimum average cost per computer?

    A. $2,000

    B. $3,000

    C. $4,000

    D. $6,000

    E. $12,000

12. If b is made the subject of the equation

$$\frac{1}{a} + \frac{1}{b} + \frac{1}{c} = \frac{1}{d} \text{ where } abcd \neq 0, \text{ then}$$

    A. $b = d - a - c$

    B. $b = \dfrac{acd}{ac - ad - cd}$

    C. $b = \dfrac{acd}{ac - ad + cd}$

    D. $b = \dfrac{acd}{ad - ac - cd}$

    E. $b = \dfrac{acd}{cd - ac - ad}$

for calculation use

13. The greatest value of $3 - 2 \cos x$ is

    A. 4

    B. 5

    C. 6

    D. 8

    E. 10

14. If $f(x) = \dfrac{1}{x^2 + 1}$ and $g(x) = \sqrt{x^2 + 2x}$, then

    $f(g(5)) =$

    A. 0.03

    B. 0.06

    C. 0.28

    D. 0.30

    E. 0.60

15. If a cube has a surface area of $36x^2$ square feet, what is its volume in cubic feet?

    A. $\sqrt{6}x^3$

    B. $6\sqrt{6}x^3$

    C. $36x^3$

    D. $36\sqrt{6}x^3$

    E. $216x^3$

for calculation use

16. M is the midpoint of line segment AB. The coordinates of points A and M are $(4, -3)$ and $(6, 1)$, respectively. What are the coordinates of point B?

   A. $(1, -2)$

   B. $(2, -7)$

   C. $(5, -1)$

   D. $(8, 5)$

   E. $(10, 5)$

17. If the average (arithmetic mean) of 5 consecutive integers is 30, what is the median of these numbers?

   A.   4

   B.   6

   C.   8

   D.   30

   E.   33

18. For any angle α,

   $(\cos^2 \alpha)(\sin^2 \alpha) + \cos^4 \alpha + \sin^2 \alpha =$

   A.   0

   B. $\sin^2 \alpha$

   C. $\cos^2 \alpha$

   D.   1

   E. $\cos \alpha$

for calculation use

19. If $a > b > c$, which of the following cannot be true?

    A. $b + c < a$

    B. $2a > b + c$

    C. $2c > a + b$

    D. $ab > bc$

    E. $a + c < 2b + c$

20. If $f(x) = \dfrac{1+x}{x}$, then $f(-x) =$

    A. 0

    B. $\dfrac{1-x}{x}$

    C. $\dfrac{x}{1+x}$

    D. $\dfrac{x-1}{x}$

    E. $\dfrac{x-1}{-x}$

for calculation use

21. x varies directly as y, and y varies inversely as z. If we know $z = 5$ when $x = 3$, what is the value of z when $x = 6$?

   A. $\dfrac{3}{5}$

   B. $2\dfrac{1}{2}$

   C.   10

   D.   30

   E.   It cannot be determined from the given information.

22. To calculate the amount of an element $A(t)$ after t seconds, the formula $A(t) = ae^{\frac{-t}{300}}$ is used where a is the initial amount of the element. How long will it take for an initial amount of 1000 grams to decay to 100 grams?

   A.   4 min 35 sec
   B.   5 min 56 sec
   C.   7 min 1 sec
   D.   8 min 50 sec
   E.   11 min 31 sec

for calculation use

23. Given that $\sin x - \cos x = 0$, then the value of $(\sin x)(\cos x) =$

    A. -1

    B. 0

    C. 0.5

    D. 1

    E.   It cannot be determined from the given information.

24. The range of $f(x) = \begin{cases} -x+4 & x<0 \\ x^{1/4}+2 & x\geq 0 \end{cases}$ if is

    A. $f(x) \geq 2$

    B. $f(x) \geq 4$

    C. $2 \leq f(x) \leq 4$

    D. $f(x) \leq 4$

    E.   All real numbers

25. For all θ, what is the value of

    $$\sin\theta + \sin(\frac{\pi}{2}-\theta) + \cos\theta + \cos(\frac{\pi}{2}-\theta)?$$

    A. $2\sin\theta$

    B. $2\cos\theta$

    C. $2(\sin\theta + \cos\theta)$

    D. $2(\sin\theta - \cos\theta)$

    E. $2(\cos\theta - \sin\theta)$

for calculation use

26. If $f(x)$ is an even function, which of the following may not be an even function?

A. $f(-x)$

B. $-f(x)$

C. $f(x)+3$

D. $|f(x)|$

E. $f(x-4)$

27. What is the domain of $\sqrt[5]{9-x^2}$?

A. $x > 2.29$

B. $x > 3.46$

C. $-3 < x < 3$

D. $-3 \le x \le 3$

E. All real numbers

28. In $\triangle ABC$, the coordinates of A, B and C are $(3, 4)$, $(6, 7)$ and $(5, 8)$ respectively. What is the length of the altitude from C to the base AB?

A. $\sqrt{2}$

B. $\sqrt{3}$

C. 2

D. $\sqrt{5}$

E. $\sqrt{6}$

for calculation use

29. Below is the graph of $y = f(x)$. Which of the following is the graph of $y = f(|x|)$?

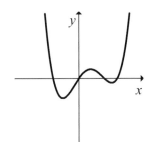

A.   B.

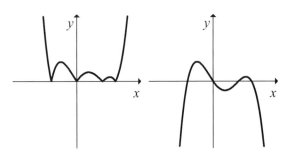

C.   D.

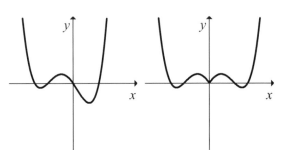

E.

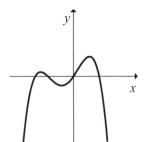

for calculation use

30. What is the length of a tangent line drawn to a circle with radius 5 units from a point 12 units away from the center of the circle?

    A.   2.4 units

    B.   7 units

    C.   13 units

    D.   17 units

    E.   None of the above

31. If two of the solutions of the equation $f(x) = 0$ are 4 and 8, then which of the following must be the solutions of the equation $f(x) + 4 = 0$?

    A.   0 and 4

    B.   4 and 8

    C.   8 and 12

    D.   No such real zeros can exist.

    E.   The real roots cannot be determined from the information given.

32. Find the values of x that will satisfy the inequality $(x-3)(x+2)(x-1) > 0$.

    A. $-2 < x < 1$ or $x > 3$

    B. $x < -2$ or $1 < x < 3$

    C. $x < -2$ or $x > 3$

    D. $-2 < x < 3$

    E. $x < 1$ or $x > 3$

for calculation use

33.　$f(x) = (1+x)^2$ is defined for $-2 \le x \le 2$. What is the range of f?

　　A.　$0 \le f(x) \le 4$

　　B.　$0 \le f(x) \le 9$

　　C.　$1 \le f(x) \le 4$

　　D.　$1 \le f(x) \le 5$

　　E.　$1 \le f(x) \le 9$

34.　Given that $i = \sqrt{-1}$, $(i+2)^3 =$

　　A.　$8 - i$

　　B.　$2 + 11i$

　　C.　$6 + 13i$

　　D.　$10 + 11i$

　　E.　$14 + 13i$

35.　If $(\sin^2 \alpha)(\cos \alpha) > 0$, then which of the following must be true?

　　A.　$\sin \alpha > 0$

　　B.　$\sin \alpha \ge 0$

　　C.　$\cos \alpha > 0$

　　D.　$\cos \alpha < 0$

　　E.　$\cos \alpha \ge 0$

for calculation use

36. A single die is thrown several times. The results are as follows:

Number thrown	Frequency
1	$6y$
2	$5y$
3	$4y$
4	$3y$
5	$2y$
6	y

What is the average (arithmetic mean) number thrown?

A. $1\dfrac{3}{4}$

B. $2\dfrac{2}{3}$

C. $3\dfrac{1}{3}$

D. $3\dfrac{1}{2}$

E. $4\dfrac{1}{3}$

37. For what value(s) of H is the x-axis tangent to the graph of the equation $y = 2x^2 - Hx - 8$?

A. -4 and 8

B. -4 and 4

C. -8 and 8

D. 8 only

E. None of the above

for calculation use

38. Given that

$$\#a = \begin{cases} a+1 & \text{if } a \text{ is even} \\ -a+1 & \text{if } a \text{ is odd} \end{cases}$$

Find $\#1 + \#2 + \#3 + \dots\dots\dots + \#99 + \#100$.

A. -100

B.   0

C.   150

D.   300

E.   5050

39. If A is the polar point $(-3, 60°)$ and B is the polar point $(3, -60°)$, then the distance $|AB|$ is equal to

A. $\sqrt{3}$

B.   3

C. $2\sqrt{3}$

D. $3 + \sqrt{3}$

E.   6

40. If $\log 2 = a$ and $\log 5 = b$, then $\log 100$ in terms of a and b is

A. $a + b$

B. $2a + b$

C. $a + 2b$

D. $2a + 2b$

E. $(a+b)^2$

for calculation use

41. If a right isosceles triangle with a leg of length 3 is rotated 360° around one of its legs, what is the volume of the solid?

    A. 9
    B. 28.27
    C. 36
    D. 84.82
    E. 113.10

42. The sides of a triangle are 6, 9, and 10 respectively. What is the degree measure of the smallest angle?

    A. 35
    B. 36
    C. 42
    D. 48
    E. 51

43. How many different ways are there to arrange 8 people of different heights in a line, if the two shortest people must stand one at either end of the line?

    A. 6
    B. 120
    C. 720
    D. 1,440
    E. 4,650

for calculation use

44.   The following sector is folded to form a right cone.

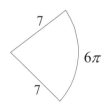

The volume of the cone is

A.   20.94

B.   47.12

C.   59.61

D.   65.97

E.   69.12

45.   If $x_1 = 1$, $x_2 = 2$ and $x_{n+1} = x_n + x_{n-1}$ for $n \geq 2$,
       then $x_5 =$

A.   4

B.   5

C.   6

D.   8

E.   10

46. Given that $f(x) = x^3 - Kx^2 - 6Kx + K$. What will be the remainder when $f(x)$ is divided by $x - 2$?

    A.   4

    B. $4 - 6K$

    C. $4 + K$

    D. $8 - 15K$

    E. $8 + 3K$

47. For the statement "If $ab = 0$, then either a or b is zero", in order to give an indirect proof, it is necessary to begin with the assumption that

    A.   both a and b are non-zero

    B.   either a or b is non-zero

    C.   both a and b are zero

    D.   either a or b is zero

    E. $ab = 0$

48. If $i = \sqrt{-1}$, then
    $$i + 2i^2 + 3i^3 + 4i^4 + 5i^5 + 6i^6 \ldots\ldots\ldots 86i^{86} + 87i^{87} =$$

    A. $-44 - 44i$

    B. $-42 - 42i$

    C. $42 - 42i$

    D. $44 - 44i$

    E. $46 - 42i$

for calculation use

49. What is the area enclosed by the lines $y = 0$, $x = 0$, $y = x + 1$ and $y = -x + 5$?

    A. $3\sqrt{5}$

    B. 7.5

    C. 8

    D. 8.5

    E. 12.5

50. If $n! = 4830(n-2)!$, then $n =$

    A. 70

    B. 71

    C. 72

    D. 73

    E. 74

Finding Your Test Score

Step 1: Count the number of correct answers and record it here:

Step 2: Count the number of wrong answers, divide it by 4 and record it here:

Step 3: Subtract the number in the second box from that in the first box and round it to the

nearest integer. This is you raw score:

Step 4: By using the conversion table below, you can find your test score.

Raw Score	Probable scaled SAT Math Level 2 score	Raw Score	Probable scaled SAT Math Level 2 score	Raw Score	Probable scaled SAT Math Level 2 score
42 - 50	800	26	650	10	510
41	790	25	640	9	500
40	780	24	630	8	480
39	770	23	620	7	460
38	760	22	610	6	450
37	750	21	600	5	430
36	740	20	600	4	400
35	730	19	590	3	390
34	720	18	580	2	370
33	720	17	570	1	360
32	710	16	570	0	350
31	700	15	560	−1	320
30	690	14	550	−2	300
29	680	13	540	−3	280
28	670	12	530	−4	260
27	660	11	520	−5	250

The College Board will convert your raw score to a **scaled score**. The highest score you can get is **800**. The lowest is **200**.

In the actual SAT Math Level 2 test, there is always some slight variation from test to test for the score boundaries. It's possible to get somewhat lower than our scores by getting very few correct and many wrong. But, to be honest, if you are getting scores this low it would be a lot better for you to try the easier SAT Math Level 1 test.

Sample Test 3

Time: **One hour**

Write your answers on the sheet overleaf by **shading in** the appropriate oval like this:

Use a pencil and if you wish to correct an answer, ensure that you erase the original answer completely.

Mark Scheme: Each answer is worth +1 mark if correct, $-\dfrac{1}{4}$ mark if incorrect and 0 mark if omitted.

Calculator Use: A calculator is necessary to answer some of the questions on the test although not all questions require calculator use. You will need a calculator that can at least perform roots, logarithms and trigonometric ratios. You may use a graphing calculator.

Diagrams: Diagrams are drawn to scale unless stated otherwise.

Function Domains: All functions have real number domains unless stated otherwise.

Formulas: The following is a list of formulas which may be used for reference:

Volume of a sphere of radius *r*: $\dfrac{4}{3}\pi r^{3}$

Surface area of a sphere of radius *r*: $4\pi r^{2}$

Volume of a pyramid of height *h* and base area *A*: $\dfrac{1}{3}Ah$

Volume of a right circular come of height *h* and base radius *r*: $\dfrac{1}{3}\pi r^{2}h$

Curved surface of a right circular cone of height *h* and slant height *l*: πrl

1. Ⓐ Ⓑ Ⓒ Ⓓ Ⓔ
2. Ⓐ Ⓑ Ⓒ Ⓓ Ⓔ
3. Ⓐ Ⓑ Ⓒ Ⓓ Ⓔ
4. Ⓐ Ⓑ Ⓒ Ⓓ Ⓔ
5. Ⓐ Ⓑ Ⓒ Ⓓ Ⓔ
6. Ⓐ Ⓑ Ⓒ Ⓓ Ⓔ
7. Ⓐ Ⓑ Ⓒ Ⓓ Ⓔ
8. Ⓐ Ⓑ Ⓒ Ⓓ Ⓔ
9. Ⓐ Ⓑ Ⓒ Ⓓ Ⓔ
10. Ⓐ Ⓑ Ⓒ Ⓓ Ⓔ
11. Ⓐ Ⓑ Ⓒ Ⓓ Ⓔ
12. Ⓐ Ⓑ Ⓒ Ⓓ Ⓔ
13. Ⓐ Ⓑ Ⓒ Ⓓ Ⓔ
14. Ⓐ Ⓑ Ⓒ Ⓓ Ⓔ
15. Ⓐ Ⓑ Ⓒ Ⓓ Ⓔ
16. Ⓐ Ⓑ Ⓒ Ⓓ Ⓔ
17. Ⓐ Ⓑ Ⓒ Ⓓ Ⓔ
18. Ⓐ Ⓑ Ⓒ Ⓓ Ⓔ
19. Ⓐ Ⓑ Ⓒ Ⓓ Ⓔ
20. Ⓐ Ⓑ Ⓒ Ⓓ Ⓔ
21. Ⓐ Ⓑ Ⓒ Ⓓ Ⓔ
22. Ⓐ Ⓑ Ⓒ Ⓓ Ⓔ
23. Ⓐ Ⓑ Ⓒ Ⓓ Ⓔ
24. Ⓐ Ⓑ Ⓒ Ⓓ Ⓔ
25. Ⓐ Ⓑ Ⓒ Ⓓ Ⓔ

26. Ⓐ Ⓑ Ⓒ Ⓓ Ⓔ
27. Ⓐ Ⓑ Ⓒ Ⓓ Ⓔ
28. Ⓐ Ⓑ Ⓒ Ⓓ Ⓔ
29. Ⓐ Ⓑ Ⓒ Ⓓ Ⓔ
30. Ⓐ Ⓑ Ⓒ Ⓓ Ⓔ
31. Ⓐ Ⓑ Ⓒ Ⓓ Ⓔ
32. Ⓐ Ⓑ Ⓒ Ⓓ Ⓔ
33. Ⓐ Ⓑ Ⓒ Ⓓ Ⓔ
34. Ⓐ Ⓑ Ⓒ Ⓓ Ⓔ
35. Ⓐ Ⓑ Ⓒ Ⓓ Ⓔ
36. Ⓐ Ⓑ Ⓒ Ⓓ Ⓔ
37. Ⓐ Ⓑ Ⓒ Ⓓ Ⓔ
38. Ⓐ Ⓑ Ⓒ Ⓓ Ⓔ
39. Ⓐ Ⓑ Ⓒ Ⓓ Ⓔ
40. Ⓐ Ⓑ Ⓒ Ⓓ Ⓔ
41. Ⓐ Ⓑ Ⓒ Ⓓ Ⓔ
42. Ⓐ Ⓑ Ⓒ Ⓓ Ⓔ
43. Ⓐ Ⓑ Ⓒ Ⓓ Ⓔ
44. Ⓐ Ⓑ Ⓒ Ⓓ Ⓔ
45. Ⓐ Ⓑ Ⓒ Ⓓ Ⓔ
46. Ⓐ Ⓑ Ⓒ Ⓓ Ⓔ
47. Ⓐ Ⓑ Ⓒ Ⓓ Ⓔ
48. Ⓐ Ⓑ Ⓒ Ⓓ Ⓔ
49. Ⓐ Ⓑ Ⓒ Ⓓ Ⓔ
50. Ⓐ Ⓑ Ⓒ Ⓓ Ⓔ

for calculation use

1. Given that $a = -1$, $b = -2$ and $c = -3$, find $a^b - b^c + c^a$.

    A. $-\dfrac{29}{24}$

    B. $-\dfrac{17}{24}$

    C. $\dfrac{5}{24}$

    D. $\dfrac{7}{24}$

    E. $\dfrac{19}{24}$

2. If $x > 1$ and $\dfrac{a}{b} = 1 - \dfrac{1}{x}$, then $\dfrac{b}{a} =$

    A. x

    B. $x - 1$

    C. $\dfrac{x-1}{x}$

    D. $\dfrac{x}{x-1}$

    E. $\dfrac{1}{x} - 1$

for calculation use

3. In the figure below, $f(x) = 2\sin x + 1$ attains its maximum at point M. What are the coordinates of M?

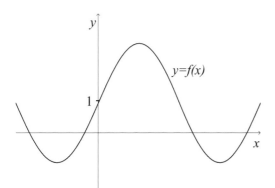

A. $\left(\dfrac{\pi}{2}, 2\right)$

B. $\left(\dfrac{\pi}{2}, 3\right)$

C. $(\pi, 1)$

D. $(\pi, 2)$

E. $\left(\dfrac{3\pi}{2}, 3\right)$

4. What is the maximum number of rectangular blocks, each measuring 3 inches by 8 inches by 12 inches, that can fit inside a rectangular box with dimensions 27 inches by 60 inches by 64 inches?

A. 72

B. 144

C. 288

D. 360

E. 540

5. When Andy and Oscar work together, they can finish a certain job in 3 days. Andy can finish the job alone in 4 days. How long will Oscar take to finish the job alone?

A. 6 days 12 hours

B. 8 days 15 hours

C. 10 days 18 hours

D. 12 days

E. 12 days 4 hours

6. If $\tan 2\theta - 2 = 0$ and $0° \le \theta \le 90°$, then the value of θ is

A. 31.7°

B. 45°

C. 63.4°

D. 64.3°

E. 73.4°

7. The range of $y = \sqrt{x+1} - 2$ is

A. $y \le -2$

B. $y \ge -2$

C. $-2 \le y \le 1$

D. $-2 \le y$ or $y \ge 1$

E. All real numbers

for calculation use

8. Jan drives at x miles per hour for y hours. David drives at $y-1$ miles per hour for $x+1$ hours. They travel for the same distance. Find $\dfrac{1}{2x-2y}$.

    A. -1

    B. $-\dfrac{1}{2}$

    C. $\dfrac{1}{2}$

    D. 1

    E. It cannot be determined from the given information.

9. Which of these numbers written in rectangular form is equivalent to the polar form $\left(\sqrt{2}, -\dfrac{3\pi}{4}\right)$?

    A. $(1, 1)$
    B. $\left(\sqrt{2}, 1\right)$
    C. $(-1, -1)$
    D. $(1, -1)$
    E. $\left(-1, \sqrt{2}\right)$

10. $\dfrac{\cos(180^\circ + \theta)}{\sin(90^\circ - \theta)} =$

   A. -1

   B. 0

   C. 1

   D. $\tan\theta$

   E. $\cot\theta$

11. Referring to the values of $f(x)$ in the given table, which of the following cannot be an equation of $f(x)$?

x	$f(x)$
-1	0
0	12
2	0
3	0

   A. $2(x+1)(x-2)(x-3)$

   B. $-(x+1)(x-2)^2(x-3)$

   C. $-(x+1)^2(x-2)^2(x-3)$

   D. $2(x+1)^2(x-2)(x-3)$

   E. $0.5(x+1)(x-2)(x-3)^2$

for calculation use

12. Peter had $ x at the end of year 2000. It increased by $a\%$ in year 2001 and then decreased by $b\%$ in year 2002. He had $ y at the end of year 2002. Find x in terms of a, b and y.

A. $x = \dfrac{10{,}000y}{(100+a)(100-b)}$

B. $x = \left(1+\dfrac{a}{100}\right)\left(1-\dfrac{b}{100}\right)\left(\dfrac{1}{y}\right)$

C. $x = \left(1+\dfrac{a}{100}-\dfrac{b}{100}\right)y$

D. $x = \dfrac{y}{(1+a)(1-b)}$

E. $x = y\left(1-\dfrac{b}{100}+\dfrac{a}{100}-\dfrac{ab}{100}\right)$

13. Given that $\sin x = -\dfrac{15}{17}$ and $\cos x < 0$, what is the value of $\tan x$?

A. $-\dfrac{17}{8}$

B. $-\dfrac{8}{15}$

C. $-\dfrac{8}{17}$

D. $\dfrac{15}{8}$

E. $\dfrac{17}{8}$

for calculation use

14. If $f(x) = 3x + 4$ and $f(g(1)) = 10$, which of the following could be $g(x)$?

   A. $7x - 5$

   B. $5x + 7$

   C. $5x - 7$

   D. $5x + 3$

   E. $-5x + 3$

15. Which of the following points is not inside a sphere with center at the origin and radius of 4?

   A. $(0, 1, 2)$

   B. $(1, 2, 3)$

   C. $(2, 3, 4)$

   D. $(3, 2, 1)$

   E. $(-2, 1, 0)$

16. If the slope of a line containing the points $(3, a)$ and $(b, 3)$ is 2, what is a in terms of b?

   A. $\dfrac{b-3}{2}$

   B. $2b - 3$

   C. $\dfrac{2b-3}{2}$

   D. $9 - 2b$

   E. $\dfrac{9-b}{2}$

for calculation use

17. How many 7-digit phone numbers are there if the first digit is a 9 and the last digit is a 2?

    A.   59,049

    B.   100,000

    C.   604,800

    D.   4,782,969

    E.   10,000,000

18. If $\sin\theta = \dfrac{3}{5}$ and $90° \le \theta \le 180°$, find $2\cos\theta + 3\tan\theta$.

    A. $\dfrac{-77}{20}$

    B. $\dfrac{-13}{20}$

    C.   0

    D. $\dfrac{13}{20}$

    E. $\dfrac{77}{20}$

19. If $a:b = 2:3$, $b:c = 6:1$ and $c:d = 4:5$, then $\left(b^2 - 2a^2 - c^2\right):\left(3d^2 - c^2\right) =$

    A. $56 : 59$

    B. $54 : 59$

    C. $52 : 59$

    D. $50 : 59$

    E. $48 : 59$

for calculation use

20. In the figure below, what is the total area of the shaded rectangles?

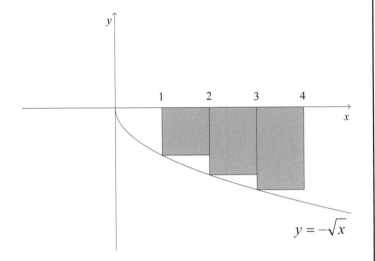

A. 2.41

B. 2.45

C. 3.59

D. 3.82

E. 4.15

21. Given that the 1st term and the 10th term of an arithmetic sequence are 10 and 28 respectively, what is the sum of the first 20 terms of this sequence?

A. 290

B. 350

C. 560

D. 580

E. 1160

for calculation use

22. Which of the following functions $f(x)$ has the property that $f(-x) = -f(x)$?

   A. $f(x) = x^4$

   B. $f(x) = \sin(x - \pi)$

   C. $f(x) = (x - 3)^5$

   D. $f(x) = x^3 + 4$

   E. $f(x) = |x|$

23. Referring to the figure of $\triangle ABC$ where $a < c < b$, which of the following is/are always true?

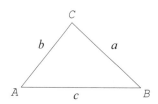

   Figure not drawn to scale

   I $\sin A = \sin(B + C)$

   II $\sin A < \sin C < \sin B$

   III $\cos(A + C) < \cos B$

   A. I and II only

   B. I and III only

   C. II only

   D. II and III only

   E. I, II and III

for calculation use

24. The domain of $f(x) = \ln \sqrt{x^2 - 1}$ is

    A. $x < -1$

    B. $x > 1$

    C. $-1 < x < 1$

    D. $x > 1$ or $x < -1$

    E.   All real numbers

25. The minimum point of $y = \dfrac{3}{3 + \sin 2x}$ for $0 \le x \le \pi$ is

    A. $\left(\dfrac{\pi}{2}, \dfrac{3}{2} \right)$

    B. $\left(\dfrac{\pi}{4}, 1 \right)$

    C. $\left(\dfrac{\pi}{2}, \dfrac{3}{4} \right)$

    D. $\left(\dfrac{\pi}{4}, \dfrac{3}{4} \right)$

    E. $(0, 1)$

26. If $f(x) = x^3 + 1$ and f^{-1} is the inverse function of f, then what is $f^{-1}(4)$?

    A.   0.02

    B.   1.44

    C.   1.71

    D.   27

    E.   65

for calculation use

27. Suppose the graph of $f(x) = x^2 + 1$ is translated 2 units left and 1 unit down. If the resulting graph is represented by $g(x)$, then what is the value of $g(2)$?

    A.   0

    B.   2

    C.   6

    D.   16

    E.   17

28. Which of the following equations defines the set of all the points in the xy-plane that are 4 units from the point $(2, -2)$?

    A. $x^2 - 4x + y^2 + 4y - 4 = 0$

    B. $x^2 - 4x + y^2 + 4y - 8 = 0$

    C. $x^2 - 4x + y^2 + 4y = 0$

    D. $x^2 - 4x + y^2 - 4y - 4 = 0$

    E. $x^2 - 4x + y^2 - 4y = 0$

29. What are the values of x for which $|x - 6| < 4$?

    A. $x < 10$ or $x > -2$

    B. $x < 10$

    C. $x > -2$

    D. $-10 < x < 2$

    E. $2 < x < 10$

for calculation use

30. There are 12 teams in a competition. In how many ways can they be divided into 2 groups of 6 teams?

    A. 360

    B. 720

    C. 462

    D. 924

    E. 1440

31. What is the range of the function defined by
    $f(x) = x^{\frac{1}{3}}$ for $x > 2$ and $f(x) = 2x - 1$ for $x \le 2$?

    A. $f(x) > 2^{\frac{1}{3}}$

    B. $f(x) \le 3$

    C. $2^{\frac{1}{3}} < f(x) < 3$

    D. $f(x) \ge 3$

    E. All real numbers

32. How many solutions for x are there if
    $\left|x\right|^3 - 7\left|x\right| + 6 = 0$?

    A. 2

    B. 3

    C. 4

    D. 5

    E. 6

33. If $f(x) = \log_2 x$, for $x > 0$, then $f^{-1}(x) =$

   A. 2^x

   B. x^2

   C. $\dfrac{x}{2}$

   D. $\dfrac{2}{x}$

   E. $\log_x 2$

34. If $\dfrac{a}{b} - 1 > 0$, which of the following can never be true?

   A. $a > b$

   B. $a < b$

   C. $a > 0$

   D. $b > 0$

   E.   None of the above

for calculation use

35. Which of the following equations have real solutions?

$$\text{I} \qquad \sin^2\theta = -\frac{1}{3}$$

$$\text{II} \qquad \cos^2\theta = 3$$

$$\text{III} \qquad \tan^2\theta = 5$$

A. I only

B. II only

C. III only

D. I and II only

E. II and III only

36. For an unfair coin, the probability of getting heads on a single toss is 0.3. What is the probability of getting no heads in 3 trials of tossing this coin?

A. 0.063

B. 0.27

C. 0.343

D. 0.7

E. 0.9

for calculation use

37. The vertices of $\triangle ABC$ are $A(-3, 0)$, $B(0, 3)$ and $C(0, -3)$. $\triangle ABC$ is therefore

        I   Scalene
        II   Isosceles
        III   Right angular

    A.   I only

    B.   II only

    C.   III only

    D.   I and III only

    E.   II and III only

38. Solve $(x^2 - 100)^{\frac{2}{3}} = 16$ for x.

    A. $x = \pm 6$ or $x = \pm 2\sqrt{41}$

    B. $x = \pm 6$

    C. $x = \pm 2\sqrt{41}$

    D. $x = \pm 3$ or $x = \pm 2\sqrt{41}$

    E. $x = \pm 12$ or $x = \pm 2\sqrt{41}$

39. Find the area of an equilateral triangle inscribed in a circle of radius 8.

    A. $16\sqrt{3}$

    B. $24\sqrt{3}$

    C. $32\sqrt{3}$

    D. $48\sqrt{3}$

    E. $64\sqrt{3}$

40. What is the sum of all integers between 1 and 100 that are divisible by 9?

    A.   540
    B.   567
    C.   594
    D.   606
    E.   648

41. A rectangular block with a volume of 250 cubic inches is sliced into 2 cubes of equal volume. How much greater, in square inches, is the combined surface area of the 2 cubes than the original surface area of the rectangular block?

    A.   5
    B.   25
    C.   40
    D.   50
    E.   250

42. A polar equation is given by the formula $r = \dfrac{1}{\sec\theta + \csc\theta}$. An equivalent Cartesian form could be

    A. $\left(x^2 + y^2\right)(x + y) = 1$
    B. $\left(x^2 + y^2\right)xy = 1$
    C. $(x + y)^3 = 1$
    D. $\left(x^2 + y^2\right)xy = x + y$
    E. $\left(x^2 + y^2\right)(x + y) = xy$

for calculation use

43. The standard deviation of a set of numbers is S. What is the standard deviation if each number in the set is doubled?

    A. $0.5S$

    B. S

    C. $2S$

    D. $4S$

    E. S^2

44. What is the volume of the solid obtained by rotating the line $y = x + 1$ around the x-axis from $x = 0$ to $x = 4$?

    A. $\dfrac{121\pi}{3}$

    B. $\dfrac{122\pi}{3}$

    C. $\dfrac{124\pi}{3}$

    D. $\dfrac{130\pi}{3}$

    E. $\dfrac{131\pi}{3}$

for calculation use

45. Given that a and b are integers, if $2a + 3b$ is odd, which of the following must be correct?

    A. a is odd

    B. a is even

    C. b is odd

    D. b is even

    E.   None of the above

46. If $f(x^2 + 1) = x^4 + 1$, then $f(x) =$

    A. x^2

    B. $x^2 + 1$

    C. $x^2 - 2x + 2$

    D. $x^2 + 2x - 2$

    E. $x^2 + 2x$

47. For an arithmetic sequence, what should the common difference be if it is also a geometric sequence at the same time?

    A. -2

    B. -1

    C.   0

    D.   1

    E.   2

for calculation use

48. Simplify $\dfrac{P^n_r}{C^n_{r-1}}$.

    A. $(n-r-1)r!$

    B. $(n-r+1)(r-1)!$

    C. $(n+r-1)r!$

    D. $(n+r+1)(r-1)!$

    E. $(n-r-1)(r-1)!$

49. The center of an ellipse is $(2, -3)$, the length of the major axis is 8, and the length of the minor axis is 4. What is the equation of the ellipse?

    A. $\left(\dfrac{x+2}{8}\right)^2 + \left(\dfrac{y-3}{4}\right)^2 = 1$

    B. $\left(\dfrac{x+2}{4}\right)^2 + \left(\dfrac{y-3}{2}\right)^2 = 1$

    C. $\left(\dfrac{x+2}{16}\right)^2 + \left(\dfrac{y-3}{4}\right)^2 = 1$

    D. $\left(\dfrac{x-2}{4}\right)^2 + \left(\dfrac{y+3}{2}\right)^2 = 1$

    E. $\left(\dfrac{x-2}{8}\right)^2 + \left(\dfrac{y+3}{4}\right)^2 = 1$

for calculation use

50. Simplify $\dfrac{2^{n+1}-8^{3-n}}{2(2^n-2^{4-n})}$.

A. $\dfrac{1-2^{8-4n}}{2^{4-2n}}$

B. 2^{8-4n}

C. $\dfrac{1-2^{3-2n}}{1-2^{4-2n}}$

D. $1-2^{4-2n}$

E. $1+2^{4-2n}$

Finding Your Test Score

Step 1: Count the number of correct answers and record it here:

Step 2: Count the number of wrong answers, divide it by 4 and record it here:

Step 3: Subtract the number in the second box from that in the first box and round it to the nearest integer. This is you raw score:

Step 4: By using the conversion table below, you can find your test score.

Raw Score	Probable scaled SAT Math Level 2 score	Raw Score	Probable scaled SAT Math Level 2 score	Raw Score	Probable scaled SAT Math Level 2 score
42 - 50	800	26	650	10	510
41	790	25	640	9	500
40	780	24	630	8	480
39	770	23	620	7	460
38	760	22	610	6	450
37	750	21	600	5	430
36	740	20	600	4	400
35	730	19	590	3	390
34	720	18	580	2	370
33	720	17	570	1	360
32	710	16	570	0	350
31	700	15	560	−1	320
30	690	14	550	−2	300
29	680	13	540	−3	280
28	670	12	530	−4	260
27	660	11	520	−5	250

The College Board will convert your raw score to a **scaled score**. The highest score you can get is **800**. The lowest is **200**.

In the actual SAT Math Level 2 test, there is always some slight variation from test to test for the score boundaries. It's possible to get somewhat lower than our scores by getting very few correct and many wrong. But, to be honest, if you are getting scores this low it would be a lot better for you to try the easier SAT Math Level 1 test.

Sample Test 4

Time: <u>One hour</u>

Write your answers on the sheet overleaf by **shading in** the appropriate oval like this:

Use a pencil and if you wish to correct an answer, ensure that you erase the original answer completely.

<u>Mark Scheme</u>: Each answer is worth +1 mark if correct, $-\dfrac{1}{4}$ mark if incorrect and 0 mark if omitted.

<u>Calculator Use</u>: A calculator is necessary to answer some of the questions on the test although not all questions require calculator use. You will need a calculator that can at least perform roots, logarithms and trigonometric ratios. You may use a graphing calculator.

<u>Diagrams</u>: Diagrams are drawn to scale unless stated otherwise.

<u>Function Domains</u>: All functions have real number domains unless stated otherwise.

<u>Formulas</u>: The following is a list of formulas which may be used for reference:

Volume of a sphere of radius *r*: $\dfrac{4}{3}\pi r^{3}$

Surface area of a sphere of radius *r*: $4\pi r^{2}$

Volume of a pyramid of height *h* and base area *A*: $\dfrac{1}{3}Ah$

Volume of a right circular come of height *h* and base radius *r*: $\dfrac{1}{3}\pi r^{2}h$

Curved surface of a right circular cone of height *h* and slant height *l*: πrl

1. (A) (B) (C) (D) (E)
2. (A) (B) (C) (D) (E)
3. (A) (B) (C) (D) (E)
4. (A) (B) (C) (D) (E)
5. (A) (B) (C) (D) (E)
6. (A) (B) (C) (D) (E)
7. (A) (B) (C) (D) (E)
8. (A) (B) (C) (D) (E)
9. (A) (B) (C) (D) (E)
10. (A) (B) (C) (D) (E)
11. (A) (B) (C) (D) (E)
12. (A) (B) (C) (D) (E)
13. (A) (B) (C) (D) (E)
14. (A) (B) (C) (D) (E)
15. (A) (B) (C) (D) (E)
16. (A) (B) (C) (D) (E)
17. (A) (B) (C) (D) (E)
18. (A) (B) (C) (D) (E)
19. (A) (B) (C) (D) (E)
20. (A) (B) (C) (D) (E)
21. (A) (B) (C) (D) (E)
22. (A) (B) (C) (D) (E)
23. (A) (B) (C) (D) (E)
24. (A) (B) (C) (D) (E)
25. (A) (B) (C) (D) (E)

26. (A) (B) (C) (D) (E)
27. (A) (B) (C) (D) (E)
28. (A) (B) (C) (D) (E)
29. (A) (B) (C) (D) (E)
30. (A) (B) (C) (D) (E)
31. (A) (B) (C) (D) (E)
32. (A) (B) (C) (D) (E)
33. (A) (B) (C) (D) (E)
34. (A) (B) (C) (D) (E)
35. (A) (B) (C) (D) (E)
36. (A) (B) (C) (D) (E)
37. (A) (B) (C) (D) (E)
38. (A) (B) (C) (D) (E)
39. (A) (B) (C) (D) (E)
40. (A) (B) (C) (D) (E)
41. (A) (B) (C) (D) (E)
42. (A) (B) (C) (D) (E)
43. (A) (B) (C) (D) (E)
44. (A) (B) (C) (D) (E)
45. (A) (B) (C) (D) (E)
46. (A) (B) (C) (D) (E)
47. (A) (B) (C) (D) (E)
48. (A) (B) (C) (D) (E)
49. (A) (B) (C) (D) (E)
50. (A) (B) (C) (D) (E)

for calculation use

1. Given that $z \neq 0$, $x = \dfrac{4}{z}$ and $yz = 8$, find $\dfrac{x}{y}$.

   A. 0.5

   B. 1

   C. 2

   D. 16

   E. 32

2. Solve for x in the equation $8(8^x) - 6(8^x) - 1 = 0$.

   A. -1

   B. $-\dfrac{2}{3}$

   C. $-\dfrac{1}{3}$

   D. $\dfrac{1}{3}$

   E. $\dfrac{2}{3}$

3. Given that $y = \arcsin(0.6)$, the value of $4\tan(y)$ is

   A. 1

   B. 2.4

   C. 3

   D. 4.6

   E. 5

for calculation use

4. What is the volume of a cube with a surface area of 96 square inches?

    A. 8 cubic inches

    B. 16 cubic inches

    C. 27 cubic inches

    D. 48 cubic inches

    E. 64 cubic inches

5. A toy car is bought for $150x$ and is sold for $648 at a profit of $2x$ percent of the cost. Find x.

    A. 4

    B. 4.5

    C. 5

    D. 6

    E. 8

6. The perimeter of the sector OPR of a circle with center O and points P and R along its circumference is 18 and $\angle POR = 4$ radians. Find the length of arc PR.

    A. 12

    B. 16

    C. 9π

    D. 36

    E. 16π

for calculation use

7.   If $f(x) = x + \sqrt{x}$ and $g(x) = f(f(x))$, then $g(2.5) =$

   A.   2.32

   B.   3.34

   C.   5.22

   D.   6.10

   E.   8.21

8.   Given that $\log 2 = a$, $\log 3 = b$ and $\log 5 = c$, find $\log \sqrt[3]{20} + \log \sqrt[5]{90} - \log \sqrt[4]{60}$ in terms of a, b and c.

   A. $\dfrac{19}{30}a + \dfrac{7}{20}b + \dfrac{13}{60}c$

   B. $\dfrac{19}{30}a + \dfrac{13}{20}b + \dfrac{11}{60}c$

   C. $\dfrac{11}{60}a + \dfrac{13}{20}b + \dfrac{17}{30}c$

   D. $\dfrac{13}{30}a + \dfrac{17}{20}b + \dfrac{23}{60}c$

   E. $\dfrac{11}{30}a + \dfrac{3}{20}b + \dfrac{17}{60}c$

for calculation use

9. Find the equation of the line passing through the point $(2,-3)$ with an inclination of $45°$ above the x-axis.

   A. $x + y = 1$

   B. $x + 2y = 0$

   C. $2x + y = 0$

   D. $3x + y = 0$

   E. $x - y - 5 = 0$

10. The greatest value of $4 - 3\cos^2 x$ is

    A. 1

    B. 3.5

    C. 4

    D. 4.5

    E. 7

11. Let $f(x) = a\sin x - b\cos x$ where a and b are constants. If $f(0) = 1$ and $f(\frac{\pi}{2}) = 2$, then $a - b =$

    A. -3

    B. -1

    C. 0

    D. 1

    E. 3

for calculation use

12. The ratio of John's amount of money to Mary's amount of money is 3 : 7. If Mary gives $224 to John, then the ratio of Mary's amount of money to John's amount of money will be 3 : 7. How much do they have altogether?

A. $520

B. $540

C. $560

D. $580

E. $600

13. In the figure below, what is the value of $\sin \theta + \cos \theta$?

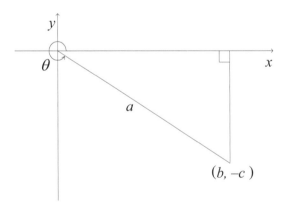

A. $b + c$

B. $b - c$

C. $\dfrac{b+c}{a}$

D. $\dfrac{b-c}{a}$

E. $c - b$

14. Two of the solutions of the equation $f(x) = 0$ are 5 and 8. Which of the following must be the solutions of the equation $f(x-3) = 0$?

   A. -5 and -2

   B.   2 and 5

   C.   5 and 8

   D.   8 and 11

   E.   None of the above

15. The diameter of the base of a cone is increased by 50% and its height is decreased by 50%. What is the percentage change in volume going from the old to the new cone?

   A.   No change

   B.   12.5% increase

   C.   25% increase

   D.   25% decrease

   E.   12.5% decrease

16. In the following diagram, if l_1 and l_2 are parallel, then what is the value of a?

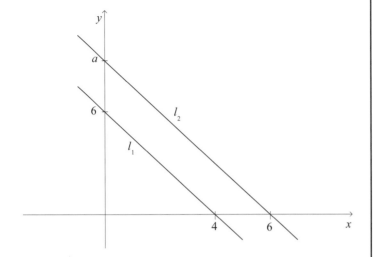

A. 4

B. 7.5

C. 8

D. 9

E. It cannot be determined from the given information.

17. Andrew has 5 shirts, 3 pairs of pants, and 2 pairs of shoes that he can choose from to wear to a dinner party. How many different combinations does he have to choose from?

A. 3

B. 10

C. 16

D. 30

E. 120

for calculation use

18. $\cos^4 \alpha - \sin^4 \alpha =$

A. 0

B. 1

C. $\cos^2 \alpha$

D. $\sin^2 \alpha$

E. $\cos^2 \alpha - \sin^2 \alpha$

19. Given that $ax^2 + bx + c = 0$ has two distinct real roots and $a = c$, find the range of b if $a > 0$.

A. $-2a < b < 2a$

B. $b < -2a$ or $b > 2a$

C. $-c < b < c$

D. All real numbers

E. It cannot be determined from the given information.

20. If $f(x) = 3^{x+2}$, then $f^{-1}(x) =$

A. $\dfrac{1}{2}\log_3 x$

B. $2\log_3 x$

C. $\log_3 x + 2$

D. $\log_3 x - 2$

E. $\log_3 2x$

for calculation use

21. If vector **u** has a magnitude of 5, and vector **v** has a magnitude of 12, then which of the following could not be the magnitude of **u** + **v**?

A. 5

B. 7

C. 12

D. 13

E. 17

22. What is the domain of $f(x) = \dfrac{1}{x^2 - 3x + 2}$?

A. All real numbers x such that $x \neq 1$

B. All real numbers x such that $x \neq 2$

C. All real numbers x such that $x \neq 1, 2$

D. All real numbers

E. None of the above gives the correct domain for $f(x)$.

23. Solve $2\cos(3\theta) = \sqrt{3}$ for $0° \leq \theta \leq 120°$.

A. $10°$ or $90°$

B. $10°$ or $110°$

C. $10°$ or $120°$

D. $20°$ or $120°$

E. $25.7°$ or $125.7°$

for calculation use

24. Below is the graph of $y = f(x)$. Which of the following is the graph of $y = |f(x)|$?

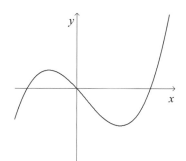

A.

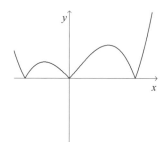

B.

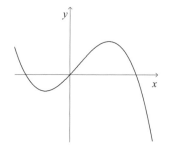

C.

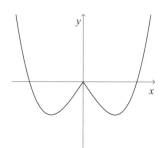

D.

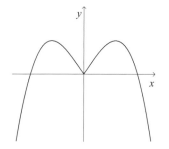

E.

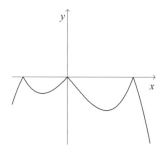

for calculation use

25. In the figure below, what is the length of XY?

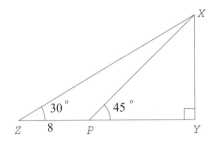

Note: Figure not drawn to scale

A. $2\sqrt{3} + 2$

B. $3\sqrt{2} + 3$

C. $2\sqrt{3} + 4$

D. $4\sqrt{3} + 4$

E. $6\sqrt{3} + 3$

26. If $(x-2)(x-3) = (a-2)(a-3)$, what are the solutions for x?

A. 0 or 5

B. 2 or 3

C. a or 2

D. a or 3

E. a or $5-a$

for calculation use

27. Given that $f(x) = x^3 - x$ and $g(x) = 6x^2 - 30$, what are the values of x such that $f(x) = g(x)$?

    A. $-5, 1, 6$

    B. $-3, 2, 5$

    C. $-2, 1, 15$

    D. $-2, 3, 5$

    E. $-1, 5, 6$

28. Which of the following inequalities represent the shaded part of the diagram?

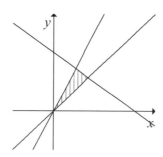

    A. $y > x$, $y > 2x$ and $3x + 4y < 12$

    B. $y < x$, $y < 2x$ and $3x + 4y < 12$

    C. $y > x$, $y < 2x$ and $3x + 4y > 12$

    D. $y < x$, $y > 2x$ and $3x + 4y > 12$

    E. $y > x$, $y < 2x$ and $3x + 4y < 12$

29. What is the range of $y = \dfrac{|x-1|}{x}$?

    A. $y \neq 0$

    B. $y > 0$

    C. $y < -1$ or $y \geq 0$

    D. $y \neq -1$

    E.   All real numbers

30. If $f(x) = ax^2 + bx + c$, with a, b and c real numbers and $a > 0$. What is the minimum value of $f(x)$?

    A. $f\left(-\dfrac{b}{2a}\right)$

    B. $f\left(\dfrac{b}{2a}\right)$

    C. $-\dfrac{b}{2a}$

    D. $\dfrac{b}{2a}$

    E. $b^2 - 4ac$

31. In polar coordinates, the graph of $r = 0$ is

    A.   a point

    B.   a circle

    C.   a horizontal line

    D.   a vertical line

    E.   a parabola

for calculation use

32. Thomas cycles a distance of l miles at x miles per hour and then he returns at $(x-4)$ miles per hour. The total time for the whole trip is t hours. Expressing l in terms of x and t gives

A. $\dfrac{tx}{x-4}$

B. $\dfrac{tx(2x-4)}{x-1}$

C. $\dfrac{t(2x-4)}{x}$

D. $\dfrac{x(x-4)}{t}$

E. $\dfrac{tx(x-4)}{2x-4}$

33. If $f(x, y) = (x+y, x-y)$ for every ordered pair (x, y) in the plane, for which point(s) is it true that $f(x, y) = (x, y)$?

A. All the points (x, y) such that $x = 0$

B. All the points (x, y) such that $y = 0$

C. All the points (x, y) such that $xy = 0$

D. All the points (x, y) such that $x = y$

E. $(0, 0)$ only

NTK

34. Given that p and q are even integers, which of the following must be an odd integer?

    A. $p+q$

    B. $p-q$

    C. pq

    D. $\dfrac{p}{q}$

    E. $(p+1)(q-1)$

35. The diagram below is a sector of a circle with radius 1. Express the shaded area in terms of θ in radian measure.

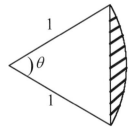

Figure not drawn to scale

    A. $\dfrac{1}{2}(\theta - \cos\theta)$

    B. $\dfrac{1}{2}(\theta - \sin\theta)$

    C. $\theta - \cos\theta$

    D. $\theta - \sin\theta$

    E. $\cos\theta - \sin\theta$

for calculation use

36. The average (arithmetic mean) height of the 12 players on a basketball team is 190 cm. Four new players with average height 185 cm are added to the team. What is the new mean height of the whole team?

    A.   186.25 cm

    B.   187.5 cm

    C.   188.75 cm

    D.   189.25 cm

    E.   189.75 cm

37. Find the coordinates of the point that divides the line segment joining the points $(6, -9)$ and $(6, 3)$ in the ratio 3 : 1.

    A. $(1, 0)$

    B. $(6, 0)$

    C. $(0, 1)$

    D. $(0, 6)$

    E. $(-4, 3)$

38. If $a < b$ and $b < c$, which of the following must be true?

    A. $b + c < 2a$

    B. $a + b < c$

    C. $a - b < b - c$

    D. $a + b < 2c$

    E. $a + c < 2b$

for calculation use

39. Given that $\sin x = \dfrac{12}{13}$ and $\cos x < 0$, what is the value of $\tan x$?

    A. $-\dfrac{12}{5}$

    B. $-\dfrac{13}{12}$

    C. $-\dfrac{5}{13}$

    D. $\dfrac{5}{12}$

    E. $\dfrac{13}{5}$

40. What is the 20th term of the sequence 50, 47, 44, 41 …?

    A. -13

    B. -10

    C. -7

    D. -4

    E. -1

41. The coordinates of points A, B and C are $(-1, 2, -3)$, $(1, -2, 3)$ and $(-1, -2, 3)$ respectively. Which of the two points has the shortest distance between them, and what is the distance?

    A. BC, 1

    B. BC, 2

    C. AC, $\sqrt{40}$

    D. AC, $\sqrt{85}$

    E. AB, $\sqrt{101}$

42. Given that $\pi < a < b < \dfrac{3\pi}{2}$, which of the following statements is/are true?

    I $\cos a < \cos b$
    II $\sin a < \sin b$
    III $\tan a < \tan b$

    A.   I only

    B.   I and II only

    C.   I and III only

    D.   II and III only

    E.   I, II and III

43. Five biased coins are tossed. For each coin, the probability of getting heads on a single toss is 0.3. What is the probability of getting 3 heads and 2 tails?

   A.   0.0794

   B.   0.1058

   C.   0.1191

   D.   0.1323

   E.   0.3087

44. If a cube is inscribed in a sphere with a radius of 6, what is the volume of the space between the sphere and the cube?

   A.   332.55

   B.   572.22

   C.   688.78

   D.   863.21

   E.   904.78

45. If $f(x) = e^{-x}$, as x approaches infinity, then $f(x)$ approaches

   A.   Negative infinity

   B. -1

   C.   0

   D.   1

   E.   Infinity

for calculation use

46. Refer to the graph of $h(x)$ below, which of the following could be its equation?

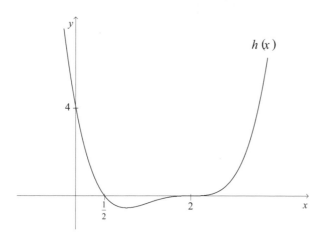

A. $-0.5(2x-1)(x-2)^2$

B. $-0.5(2x-1)(x-2)^3$

C. $0.5(2x-1)(x-2)^3$

D. $0.5(2x-1)^2(x-2)^3$

E. $(2x-1)^2(x-2)^2$

47. Simplify $\dfrac{(a-2)!-(a-3)!}{(a-1)!}$.

A. $\dfrac{a-3}{a^2-2a}$

B. $\dfrac{a-2}{a^2-2a-1}$

C. $\dfrac{a-2}{a^2-2a-3}$

D. $\dfrac{a-3}{a^2-2a-3}$

E. $\dfrac{a-3}{a^2-3a+2}$

for calculation use

48. A group of students took either an easy mathematics test or a hard mathematics test. Each student took exactly one test. Of those who took the easy mathematics test, 80% students passed. Of those who took the hard mathematics test, $33\frac{1}{3}\%$ students passed. It is known that $\frac{4}{7}$ of the students took the easy mathematics test. What percent of the students of the whole group did not pass either of the mathematics tests?

    A.   40%

    B.   45%

    C.   55%

    D.   60%

    E.   65%

49. What is the polar equation of the circle centered at $(-3, 4)$ with radius 5?

    A. $r + 6\cos\theta + 8\sin\theta = 0$

    B. $r + 8\cos\theta + 6\sin\theta = 0$

    C. $r - 6\cos\theta - 8\sin\theta = 0$

    D. $r + 6\cos\theta - 8\sin\theta = 0$

    E. $r - 8\cos\theta + 6\sin\theta = 0$

for calculation use

50. Solve for x in the inequality $|2-x| > |2x-1|$.

    A. $-1 < x < 1$

    B. $x > 1$ or $x < -1$

    C. $\dfrac{1}{2} < x < 2$

    D. $x > 2$ or $x < \dfrac{1}{2}$

    E. $1 < x < 2$

Finding Your Test Score

Step 1: Count the number of correct answers and record it here:

Step 2: Count the number of wrong answers, divide it by 4 and record it here:

Step 3: Subtract the number in the second box from that in the first box and round it to the

nearest integer. This is you raw score:

Step 4: By using the conversion table below, you can find your test score.

Raw Score	Probable scaled SAT Math Level 2 score	Raw Score	Probable scaled SAT Math Level 2 score	Raw Score	Probable scaled SAT Math Level 2 score
42 - 50	800	26	650	10	510
41	790	25	640	9	500
40	780	24	630	8	480
39	770	23	620	7	460
38	760	22	610	6	450
37	750	21	600	5	430
36	740	20	600	4	400
35	730	19	590	3	390
34	720	18	580	2	370
33	720	17	570	1	360
32	710	16	570	0	350
31	700	15	560	−1	320
30	690	14	550	−2	300
29	680	13	540	−3	280
28	670	12	530	−4	260
27	660	11	520	−5	250

The College Board will convert your raw score to a **scaled score**. The highest score you can get is **800**. The lowest is **200**.

In the actual SAT Math Level 2 test, there is always some slight variation from test to test for the score boundaries. It's possible to get somewhat lower than our scores by getting very few correct and many wrong. But, to be honest, if you are getting scores this low it would be a lot better for you to try the easier SAT Math Level 1 test.

Sample Tests Answers

Sample Test 1

1.	D	11.	C	21.	B	31.	E	41.	B
2.	D	12.	B	22.	E	32.	B	42.	A
3.	B	13.	E	23.	C	33.	D	43.	A
4.	D	14.	B	24.	A	34.	C	44.	A
5.	C	15.	E	25.	D	35.	D	45.	C
6.	C	16.	E	26.	C	36.	E	46.	A
7.	E	17.	D	27.	E	37.	D	47.	B
8.	C	18.	A	28.	B	38.	B	48.	C
9.	A	19.	C	29.	C	39.	A	49.	A
10.	C	20.	D	30.	C	40.	D	50.	D

Sample Test 2

1.	C	11.	C	21.	B	31.	E	41.	B
2.	B	12.	B	22.	E	32.	A	42.	B
3.	C	13.	B	23.	C	33.	B	43.	D
4.	C	14.	A	24.	A	34.	B	44.	C
5.	A	15.	B	25.	C	35.	C	45.	D
6.	E	16.	D	26.	E	36.	B	46.	D
7.	D	17.	D	27.	E	37.	E	47.	A
8.	E	18.	D	28.	A	38.	C	48.	A
9.	D	19.	C	29.	D	39.	B	49.	D
10.	C	20.	D	30.	E	40.	D	50.	A

Sample Test 3

1.	E	11.	E	21.	D	31.	E	41.	D
2.	D	12.	A	22.	B	32.	C	42.	E
3.	B	13.	D	23.	A	33.	A	43.	C
4.	D	14.	A	24.	D	34.	E	44.	C
5.	D	15.	C	25.	D	35.	C	45.	C
6.	A	16.	D	26.	B	36.	C	46.	C
7.	B	17.	B	27.	D	37.	E	47.	C
8.	B	18.	A	28.	B	38.	A	48.	B
9.	C	19.	E	29.	E	39.	D	49.	D
10.	A	20.	E	30.	C	40.	C	50.	E

Sample Test 4

1.	A	11.	E	21.	A	31.	A	41.	B
2.	C	12.	C	22.	C	32.	E	42.	C
3.	C	13.	D	23.	B	33.	E	43.	D
4.	E	14.	D	24.	A	34.	E	44.	B
5.	A	15.	B	25.	D	35.	B	45.	C
6.	A	16.	D	26.	E	36.	C	46.	C
7.	D	17.	D	27.	D	37.	B	47.	E
8.	E	18.	E	28.	E	38.	D	48.	A
9.	E	19.	B	29.	C	39.	A	49.	D
10.	C	20.	D	30.	A	40.	C	50.	A

Solutions To Sample Test 1

1.   Answer: **D**

Algebra (Easy)

$$\frac{3}{x-1}-6=0 \Rightarrow \frac{3}{x-1}=6 \Rightarrow \frac{3}{6}=x-1 \Rightarrow \frac{1}{2}=x-1 \Rightarrow x=\frac{3}{2}$$

The answer is D.

2.   Answer: **D**

Algebra (Easy)

For the equation here, we transform it to $x^2 - 8x - 5 = 0$. For this quadratic equation, we cannot factor it directly: we need to use the quadratic formula. Here, $a = 1$, $b = -8$ and $c = -5$.

$$x = \frac{-b \pm \sqrt{b^2 - 4ac}}{2a} = \frac{-(-8) \pm \sqrt{(-8)^2 - 4(1)(-5)}}{2(1)} = \frac{8 \pm \sqrt{84}}{2} = \frac{8 \pm 2\sqrt{21}}{2} = 4 \pm \sqrt{21}$$

The answer is D.

(For those who are not comfortable with square roots, you could find the answer by checking the values of the choices in the calculator directly.)

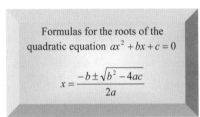

Formulas for the roots of the quadratic equation $ax^2 + bx + c = 0$

$$x = \frac{-b \pm \sqrt{b^2 - 4ac}}{2a}$$

Plugging-in Tips:

We can plug the numbers in the choices into the given equation to see whether the equality holds or not:

Choice A: Plug $x = 23$

$23^2 - 8 \times 23 = 345 \neq 5$, so choice A is not the answer.

Choice B: Plug $x = 25$

$25^2 - 8 \times 25 = 425 \neq 5$, so choice B is not the answer.

Choice C: Plug $x = 29$

$29^2 - 8 \times 29 = 609 \neq 5$, so choice C is not the answer.

Choice D: Plug $x = 4 + \sqrt{21}$

$(4 + \sqrt{21})^2 - 8 \times (4 + \sqrt{21}) = 5$ and $(4 - \sqrt{21})^2 - 8 \times (4 - \sqrt{21}) = 5$, the

equation **is** satisfied for both values, so choice D **should be** the answer.

Choice E: Plug $x = 8 + \sqrt{21}$

$(8 + \sqrt{21})^2 - 8 \times (8 + \sqrt{21}) = 57.66 \neq 5$, so choice E is not the answer.

The answer is D.

3.   Answer: **B**

Trigonometry (Easy)

$\sqrt{3} \sin x - \cos x = 0 \Rightarrow \sqrt{3} \sin x = \cos x \Rightarrow \dfrac{\sqrt{3} \sin x}{\cos x} = 1 \Rightarrow \dfrac{\sin x}{\cos x} = \dfrac{1}{\sqrt{3}} \Rightarrow \tan x = \dfrac{1}{\sqrt{3}}$

$\Rightarrow x = \tan^{-1} \dfrac{1}{\sqrt{3}} = 30°$

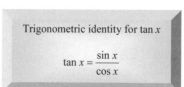

Trigonometric identity for $\tan x$

$\tan x = \dfrac{\sin x}{\cos x}$

The answer is B.

Plugging-in Tips:

We can plug the numbers in the choices into the given equation to see whether the equality holds or not.

Choice A: Plug $x = 0°$

$\sqrt{3} \sin 0° - \cos 0° = -1 \neq 0$, so choice A is not the answer.

Choice B: Plug $x = 30°$

$\sqrt{3} \sin 30° - \cos 30° = 0$, so choice B **should be** the answer.

Choice C: Plug $x = 45°$

$\sqrt{3} \sin 45° - \cos 45° = 0.52 \neq 0$, so choice C is not the answer.

Choice D: Plug $x = 60°$

$\sqrt{3} \sin 60° - \cos 60° = 1 \neq 0$, so choice D is not the answer.

Choice E: Plug $x = 90°$

$\sqrt{3} \sin 90° - \cos 90° = 1.73 \neq 0$, so choice E is not the answer.

The answer is B.

4.   Answer: **D**

Solid Geometry (Easy)

For a rectangular box with dimensions 3cm by 4cm and 5cm, there are 4 edges of each dimension. Therefore, the sum of the lengths of all the edges is $3 \times 4 + 4 \times 4 + 5 \times 4 = 48$ cm.

The answer is D.

5.   Answer: **C**

Algebra (Medium)

By making use of the corresponding logarithmic identity, we have

$$2^x = 7^{x+3} \Rightarrow \log 2^x = \log 7^{x+3} \Rightarrow x \log 2 = (x+3)\log 7 \Rightarrow x \log 2 = x \log 7 + 3\log 7$$

$$\Rightarrow x \log 2 - x \log 7 = 3\log 7 \Rightarrow x(\log 2 - \log 7) = 3\log 7 \Rightarrow x = \frac{3\log 7}{\log 2 - \log 7} = -4.66$$

The answer is C.

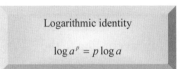

Logarithmic identity

$\log a^p = p \log a$

Plugging-in Tips:

We can plug the numbers in the choices into the given equation to see whether the equality holds or not.

Choice A: Plug $x = 4.66$

LHS $= 2^{4.66} = 25.28$, RHS $= 7^{4.66+3} = 2974753$. The equation is not satisfied, so choice A is not the answer.

Choice B: Plug $x = 3.99$

LHS $= 2^{3.99} = 15.89$, RHS $= 7^{3.99+3} = 807673$. The equation is not satisfied, so choice B is not the answer.

Choice C: Plug $x = -4.66$

LHS $= 2^{-4.66} = 0.03955$, RHS $= 7^{-4.66+3} = 0.03955$. The equation **is** satisfied, so choice C **should be** the answer.

Choice D: Plug $x = -3.99$

LHS $= 2^{-3.99} = 0.06293$, RHS $= 7^{-3.99+3} = 0.1457$. The equation is not satisfied, so choice D is not the answer.

Choice E: Plug $x = 0$

LHS $= 2^0 = 1$, RHS $= 7^{0+3} = 343$. The equation is not satisfied, so choice E is not the answer.

The answer is C.

6.   Answer: **C**

Trigonometry (Easy)

In this question, obviously $\dfrac{\pi}{3}$ could be one of the solutions to the equation. However, it is not provided as any of the choices here. Therefore, we can only take $\dfrac{\pi}{3}$ as the reference angle. Now according to the "CAST" rule, we know that the possible values of x are only in quadrant I and III because both of them have the same sign for tangent. In quadrant III, with reference angle $\dfrac{\pi}{3}$, the corresponding angle is $\pi + \dfrac{\pi}{3} = \dfrac{4\pi}{3}$, which is given in choice C.

The answer is C.

"CAST" rule

The stated trigonometric functions are positive in the corresponding quadrants.

	90° or $\dfrac{\pi}{2}$	
Sin		**All**
180° or π		0° or 0
Tan		**Cos**
	270° or $\dfrac{3\pi}{2}$	

Corresponding angles with reference angle θ in the different quadrants

With reference angle θ, the corresponding angles in each quadrant are as follows:

90° or $\dfrac{\pi}{2}$

180° $-\theta$ or $\pi - \theta$ θ

180° or π θ θ 0° or 0

180° $+\theta$ or $\pi + \theta$ 360° $-\theta$ or $2\pi - \theta$

270° or $\dfrac{3\pi}{2}$

Plugging-in Tips:

We can plug the numbers in the choices into the given equation to see whether the equality holds or not. First of all, we have $\dfrac{\pi}{3} = 1.05$.

Choice A: Plug $x = \dfrac{2\pi}{3}$

         $\arctan(\tan \dfrac{2\pi}{3}) = -1.05 \neq 1.05$, so choice A is not the answer.

Choice B: Plug $x = \pi$

         $\arctan(\tan \pi) = 0 \neq 1.05$, so choice B is not the answer.

Choice C: Plug $x = \dfrac{4\pi}{3}$

         $\arctan(\tan \dfrac{4\pi}{3}) = 1.05$, so choice C **should be** the answer.

Choice D: Plug $x = \dfrac{5\pi}{3}$

$\arctan(\tan\dfrac{5\pi}{3}) = -1.05 \neq 1.05$, so choice D is not the answer.

Choice E: Plug $x = 2\pi$

$\arctan(\tan 2\pi) = 0 \neq 1.05$, so choice E is not the answer.

The answer is C.

7.   Answer: **E**

Functions (Easy)

$h(2x) = (2x)^2 + 2(2x) = 4x^2 + 4x$

The answer is E.

Plugging-in Tips:

Taking an arbitrary number as the value of x, we can plug it into the expressions in the choices and see which one is correct. Let's take $x = 7$ here. Then,

$h(2 \times 7) = h(14) = 14^2 + 2(14) = 224$

Choice A: $2(7)^3 = 686 \neq 224$, so choice A is not the answer.

Choice B: $2(7)^2 + 2(7) = 112 \neq 224$, so choice B is not the answer.

Choice C: $2(7)^2 + 4(7) = 126 \neq 224$, so choice C is not the answer.

Choice D: $4(7)^2 + 2(7) = 210 \neq 224$, so choice D is not the answer.

Choice E: $4(7)^2 + 4(7) = 224$, so choice E **could be** the answer.

The answer is E.

8.   Answer: **C**
Algebra (Medium)

We can solve the equation directly as follows:

$$\frac{1}{x+2}-\frac{2}{x-3}=\frac{-3}{2-3x}\Rightarrow\frac{x-3-2(x+2)}{(x+2)(x-3)}=\frac{-3}{2-3x}\Rightarrow\frac{-x-7}{(x+2)(x-3)}=\frac{-3}{2-3x}$$

$$\Rightarrow(-x-7)(2-3x)=-3(x+2)(x-3)\Rightarrow 3x^2+19x-14=-3x^2+3x+18$$

$$\Rightarrow 6x^2+16x-32=0\Rightarrow 3x^2+8x-16=0\Rightarrow(3x-4)(x+4)=0$$

$$\Rightarrow x=\frac{4}{3}\text{ or }-4$$

(You could use the quadratic formula to solve the above quadratic equation.)
Here, $a=3$, $b=8$ and $c=-16$.

Formulas for the roots of the quadratic equation $ax^2+bx+c=0$

$$x=\frac{-b\pm\sqrt{b^2-4ac}}{2a}$$

$$x=\frac{-b\pm\sqrt{b^2-4ac}}{2a}=\frac{-8\pm\sqrt{8^2-4(3)(-16)}}{2(3)}=\frac{-8\pm16}{6}=\frac{4}{3}\text{ or }-4$$

Plugging-in Tips:

We can plug the numbers in the choices into the given equation to see whether the equality holds or not.

Choice A: Plug $x=4$

$$\text{LHS}=\frac{1}{4+2}-\frac{2}{4-3}=\frac{-11}{6}\text{, RHS}=\frac{-3}{2-3(4)}=\frac{3}{10}.\text{ The equation is not}$$

satisfied, so choice A is not the answer.

Choice B: As $x=4$ cannot be the solution, automatically, choice B is not the answer.

Choice C: Plug $x = -4$

$$\text{LHS} = \frac{1}{-4+2} - \frac{2}{-4-3} = \frac{-3}{14}, \text{RHS} = \frac{-3}{2-3(-4)} = \frac{-3}{14}. \text{ The equation } \textbf{is}$$

satisfied.

Plug $x = \dfrac{4}{3}$

$$\text{LHS} = \frac{1}{\frac{4}{3}+2} - \frac{2}{\frac{4}{3}-3} = \frac{3}{2}, \text{RHS} = \frac{-3}{2-3(\frac{4}{3})} = \frac{3}{2}. \text{ The equation } \textbf{is} \text{ also satisfied,}$$

so choice C **should be** the answer.

Choice D: We do not need to check $x = -4$ as we have checked this in choice C.

Plug $x = \dfrac{2}{3}$

$$\text{LHS} = \frac{1}{\frac{2}{3}+2} - \frac{2}{\frac{2}{3}-3} = \frac{69}{56}, \text{RHS} = \frac{-3}{2-3(\frac{2}{3})} = \text{undefined. The equation is not}$$

satisfied, so choice D is not the answer.

Choice E: We do not need to check $x = -4$ as we have checked this in choice C.

The answer is C.

9.   Answer: **A**

Coordinate Geometry (Medium)

On the x-axis, the y-coordinate is always 0. Therefore, the y-coordinate of the point C must be 0. By letting the required ratio be $m : n$ and using the formula on the right, we have

$$\frac{n(-2) + m(9)}{m+n} = 0 \Rightarrow -2n + 9m = 0$$

$$\Rightarrow 9m = 2n \Rightarrow \frac{m}{n} = \frac{2}{9} \Rightarrow m : n = 2 : 9$$

The answer is A.

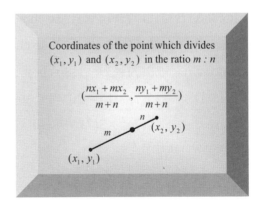

Coordinates of the point which divides (x_1, y_1) and (x_2, y_2) in the ratio $m : n$

$$\left(\frac{nx_1 + mx_2}{m+n}, \frac{ny_1 + my_2}{m+n}\right)$$

10.   Answer: **C**

Trigonometry (Medium)

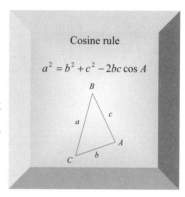

We need to use the cosine rule to solve this question. First of all, we know that the corresponding side of the angle with the smallest measure should be the shortest side. So we should make a to be 8, as in the diagram below.

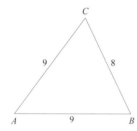

Then, by directly applying the cosine rule, we have

$$8^2 = 9^2 + 9^2 - 2(9)(9)\cos A \Rightarrow A = \cos^{-1}(\frac{8^2 - 9^2 - 9^2}{-2(9)(9)}) = 52.78°$$

The answer is C.

11.   Answer: **C**

Functions (Easy)

$$f(g(x)) = f(x-3) = 2(x-3) + 3 = 2x - 6 + 3 = 2x - 3$$
The answer is C.

Plugging-in Tips:

Taking an arbitrary number as the value of x, we can plug it into the expressions in the choices and see which one is correct. Let's take $x = 7$ here. Then,

$$g(7) = 7 - 3 = 4 \Rightarrow f(g(7)) = f(4) = 2(4) + 3 = 11$$

Choice A: $2(7) = 14 \neq 11$, so choice A is not the answer.

Choice B: $2(7) - 6 = 8 \neq 11$, so choice B is not the answer.

Choice C: $2(7) - 3 = 11$, so choice C **could be** the answer.

Choice D: $5(7) - 15 = 20 \neq 11$, so choice D is not the answer.

Choice E: $2(7)^2 - 3(7) - 9 = 68 \neq 11$, so choice E is not the answer.

The answer is C.

12.   Answer: **B**
Algebra (Medium)

In order to make p the subject, we need to express p in terms of the other variables.

$$\frac{2p+m-n}{4a-p} = \frac{c}{d}$$

$$d(2p+m-n) = c(4a-p) \qquad \text{to eliminate the denominators}$$

$$2dp+dm-dn = 4ac-pc$$

$$2dp+pc = 4ac-dm+dn \qquad \text{to put the terms with } p \text{ on one side}$$

$$p(2d+c) = 4ac-dm+dn$$

$$p = \frac{4ac-dm+dn}{2d+c} = \frac{4ac+nd-md}{c+2d}$$

The answer is B.

Plugging-in Tips:

Taking arbitrary numbers as the values of a, c, d, m and n, we can get a value of p. Then, we can plug them into the expressions given in the choices and see which one is correct. Let's take $a=2$, $c=3$, $d=4$, $m=5$ and $n=6$ here. Then,

$$\frac{2p+5-6}{4(2)-p} = \frac{3}{4} \Rightarrow 4(2p-1) = 3(8-p) \Rightarrow 8p-4 = 24-3p \Rightarrow 11p = 28 \Rightarrow p = \frac{28}{11}$$

Choice A: $p = 4md-na-cd = 4(5)(4)-6(2)-3(4) = 56 \neq \dfrac{28}{11}$,

so choice A is not the answer.

Choice B: $p = \dfrac{4ac+nd-md}{c+2d} = \dfrac{4(2)(3)+6(4)-5(4)}{3+2(4)} = \dfrac{28}{11}$,

so choice B **could be** the answer.

Choice C: $p = \dfrac{2cd}{4md-ad+cn} = \dfrac{2(3)(4)}{4(5)(4)-2(4)+3(6)} = \dfrac{4}{15} \neq \dfrac{28}{11}$,

so choice C is not the answer.

Choice D: $p = \dfrac{4nd-ad-2ac}{ad+2c} = \dfrac{4(6)(4)-2(4)-2(2)(3)}{2(4)+2(3)} = \dfrac{38}{7} \neq \dfrac{28}{11}$,

so choice D is not the answer.

Choice E: $p = \dfrac{ac+4md-nd}{cd+2ad} = \dfrac{2(3)+4(5)(4)-6(4)}{3(4)+2(2)(4)} = \dfrac{31}{14} \neq \dfrac{28}{11}$,

so choice E is not the answer.

The answer is B.

13.   Answer: **E**

Trigonometry (Medium)

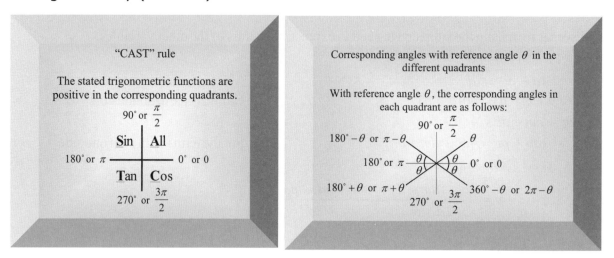

Since we have the restriction $\pi < x < 2\pi$ and $\tan x = 1.234 > 0$, by the "CAST" rule and corresponding angles in different quadrants, x must be in Quadrant III, that is,

$x = \tan^{-1} 1.234 + \pi$. Then, $\sin\left(\dfrac{x}{2}\right) = \sin(\dfrac{\tan^{-1} 1.234 + \pi}{2}) = 0.90$

The answer is E.

14.   Answer: **B**

Functions (Easy)

Given that $f(0) = 3$ and $f(1) = 2$, we have the following:

$3 = a(0)^2 + b(0) + c = c$

$2 = a(1)^2 + b(1) + c = a + b + c$

With $c = 3$, we can do the substitution and have $2 = a + b + 3 \Rightarrow -1 = a + b$

The answer is B.

15.   Answer: **E**

Solid Geometry (Medium)

Given that the radius of the sphere is 3, its diameter is 6. Since we know that the cube is circumscribed about the sphere, the side of the cube will also be 6. Therefore, the volume of the cube is $6^3 = 216$. The answer is E.

> Relationship between a cube and a sphere where the cube is circumscribed about the sphere
>
> Diameter of the sphere = Length of one side of the cube

16.   Answer: **E**

Coordinate Geometry (Medium)

Algebraic Method:

By putting the second equation into the first equation, we have

$$x^2 + (x^2 - 6)^2 = 25 \Rightarrow x^2 + x^4 - 12x^2 + 36 = 25 \Rightarrow x^4 - 11x^2 + 11 = 0$$

This seems to be an equation with degree 4. In fact, we can let $w = x^2$ here, so as to convert it

to a quadratic equation: $x^4 - 11x^2 + 11 = 0 \Rightarrow (x^2)^2 - 11x^2 + 11 = 0 \Rightarrow w^2 - 11w + 11 = 0$.

Now having a, b and c equal to 1, -11 and 11, we have

$$w = \frac{-(-11) \pm \sqrt{(-11)^2 - 4(1)(11)}}{2(1)} = \frac{11 \pm \sqrt{77}}{2} = 15.38 \text{ or } 6.61.$$

> Formulas for the roots of the quadratic equation $ax^2 + bx + c = 0$
>
> $$x = \frac{-b \pm \sqrt{b^2 - 4ac}}{2a}$$

Then $x = \pm\sqrt{15.38}$ or $\pm\sqrt{6.61}$. Here, we have four possible

values of x. If we plug these values back into the second equation given in the question, we can

find the corresponding values of y. There are 4 intersection points between the graphs of the two

functions given.

The answer is E.

(Caution: We do **NOT** need to calculate the values of y here as we only need the **number** of

intersection points, not their coordinates.)

Graphical Method:

For the first equation given in the question, it is a circle with center $(0, 0)$ and radius 5. Below is a sketch of it.

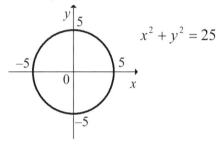

$$x^2 + y^2 = 25$$

Equation of a circle

$$(x-h)^2 + (y-k)^2 = r^2$$

(h, k) denotes the center of the circle
r denotes the radius of the circle

For the second equation, it is a parabola made by moving x^2 down by 6 units. Below is a sketch of it.

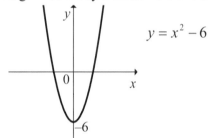

$$y = x^2 - 6$$

In order to determine the number of intersection points between them, we need to calculate the x-intercepts of the parabola so that we can know how the parabola cuts the circle. By setting $y = 0$, we have $0 = x^2 - 6 \Rightarrow x^2 = 6 \Rightarrow x = \pm\sqrt{6} = x = \pm2.45$.

With the above information, we can combine the two graphs as follows:

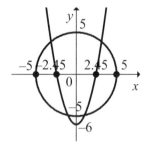

There are 4 points of intersection.

The answer is E.

Graphing Calculator Tips:

We can put the two equations into the graphing calculator to determine the answer. However, we need to make a little bit of adjustment to the first equation because it is necessary to express y in terms of x before entering the equation into the graphing calculator.

$$x^2 + y^2 = 25 \Rightarrow y^2 = 25 - x^2 \Rightarrow y = \pm\sqrt{25 - x^2}$$

Therefore, when you put the first equation into the graphing calculator, you need to input it as **two functions:** $y_1 = \sqrt{25 - x^2}$ and $y_2 = -\sqrt{25 - x^2}$. Together with $y_3 = x^2 - 6$, on the display of the graphing calculator, you can see there are four intersection points.

The answer is E.

17.   Answer: **D**

Probability & Statistics (Easy)

When drawing out the first ball, there are 10 balls in the bag where 6 are red, so the probability of getting the first red ball is $\dfrac{6}{10}$. After drawing out the first red ball, there are 9 balls in the bag where 5 are red, so the probability of getting the second red ball is $\dfrac{5}{9}$. Therefore, the probability of getting 2 red balls is $\dfrac{6}{10} \times \dfrac{5}{9} = \dfrac{1}{3} = 0.33$.

The answer is D.

Common Mistake:

It would be wrong to find the probability this way: $\dfrac{6}{10} \times \dfrac{6}{10} = \dfrac{36}{100} = 0.36$.

This is wrong because the question says that "Two balls are drawn out **WITHOUT** replacement". Therefore, when drawing out the second ball, there are only a total of 9 balls left instead of 10 balls.

18.   Answer: **A**

Trigonometry (Medium)

By the trigonometric identities, we have

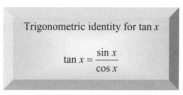

Trigonometric identity for tan x

$$\tan x = \frac{\sin x}{\cos x}$$

$$\tan^2 \theta - \sec^2 \theta = \frac{\sin^2 \theta}{\cos^2 \theta} - \frac{1}{\cos^2 \theta} = \frac{\sin^2 \theta - 1}{\cos^2 \theta}$$

$$= \frac{\sin^2 \theta - (\sin^2 \theta + \cos^2 \theta)}{\cos^2 \theta} = \frac{-\cos^2 \theta}{\cos^2 \theta} = -1$$

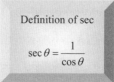

Definition of sec

$$\sec \theta = \frac{1}{\cos \theta}$$

The answer is A.

Plugging-in Tips:

Trigonometric identity for the sum of squares of sin and cos

$$\sin^2 \theta + \cos^2 \theta = 1$$

Taking an arbitrary number as the value of θ, we can plug it into the expressions in the choices and see which one is correct. Let's take $\theta = 40°$ here. Then, $\tan^2 40° - \sec^2 40° = -1$.

Choice A: It is given as -1, so choice A **could be** the answer.

Choice B: It is given as 0, so choice B is not the answer.

Choice C: It is given as 1, so choice C is not the answer.

Choice D: $\csc^2 40° = 2.42 \neq -1$, so choice D is not the answer.

Choice E: $\cot^2 40° = 1.42 \neq -1$, so choice E is not the answer.

The answer is A

19.   Answer: **C**

Algebra (Medium)

In order to get $(abc)^3$, we can combine the three given equations by multiplication to get abc first as follows:

$$(ab)(bc)(ac) = 6(12)(32) \Rightarrow (abc)^2 = 2304 \Rightarrow abc = 48 \Rightarrow (abc)^3 = 110,592$$

(Note: Here we only need to take the positive root of $(abc)^2$ because it is given that all of a, b and c are positive.)

The answer is C.

20.   Answer: **D**

Functions (Easy)

Following the definition of $\otimes$ given in the question, we have

$$-2 \otimes x = 36 \Leftrightarrow (-2)^2 + 2(-2)x + x^2 = 36 \Leftrightarrow 4 - 4x + x^2 = 36 \Leftrightarrow x^2 - 4x - 32 = 0$$

In order to solve this equation, we have the following factorization:

$$x^2 - 4x - 32 = 0 \Rightarrow (x-8)(x+4) = 0 \Rightarrow x = 8 \text{ or } -4$$

The answer is D.

(You could use the quadratic formula to solve the above quadratic equation.)

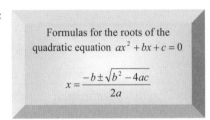

Formulas for the roots of the quadratic equation $ax^2 + bx + c = 0$

$$x = \frac{-b \pm \sqrt{b^2 - 4ac}}{2a}$$

Here, a, b and c are 1, -4 and -32, respectively, then

$$x = \frac{-(-4) \pm \sqrt{(-4)^2 - 4(1)(-32)}}{2(1)} = 8 \text{ or } -4.$$

21.   Answer: **B**

Miscellaneous (Medium)

n^{th} term of a geometric sequence

$$a_n = ar^{n-1}$$

a denotes the first term
r denotes the common ratio
a_n denotes the nth term

By the information given in the question, we have

$$a_4 = ar^{4-1} = ar^3 = -24$$

$$a_9 = ar^{9-1} = ar^8 = 768$$

By dividing a_9 by a_4, we have $\dfrac{768}{-24} = \dfrac{ar^8}{ar^3} \Rightarrow -32 = r^5 \Rightarrow r = -2$

The answer is B.

22.   Answer: **E**

Functions (Easy)

For $f(9)$, as we have $9 > 0$, we should take the first expression, so $f(9) = \sqrt{9} + 2 = 5$.

For $f(-3)$, as we have $-3 < 0$, we should take the second expression, so

$$f(-3) = -(-3) + 2 = 5.$$

Therefore, $f(9) - f(-3) = 5 - 5 = 0$

The answer is E.

23.   Answer: **C**
Trigonometry (Medium)

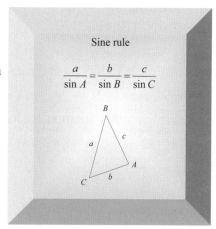

Sine rule

$$\frac{a}{\sin A} = \frac{b}{\sin B} = \frac{c}{\sin C}$$

Based on the figure given, we can easily find the two unknown angles as follows:

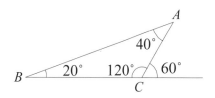

With the above information, we can apply the sine rule:

$$\frac{AC}{\sin \angle ABC} = \frac{3}{\sin \angle ACB} \Rightarrow \frac{AC}{\sin 20°} = \frac{3}{\sin 120°} \Rightarrow AC = \frac{3\sin 20°}{\sin 120°}$$

With $\sin 120° = \frac{\sqrt{3}}{2}$, we have $AC = \dfrac{3\sin 20°}{\dfrac{\sqrt{3}}{2}} = 2\sqrt{3}\sin 20°$.

The answer is C.

(For those who are not familiar with the values of sine and division of fractions, you could plug the formula above and the choices given into the calculator to find the answer.)

24.   Answer: **A**
Functions (Medium)

To find the remainder when $f(x)$ is divided by $(x+1)$, we need to use the remainder theorem, which is equivalent to finding $f(-1)$. We have $f(-1) = 3(-1)^3 + 4(-1)^2 - 5 = -4$.
The answer is A.

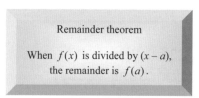

Remainder theorem

When $f(x)$ is divided by $(x-a)$, the remainder is $f(a)$.

Plugging-in Tips:

Taking an arbitrary number as the value of x, we can plug it into the expressions given in the question and find the answer directly. Note that we must take x to be greater than 7 here. The reason is that one of the choices given is 7, and the divisor must be greater than the remainder.

Let's take $x = 9$ here. Then,

$f(9) = 3(9)^3 + 4(9)^2 - 5 = 2506$ and $9 + 1 = 10$

When 2506 is divided by 10, the remainder is 6, but there is no choice given as 6. However, having a remainder 6 is equivalent to having a remainder $6 - 10 = -4$.

The answer is A.

---

25.   Answer: D
Trigonometry (Medium)

For this question, we can use the following trick to solve:

$\sin x + \cos x = \sqrt{2} \Rightarrow (\sin x + \cos x)^2 = 2$

$\Rightarrow \sin^2 x + 2\sin x \cos x + \cos^2 x = 2$

But $\sin^2 x + \cos^2 x = 1$, so we have

$2\sin x \cos x + 1 = 2 \Rightarrow 2\sin x \cos x = 1 \Rightarrow \sin x \cos x = 0.5$

The answer is D.

> Identity for the square $(a+b)^2$
>
> $(a+b)^2 = a^2 + 2ab + b^2$

> Trigonometric identity for the sum of squares of sin and cos
>
> $\sin^2 \theta + \cos^2 \theta = 1$

Graphing Calculator Tips:

In this question, you can graph the function $y = \sin x + \cos x$ and trace when the function equals $\sqrt{2} = 1.414$. After finding the value of x to be $45°$, we can put it back to the expression $\sin x \cos x$ and find $\sin 45° \cos 45° = 0.5$.

The answer is D.

---

26.   Answer: C
Functions (Medium)

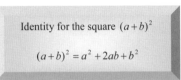

> Definition of natural logarithmic (ln) function
>
> $y = e^x \Leftrightarrow \ln y = x$

With $g(f(x)) = x$ and $g(x) = 5e^x - 4$, we have

$5e^{f(x)} - 4 = x \Rightarrow 5e^{f(x)} = x + 4 \Rightarrow e^{f(x)} = \dfrac{x+4}{5} \Rightarrow f(x) = \ln\left(\dfrac{x+4}{5}\right)$

The answer is C.

Plugging-in Tips:

Taking an arbitrary number as the value of x, we can plug it into the expressions in the choices and see which one is correct. Let's take $x = 7$ here. Then, for each choice, we can put it back into the given expression $g(f(x))$ and see which one will return the original value of 7.

Choice A: $5(7) - 4 = 31$

$g(31) = 1.4 \times 10^{14} \neq 7$, so choice A is not the answer.

Choice B: $0.2\, e^7 + 4 = 223$

$g(223) = 3.5 \times 10^{97} \neq 7$, so choice B is not the answer.

Choice C: $\ln\left(\dfrac{7+4}{5}\right) = 0.788$

$g(0.788) = 6.99$, which is approximately 7, so choice C **could be** the answer.

Choice D: $\ln\left(\dfrac{7}{5} + 4\right) = 1.686$

$g(1.686) = 22.989 \neq 7$, so choice D is not the answer.

Choice E: $\ln\left(7 + \dfrac{4}{5}\right) = 2.054$

$g(2.054) = 34.995 \neq 7$, so choice E is not the answer.

The answer is C.

27.   Answer: **E**
Functions (Medium)

In order to have $f(x, y) = g(x, y)$, we must have $xy = 2x$ and $x^2 + y^2 = 2y$. From the first equation, we have $xy = 2x \Rightarrow xy - 2x = 0 \Rightarrow x(y - 2) = 0 \Rightarrow x = 0$ or $y = 2$.

For $x = 0$, $0^2 + y^2 = 2y \Rightarrow y^2 - 2y = 0 \Rightarrow y(y - 2) = 0 \Rightarrow y = 0$ or $y = 2$ which gives the points $(0, 0)$ and $(0, 2)$.

For $y = 2$, $x^2 + 2^2 = 2(2) \Rightarrow x^2 + 4 = 4 \Rightarrow x^2 = 0 \Rightarrow x = 0$ which gives the point $(0, 0)$.

Therefore, the points required are $(0, 0)$ and $(0, 2)$.

The answer is E.

Common Mistakes:

When solving $xy = 2x$, some students divide both sides by x and conclude that $y = 2$. Note that the case $x = 0$ **will be omitted** if you do it this way. Remember, **do not divide both sides by a variable** (unless you are sure it cannot be zero); always move it to one side and factor it out.

28.   Answer: **B**

Functions (Medium)

In the given quadratic equation, a, b and c are 2, -4 and $-K$, respectively. In order to have no real roots, we use the condition $b^2 - 4ac < 0$

$(-4)^2 - 4(2)(-K) < 0 \Rightarrow 16 + 8K < 0 \Rightarrow K < -2$

The answer is B.

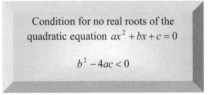

Condition for no real roots of the quadratic equation $ax^2 + bx + c = 0$

$b^2 - 4ac < 0$

29.   Answer: **C**

Functions (Medium)

In this question, since there may be more than one possible expression for $g(x)$, we cannot find the answer directly. We need to use trial and error to solve this question. In order to have $f(x) = 1$,

we must have $e^x = 1 \Rightarrow x = \ln 1 \Rightarrow x = 0$.

Therefore, $f(g(\pi)) = 1 \Rightarrow g(\pi) = 0$.

By putting π into each of the choices, we have

Choice A: $\sin \pi + \cos \pi = -1 \neq 0$, so choice A is not the answer.

Choice B: $\sin \pi - \cos \pi = 1 \neq 0$, so choice B is not the answer.

Choice C: $\tan \pi = 0$, so choice C **could be** the answer.

Choice D: $\tan \pi + \cos \pi = -1 \neq 0$, so choice D is not the answer.

Choice E: $\tan \pi - \cos \pi = 1 \neq 0$, so choice E is not the answer.

The answer is C.

Definition of natural logarithmic (ln) function

$y = e^x \Leftrightarrow \ln y = x$

Plugging-in Tips:

We can plug the numbers in the choices into the given equation to see whether the equality is held or not.

Choice A: $f(g(\pi)) = e^{\sin \pi + \cos \pi} = 0.368 \neq 1$, so choice A is not the answer.

Choice B: $f(g(\pi)) = e^{\sin \pi - \cos \pi} = 2.718 \neq 1$, so choice B is not the answer.

Choice C: $f(g(\pi)) = e^{\tan \pi} = 1$, so choice C **should be** the answer.

Choice D: $f(g(\pi)) = e^{\tan \pi + \cos \pi} = 0.368 \neq 1$, so choice D is not the answer.

Choice E: $f(g(\pi)) = e^{\tan \pi - \cos \pi} = 2.718 \neq 1$, so choice E is not the answer.

The answer is C.

30.   Answer: **C**
Coordinate Geometry (Medium)

The perpendicular bisector of the line segment $\overline{AB}$ is the line which bisects $\overline{AB}$ and perpendicular to $\overline{AB}$. To find its equation, we need the following information.

Mid-point of $AB = (\dfrac{-2+4}{2}, \dfrac{3+7}{2}) = (1, 5)$

Slope of $AB = \dfrac{7-3}{4-(-2)} = \dfrac{2}{3}$, so the slope of the perpendicular bisector of AB is $-1 \div \dfrac{2}{3} = \dfrac{-3}{2}$.

Therefore, the required equation is

$y - 5 = \dfrac{-3}{2}(x-1) \Rightarrow 2(y-5) = -3(x-1)$
$\Rightarrow 2y - 10 = -3x + 3 \Rightarrow 3x + 2y - 13 = 0$

The answer is C.

Perpendicular bisector to a line segment $\overline{AB}$

the perpendicular line passing through the mid-point of $\overline{AB}$:

A ——————— B

perpendicular bisector of $\overline{AB}$

Coordinates of the mid-point between two points (x_1, y_1) and (x_2, y_2) in the xy-plane

$(\dfrac{x_1+x_2}{2}, \dfrac{y_1+y_2}{2})$

Slope for the line passing through two points (x_1, y_1) and (x_2, y_2) in the xy-plane

$\dfrac{y_2-y_1}{x_2-x_1}$

Slopes of perpendicular lines

Let m_1 and m_2 be the slopes of the perpendicular lines, then

$m_1 m_2 = -1 \Leftrightarrow m_1 = \dfrac{-1}{m_2}$

OR

One of them is vertical and the other one is horizontal.

Equation of a straight line

$y - y_1 = m(x - x_1)$
m denotes the slope of the straight line
(x_1, y_1) denotes a point on the straight line

31.   Answer: **E**
Miscellaneous (Hard)

In this question, we need to use logical reasoning to check every choice to find the answer.

Choice A: From the second statement, we know that for those who pass physics, they must also pass mathematics. Therefore, choice A is not the answer.

Choice B: Based on the given statements, for students passing mathematics, we cannot conclude whether they pass physics or not. Therefore, choice B is not the answer.

Choice C: From the third statement, we know that those who pass English must fail physics. Therefore, choice C is not the answer.

Choice D: From the first statement, it is given there are some students failing mathematics. Combining this with the second statement, we know that there are some students failing mathematics and physics at the same time. Therefore, choice D is not the answer.

Choice E: From the fourth statement, it is given that some students fail English and mathematics. From the second statement, we know that they fail physics also, so there are some students failing all three subjects. Therefore, choice E **could be** the answer.

The answer is E.

32.   Answer: **B**

Algebra (Medium)

Logarithmic identity

$$\log(\frac{a}{b}) = \log a - \log b$$

By the corresponding logarithmic identity, we have

$$\log_2 x = \log_2(x+8) - \log_2 5 \Rightarrow \log_2 x = \log_2 \frac{x+8}{5} \Rightarrow x = \frac{x+8}{5}$$

$$\Rightarrow 5x = x+8 \Rightarrow 4x = 8 \Rightarrow x = 2$$

The answer is B.

Plugging-in Tips:

We can plug the numbers in the choices into the given equation to see whether the equality holds or not.

Definition of logarithmic function

$$y = a^x \Leftrightarrow \log_a y = x \Leftrightarrow \frac{\log y}{\log a} = x$$

$$(a > 0 \text{ and } y > 0)$$

Choice A: Plug $x = 1$

$$\text{LHS} = \log_2 1 = \frac{\log 1}{\log 2} = 0,$$

$$\text{RHS} = \log_2(1+8) - \log_2 5 = \frac{\log 9}{\log 2} - \frac{\log 5}{\log 2} = 0.85.$$

The equation is not satisfied, so choice A is not the answer.

Choice B: Plug $x = 2$

$$\text{LHS} = \log_2 2 = \frac{\log 2}{\log 2} = 1,$$

$$\text{RHS} = \log_2(2+8) - \log_2 5 = \frac{\log 10}{\log 2} - \frac{\log 5}{\log 2} = 1.$$

The equation **is** satisfied, so choice B **should be** the answer.

Choice C: Plug $x = 3$

$$\text{LHS} = \log_2 3 = \frac{\log 3}{\log 2} = 1.58,$$

$$\text{RHS} = \log_2 (3+8) - \log_2 5 = \frac{\log 11}{\log 2} - \frac{\log 5}{\log 2} = 1.14.$$

The equation is not satisfied, so choice C is not the answer.

Choice D: Plug $x = 4$

$$\text{LHS} = \log_2 4 = \frac{\log 4}{\log 2} = 2,$$

$$\text{RHS} = \log_2 (4+8) - \log_2 5 = \frac{\log 12}{\log 2} - \frac{\log 5}{\log 2} = 1.26.$$

The equation is not satisfied, so choice D is not the answer.

Choice E: Plug $x = 5$

$$\text{LHS} = \log_2 1 = \frac{\log 5}{\log 2} = 2.32,$$

$$\text{RHS} = \log_2 (5+8) - \log_2 5 = \frac{\log 13}{\log 2} - \frac{\log 5}{\log 2} = 1.38.$$

The equation is not satisfied, so choice E is not the answer.

The answer is B.

33.   Answer: **D**

Miscellaneous (Medium)

By the formula for the modulus of a complex number, we have

$$|i - 2| = |-2 + 1i| = \sqrt{(-2)^2 + 1^2} = \sqrt{5}.$$

The answer is D.

> Modulus of a complex number $a + bi$
>
> $$|a + bi| = \sqrt{a^2 + b^2}$$

Graphing Calculator Tips:

By putting $|i - 2|$ into the graphing calculator, you can get the value 2.236 directly. Then, by checking the choices, it is easy to get $\sqrt{5}$ as your answer.

The answer is D.

34. **Answer: C**
Miscellaneous (Medium)

In this question, note that x only approaches 3, but it is not exactly 3, so we can simplify $f(x)$ as follows:

$$f(x) = \frac{x^2 - 9}{x - 3} = \frac{(x+3)(x-3)}{x-3} = x + 3$$

Therefore, we can see that when x approaches 3, $f(x)$ approaches $3 + 3 = 6$.

The answer is C.

Calculator Tips:

From the question, we know that x approaches 3, so we can pick x to be 3.1, 3.01, 3.001,......
and substitute the values into $f(x)$ and we will have

$f(3.1) = 6.1$

$f(3.01) = 6.01$

$f(3.001) = 6.001$

It is obvious from the above calculations that $f(x)$ approaches 6.

The answer is C.

35. **Answer: D**
Trigonometry (Medium)

First of all, let's solve the equation directly:

$\tan^2 \theta - 3 = 0 \Rightarrow \tan^2 \theta = 3 \Rightarrow \tan \theta = \pm\sqrt{3}$

Since θ is restricted in Quadrant III, $\tan \theta$ must be positive. That is, it must be $\sqrt{3}$. With $\tan^{-1} \sqrt{3} = 60°$ as the reference angle, the corresponding angle is $180° + 60° = 240°$.

The answer is D.

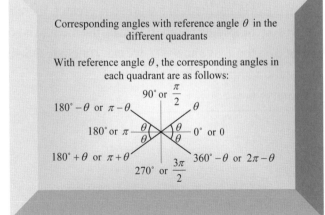

Corresponding angles with reference angle θ in the different quadrants

With reference angle θ, the corresponding angles in each quadrant are as follows:

Plugging-in Tips:

We can plug the numbers in the choices into the given equation to see whether the equality holds or not. For choices A and B, we <u>do not need to check</u> because it is <u>out of the range</u> stated in the question.

Choice C: $\tan^2 210° - 3 = -2.67 \neq 0$, so choice C is not the answer.

Choice D: $\tan^2 240° - 3 = 0$, so choice D **should be** the answer.

Choice E: $\tan^2 251.6° - 3 = 6.04 \neq 0$, so choice E is not the answer.

The answer is D.

36.   Answer: **E**
Probability & Statistics (Medium)

Below are the calculations for the new mean, mode and median after the addition of the two numbers 2 and 8:

New mean:

The original total sum of numbers is $8(5) = 40$, so the new total sum of numbers is $40 + 8 + 2 = 50$. Therefore, the new mean is 50 divided by 10 (since there are 10 numbers in the set after the addition of 2 and 8), which is 5; so the mean does not change.

New Mode:

Since the original mode is 2 and one of the two new numbers is 2, 2 must still be the number that occurs most. The new mode is still 2.

New Median:

Since in the addition of the two new numbers, 2 is smaller than the original median 5 while 8 is greater, there is no effect on the middle number. That is, the median is still 5.

> **Definition of average (arithmetic mean)**
>
> total sum of the numbers in the set divided by number of items in the set

> **Definition of median**
>
> If the number of items is odd, the median is the middle number of the set in ascending order.
> OR
> If the number of items is even, the median is the average of the middle two numbers of the set in ascending order.

> **Definition of mode**
>
> the number in the set that occurs most

Based on the above analysis, we can conclude that mean, mode and median will **not** be changed after the addition of the 2 numbers.

The answer is E.

37.　　Answer: **D**
Coordinate Geometry (Hard)

Given that $ABCD$ is a square and $\triangle ABE$ is an equilateral triangle, we can write down the size of some of the angles very quickly:

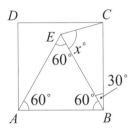

Since x is in $\triangle BCE$, we need to investigate this triangle. Below is the analysis:
Since $ABCD$ is a square, $AB = BC$.
Since $\triangle ABE$ is an equilateral triangle, $AB = BE$.
Therefore, $BE = EC$.
Now we know $\triangle BCE$ as an isosceles triangle, therefore the diagram becomes:

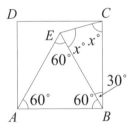

Then, we have $x + x + 30° = 180° \Rightarrow x = 75°$.
The answer is D.

38.　　Answer: **B**
Algebra (Hard)

Let $\dfrac{p}{r} = k$ where k is a whole number, then $p = kr$. We substitute this into the given expressions and have the following:

$$\frac{p^2 - 2pr + r^2}{r^2} = \frac{(kr)^2 - 2(kr)r + r^2}{r^2} = \frac{k^2r^2 - 2kr^2 + r^2}{r^2} = \frac{r^2(k^2 - 2k + 1)}{r^2} = k^2 - 2k + 1$$

It is a whole number, since k is.

$$\frac{p^4 - r^4}{r^2} = \frac{(kr)^4 - r^4}{r^2} = \frac{k^4r^4 - r^4}{r^2} = \frac{r^4(k^4 - 1)}{r^2} = r^2(k^4 - 1)$$

It is a whole number, since k and r are.

$$\frac{(kr)^3 - r^3}{(kr)^3} = \frac{k^3r^3 - r^3}{k^3r^3} = \frac{r^3(k^3 - 1)}{k^3r^3} = \frac{k^3 - 1}{k^3}$$

We are not sure whether it is a whole number.

The answer is B.

Plugging-in Tips:

Taking arbitrary numbers for p and r, where $\dfrac{p}{r}$ is a whole number, we can plug them into the expressions in the choices and find which one is a whole number. Let's take $p = 6$ and $r = 2$ here. Then,

$$\frac{p^2 - 2pr + r^2}{r^2} = \frac{6^2 - 2(6)(2) + 2^2}{2^2} = 4 \text{. It's a whole number.}$$

$$\frac{p^4 - r^4}{r^2} = \frac{6^4 - 2^4}{2^2} = 320 \text{. It's a whole number.}$$

$$\frac{(kr)^3 - r^3}{(kr)^3} = \frac{(6(2))^3 - 2^3}{(6(2))^3} = 1.037 \text{. It isn't a whole number.}$$

The answer is B.

39.   Answer: **A**
Trigonometry (Medium)

Given that $\sin\alpha\cos\alpha > 0$, $\sin\alpha$ and $\cos\alpha$ must both be positive or both be negative at the same time, By the "CAST" rule, α can only be in Quadrants I or III. For the choices given here, the possible quadrants of α are:

"CAST" rule

The stated trigonometric functions are positive in the corresponding quadrants.

90° or $\dfrac{\pi}{2}$

	Sin	All	
180° or π			0° or 0
	Tan	Cos	

270° or $\dfrac{3\pi}{2}$

Choice A: $\tan \alpha > 0$, α can be in Quadrants I or III, so choice A **could be** the answer.

Choice B: $\sin \alpha > 0$, α can be in Quadrants I or II, so choice B is not the answer.

Choice C: $\cos \alpha > 0$, α can be in Quadrants I or IV, so choice C is not the answer.

Choice D: $\cos \alpha < 0$, α can be in Quadrants II or III, so choice D is not the answer.

Choice E: $\tan \alpha < 0$, α can be in Quadrants II or IV, so choice E is not the answer.

The answer is A.

40. Answer: **D**
Miscellaneous (Medium)

Let c be the first term of this arithmetic sequence. Then, based on the given information and the formula for an arithmetic sequence,

n^{th} term of an arithmetic sequence
$a_n = a + (n-1)d$
a denotes the first term
d denotes the common difference
a_n denotes the nth term

we have the following two equations: $\begin{cases} c + (a-1)d = b \\ c + (b-1)d = a \end{cases}$

In order to get the common difference, we can take the difference of the two equations to eliminate c:

$$(c + (a-1)d) - (c + (b-1)d) = b - a \Rightarrow c + (a-1)d - c - (b-1)d = b - a$$

$$\Rightarrow (a - 1 - b + 1)d = b - a \Rightarrow (a - b)d = b - a \Rightarrow d = \frac{b-a}{a-b} = -1$$

The answer is D.

Plugging-in Tips:

Taking arbitrary numbers for a and b, we can plug them into the expressions in the choices and find the answer. Let's take $a = 3$ and $b = 5$ here. Then, we have the 3rd and the 5th terms to be 5

and 3, respectively. Therefore, the common difference is $\dfrac{5^{th}\ term - 3^{rd}\ term}{5 - 3} = \dfrac{3 - 5}{5 - 3} = -1$.

Choice A: $2a = 2(3) = 6 \neq -11$, so choice A is not the answer.

Choice B: $b - a = 5 - 3 = 2 \neq -11$, so choice B is not the answer.

Choice C: $a - b = 3 - 5 = -2 \neq -1$, so choice C is not the answer.

Choice D: It is given as -1 here, so choice D **could be** the answer.

Choice E: We can determine the common difference, so choice E is not the answer.

(For security, you may plug another set of numbers to confirm the common difference must be -1.)

The answer is D.

41.   Answer: **B**

Solid Geometry (Hard)

Let's label the points $(0, 0, 1)$, $(0, 1, 0)$, and $(1, 0, 0)$ as A, B and C, respectively. Then, we have

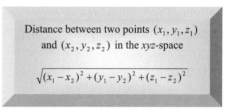

Distance between two points (x_1, y_1, z_1) and (x_2, y_2, z_2) in the xyz-space

$$\sqrt{(x_1 - x_2)^2 + (y_1 - y_2)^2 + (z_1 - z_2)^2}$$

$$AB = \sqrt{(0-0)^2 + (0-1)^2 + (1-0)^2} = \sqrt{2}$$
$$AC = \sqrt{(0-1)^2 + (0-0)^2 + (1-0)^2} = \sqrt{2}$$
$$BC = \sqrt{(0-1)^2 + (1-0)^2 + (0-0)^2} = \sqrt{2}$$

With all three sides equal, we know that this is an equilateral triangle, so all its angles are 60°. Then, its area is

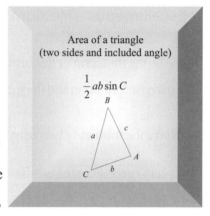

Area of a triangle
(two sides and included angle)

$$\frac{1}{2} ab \sin C$$

$$\frac{1}{2}(\sqrt{2})(\sqrt{2}) \sin 60° = \frac{\sqrt{3}}{2}.$$

The answer is B.

(Note: If you do not know $\sin 60° = \dfrac{\sqrt{3}}{2}$, you can compute the exact value of the above expression and compare it with the numbers given in the choices. After checking with the calculator, the answer is B.)

42.   Answer: **A**

Trigonometry (Medium)

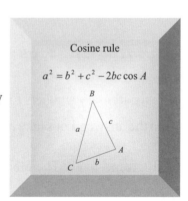

Cosine rule

$$a^2 = b^2 + c^2 - 2bc \cos A$$

Given that $\tan \angle A = 2.4$, we know that $\angle A = \tan^{-1} 2.4$. Then, by directly applying the cosine rule, we have

$$a^2 = 14^2 + 13^2 - 2(14)(13)\cos(\tan^{-1} 2.4)$$

$$\Rightarrow a = \sqrt{14^2 + 13^2 - 2(14)(13)\cos(\tan^{-1} 2.4)} = 15$$

The answer is A.

43.   Answer: **A**

Probability & Statistics (Medium)

According to the question and formula for conditional probability, we can define the following:

Event X: the probability of picking a non-defective light bulb from sample A.

Event Y: the probability of picking a non-defective light bulb.

With the above definition, the required probability is just $P(X \mid Y)$, the probability of event X happening given that event Y has happened.

Since we have a total of $(x + 2x) = 3x$ bulbs, we therefore have the following probabilities:

> **Conditional probability**
>
> The probability of event A happening given that event B has already happened:
> $$P(A \mid B) = \frac{P(A \cap B)}{P(B)}$$
> $P(A \cap B)$ denotes the probability of events A and B happening together

Probability of picking a bulb from sample $A = \dfrac{x}{3x} = \dfrac{1}{3}$

Probability of picking a bulb from sample $B = \dfrac{2x}{3x} = \dfrac{2}{3}$

The probability of getting a non-defective bulb from each sample can be calculated:

Probability of picking a non-defective light bulb from sample $A = \dfrac{1}{3} \times (1 - 10\%) = 0.3$

Probability of picking a non-defective light bulb from sample $B = \dfrac{2}{3} \times (1 - 25\%) = 0.5$

Therefore, the probability of picking a non-defective light bulb $= 0.3 + 0.5 = 0.8$

Combining the above information, we have $P(X \mid Y) = \dfrac{P(X \cap Y)}{P(Y)} = \dfrac{0.3}{0.8} = \dfrac{3}{8}$.

The answer is A.

Plugging-in Tips:

Taking an arbitrary value of x here, we can calculate the required probability directly. Let's assume x to be 10.

In sample A, there are 10 light bulbs, $10 \times 10\% = 1$ of them is defective. That is, 9 of them are non-defective.

In sample B, there are 20 light bulbs, $20 \times 25\% = 5$ of them are defective. That is, 15 of them are non-defective.

In total, there are $(9+15) = 24$ non-defective light bulbs.

Therefore, given that the picked light bulb is non-defective, the probability that the light bulb is from sample A is $\dfrac{9}{24} = \dfrac{3}{8}$.

The answer is A.

44.   Answer: **A**
Solid Geometry (Medium)

By referring to the diagrams below, we can see clearly that only the triangle cannot be formed by the intersection of a cylinder and a plane.

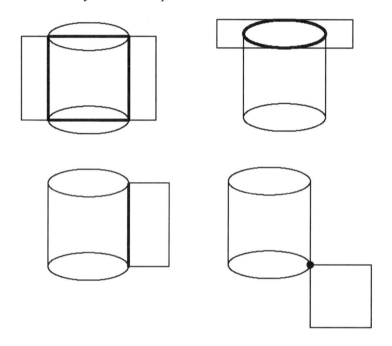

The answer is A.
(Caution: Remember that "intersection" can also mean touching.)

45.   Answer: **C**
Algebra (Hard)

Based on the formulas for the sum and product of roots of a quadratic equation, we have the following:

> Formulas for the sum and product of roots of the quadratic equation $ax^2 + bx + c = 0$
>
> $$\text{sum of roots} = \frac{-b}{a}$$
>
> $$\text{product of roots} = \frac{c}{a}$$

$$\frac{-b}{a} = p+q = -1, \quad \frac{c}{a} = pq = -6 \text{ and } a+b+c = -4.$$

From the first two equations here, we have $b = a$ and $c = -6a$. By direct substitution into the third equation, we have $a + a + -6a = -4 \Rightarrow -4a = -4 \Rightarrow a = 1$

Therefore, we will have $b = 1$ and $c = -6(1) = -6$. Then $a^2 + b^2 - c^2 = 1^2 + 1^2 - (-6)^2 = -34$.
The answer is C.

46.   Answer: **A**

Miscellaneous (Medium)

First of all, we have $\sqrt{ab} = 6 \Rightarrow ab = 36$. Therefore, the possible combinations of a and b are 1 and 36, 2 and 18, 3 and 12, 4 and 9. The sum of these four sets of numbers are 37, 20, 15 and 13, so 12 could not be a value of $a + b$.

The answer is A.

47.   Answer: **B**

Solid Geometry (Hard)

First of all, by using the Pythagorean Theorem, we can get the height of the smaller cone:

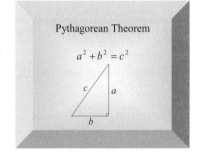

Pythagorean Theorem

$$a^2 + b^2 = c^2$$

$$3^2 + h_1^2 = 5^2 \Rightarrow h_1^2 = 16 \Rightarrow h_1 = 4$$

(Note: we only take positive h_1 here because height must always be positive)

In order to get the height of the bigger cone, we need to use the conditions on the sides of similar triangles.

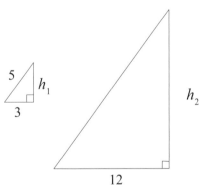

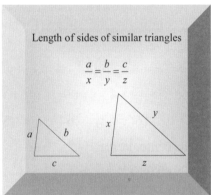

Length of sides of similar triangles

$$\frac{a}{x} = \frac{b}{y} = \frac{c}{z}$$

$$\frac{h_2}{h_1} = \frac{12}{3} \Rightarrow h_2 = 4h_1 \Rightarrow h_2 = 4(4) = 16$$

Therefore, we can get the volume of the remaining part as follows: volume of the bigger cone – volume of the smaller cone

$$= \frac{1}{3}\pi(12)^2(16) - \frac{1}{3}\pi(3)^2(4) = 756\pi$$

The answer is B.

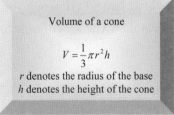

Volume of a cone

$$V = \frac{1}{3}\pi r^2 h$$

r denotes the radius of the base
h denotes the height of the cone

48.   Answer: **C**
Miscellaneous (Hard)

By using the formula for an arithmetic sequence and the information in the question, we can set up the following 2 equations:

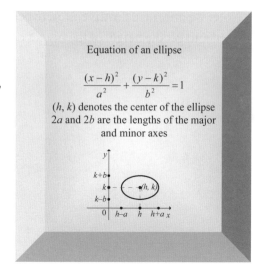

n^{th} term of an arithmetic sequence

$$a_n = a + (n-1)d$$
a denotes the first term
d denotes the common difference
a_n denotes the nth term

$$a + (5-1)d = x \Rightarrow a + 4d = x$$
$$a + (2-1)d = -x \Rightarrow a + d = -x$$

To solve the simultaneous equations here, we can subtract the second one from the first one to eliminate a in order to first find the value of d.

$$a + 4d - (a+d) = x - (-x) \Rightarrow a + 4d - a - d = 2x \Rightarrow 3d = 2x \Rightarrow d = \frac{2x}{3}$$

By substituting for d into the second equation, we have $a + d = -x \Rightarrow a + \dfrac{2x}{3} = -x \Rightarrow a = \dfrac{-5x}{3}$

Therefore, the yth term is $a + (y-1)d = \dfrac{-5x}{3} + (y-1)\dfrac{2x}{3} = \dfrac{-5x + 2xy - 2x}{3} = \dfrac{2xy - 7x}{3}$.

The answer is C.

49.   Answer: **A**
Coordinate Geometry (Hard)

By completing the squares for both x and y variables, we have

Equation of an ellipse

$$\frac{(x-h)^2}{a^2} + \frac{(y-k)^2}{b^2} = 1$$

(h, k) denotes the center of the ellipse
$2a$ and $2b$ are the lengths of the major and minor axes

$$16(x^2 + 4x) + 9(y^2 + 6y) + 1 = 0$$
$$16(x^2 + 4x + 4 - 4) + 9(y^2 + 6y + 9 - 9) + 1 = 0$$
$$16(x+2)^2 - 64 + 9(y+3)^2 - 81 + 1 = 0$$

The center here is $(-2, -3)$.
The answer is A.

(Caution: **STOP** when you get the answer. We only need to find the center of the ellipse here. It would waste a lot of time to keep going and arrange the ellipse in standard form. Don't bother!)

50. Answer: **D**

Algebra (Hard)

In order to get $x^2 + \dfrac{1}{x^2}$, we can square both sides of the given equation and get the following:

$$(x + \frac{1}{x})^2 = 25 \Rightarrow x^2 + 2x(\frac{1}{x}) + \frac{1}{x^2} = 25$$

$$\Rightarrow x^2 + 2 + \frac{1}{x^2} = 25 \Rightarrow x^2 + \frac{1}{x^2} = 23$$

Identity for the square $(a+b)^2$

$$(a+b)^2 = a^2 + 2ab + b^2$$

The answer is D.

Solutions To Sample Test 2

1.   Answer: **C**

Algebra (Easy)

$g(f(x)) = g(1-x) = (1-x)^2 - 3 = 1 - 2x + x^2 - 3 = x^2 - 2x - 2$

The answer is C.

> Identity for the square $(a-b)^2$
>
> $(a-b)^2 = a^2 - 2ab + b^2$

2.   Answer: **B**

Algebra (Easy)

Let's try to express d in terms of a and then solve for e.

$5c = 6d$, so $d = \dfrac{5c}{6}$.

$3b = 4c$, so $c = \dfrac{3b}{4} \Rightarrow d = \dfrac{5}{6}(\dfrac{3b}{4}) = \dfrac{5b}{8}$.

$a = 2b$, so $b = \dfrac{a}{2} \Rightarrow d = \dfrac{5}{8}(\dfrac{a}{2}) = \dfrac{5a}{16}$.

Then, by putting it back into $de = a$, we have

$\dfrac{5a}{16}(e) = a \Rightarrow ae = \dfrac{16a}{5} \Rightarrow e = \dfrac{16}{5} = 3.2$

(Here, we can divide both sides by a because a is non-zero.)

The answer is B.

Plugging-in Tips:

Taking an arbitrary number as the value of a, we can plug it into the expressions given in the question and find the answer directly. Let's take $a = 10$ here. Then,

$a = 2b \Rightarrow 10 = 2b \Rightarrow b = 5$

$3b = 4c \Rightarrow 3(5) = 4c \Rightarrow c = \dfrac{15}{4}$

$5c = 6d \Rightarrow 5(\dfrac{15}{4}) = 6d \Rightarrow d = \dfrac{25}{8}$

$de = a \Rightarrow \dfrac{25}{8}(e) = 10 \Rightarrow e = \dfrac{80}{25} = 3.2$

The answer is B.

3.   Answer: **C**
Trigonometry (Easy)

Based on the information given in the question, we get the following sketch by making x the distance between the ship and the shore:

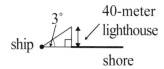

ship

3°

40-meter lighthouse

shore

Note: Figure not drawn to scale

Definition of tan

$$\tan \theta = \frac{opp}{adj}$$

hyp opp

θ

adj

Therefore, we have

$$\tan 3^\circ = \frac{40}{x} \Rightarrow x = \frac{40}{\tan 3^\circ} = 763.2... = 763 \text{ (correct to the nearest meter)}$$

The answer is C.

4.   Answer: **C**
Solid Geometry (Easy)

With the formula for the volume of a cylinder, we can find the original radius r as follows:

$$V = \pi r^2 h \Rightarrow 72\pi = \pi r^2 (8) \Rightarrow r^2 = 9 \Rightarrow r = 3 \text{ inches}$$

(Here, we only need to take the positive root of r because the radius must be positive.)

The new height is (8+4) inches, which is 12 inches. Therefore, the new volume is $\pi(3)^2(12) = 108\pi$ cubic inches.

The answer is C.

Volume of a cylinder

$V = \pi r^2 h$

r denotes the radius of the base
h denotes the height of the cylinder

5.　　Answer: **A**

Function (Medium)

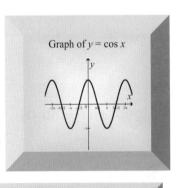

Meaning of x^{-n}

$$x^{-n} = \frac{1}{x^n}$$

Method 1:

In this method, we change both sides of the equation to the same base to solve it:

$$g(3, x) = \frac{1}{4} \Rightarrow 2^{3+x} = \frac{1}{2^2} \Rightarrow 2^{3+x} = 2^{-2} \Rightarrow 3 + x = -2 \Rightarrow x = -2 - 3 = -5$$

The answer is A.

Method 2:

In this method, we take logarithms of both sides of the equation to solve it:

$$g(3, x) = \frac{1}{4} \Rightarrow 2^{3+x} = \frac{1}{4} \Rightarrow \log 2^{3+x} = \log\frac{1}{4} \Rightarrow (3 + x)\log 2 = \log\frac{1}{4}$$

$$\Rightarrow 3 + x = \frac{\log\frac{1}{4}}{\log 2} \Rightarrow x = \frac{\log\frac{1}{4}}{\log 2} - 3 = -5$$

Logarithmic identity

$$\log a^p = p\log a$$

The answer is A.

6.　　Answer: **E**

Trigonometry (Easy)

Comparing the given graph and the original graph of $\cos x$, the original y-intercept is changed from 1 to 2, that is, it is doubled. Therefore, there is a vertical stretch by a factor of 2, which indicates that $a = 2$. For the x-intercepts, they change from $\frac{\pi}{2}, \frac{3\pi}{2}, \ldots\ldots$ to $\frac{\pi}{4}, \frac{3\pi}{4}, \ldots\ldots,$ that is, they are halved. Therefore, there is a horizontal compression by a factor of 2, which gives $k = 2$.

The answer is E.

Graph of $y = \cos x$

Effect of $f(kx)$ on the graph of $f(x)$ ($k > 0$)	Effect of $kf(x)$ on the graph of $f(x)$ ($k > 0$)
If $k > 1$, there is a horizontal compression by a factor of k. If $0 < k < 1$, there is a horizontal stretch by a factor of k.	If $k > 1$, there is a vertical stretch by a factor of k. If $0 < k < 1$, there is a vertical compression by a factor of k.

7.   Answer: **D**

Functions (Easy)

Identity for the difference of squares $a^2 - b^2$

$$a^2 - b^2 = (a+b)(a-b)$$

By expressing every function in the choices as a quadratic function and using the condition for one real root of a quadratic equation, we can solve this problem as follows.

Condition for one real root of the quadratic equation $ax^2 + bx + c = 0$

$$b^2 - 4ac = 0$$

Choice A: $f(-x) = (-x)^2 - 8(-x) + 12 = x^2 + 8x + 12$
$b^2 - 4ac = 8^2 - 4(1)(12) = 16 \neq 0$, so choice A is not the answer.

Choice B: $f(x-4) = (x-4)^2 - 8(x-4) + 12 = x^2 - 8x + 16 - 8x + 32 + 12$
$= x^2 - 16x + 60$
$b^2 - 4ac = (-16)^2 - 4(1)(60) = 16 \neq 0$, so choice B is not the answer.

Choice C: $-f(x) = -(x^2 - 8x + 12) = -x^2 + 8x - 12$
$b^2 - 4ac = 8^2 - 4(-1)(-12) = 112 \neq 0$, so choice C is not the answer.

Choice D: $f(x) + 4 = x^2 - 8x + 12 + 4 = x^2 - 8x + 16$
$b^2 - 4ac = (-8)^2 - 4(1)(16) = 0$, so choice D **could be** the answer.

Choice E: $f(x) - 4 = x^2 - 8x + 12 - 4 = x^2 - 8x + 8$
$b^2 - 4ac = (-8)^2 - 4(1)(8) = 32 \neq 0$, so choice E is not the answer.

The answer is D.

Graphing Calculator Tips:

By expressing the functions as above, you can plug all of them into your graphing calculator and find which one touches the x-axis, that is, has only one intersection point with the x-axis. With the graphing calculator, you can find the answer is D.

8.   Answer: **E**

Algebra (Medium)

Identity for the difference of squares $a^2 - b^2$

$$a^2 - b^2 = (a+b)(a-b)$$

$$\frac{\sqrt{a} + \sqrt{b}}{\sqrt{a} - \sqrt{b}} - \frac{\sqrt{a} - \sqrt{b}}{\sqrt{a} + \sqrt{b}}$$

$$= \frac{(\sqrt{a} + \sqrt{b})(\sqrt{a} + \sqrt{b}) - (\sqrt{a} - \sqrt{b})(\sqrt{a} - \sqrt{b})}{(\sqrt{a} - \sqrt{b})(\sqrt{a} + \sqrt{b})}$$

Identities for the squares $(a+b)^2$ and $(a-b)^2$

$$(a+b)^2 = a^2 + 2ab + b^2$$
$$(a-b)^2 = a^2 - 2ab + b^2$$

$$= \frac{(\sqrt{a})^2 + 2\sqrt{ab} + (\sqrt{b})^2 - ((\sqrt{a})^2 - 2\sqrt{ab} + (\sqrt{b})^2)}{(\sqrt{a})^2 - (\sqrt{b})^2}$$

$$= \frac{a + 2\sqrt{ab} + b - a + 2\sqrt{ab} - b}{a - b} = \frac{4\sqrt{ab}}{a - b}$$

The answer is E.

Plugging-in Tips:

Taking arbitrary numbers as the values of a and b, we can plug them into the expressions in the choices and see which one is correct. Let's take $a = 3$ and $b = 2$ here. Then,

$$\frac{\sqrt{a} + \sqrt{b}}{\sqrt{a} - \sqrt{b}} - \frac{\sqrt{a} - \sqrt{b}}{\sqrt{a} + \sqrt{b}} = \frac{\sqrt{3} + \sqrt{2}}{\sqrt{3} - \sqrt{2}} - \frac{\sqrt{3} - \sqrt{2}}{\sqrt{3} + \sqrt{2}} = 9.80$$

Choice A: $\dfrac{2\sqrt{2}}{3 - 2} = 2.83 \neq 9.80$, so choice A is not the answer.

Choice B: $\dfrac{3 + 2}{3 - 2} = 5 \neq 9.80$, so choice B is not the answer.

Choice C: $\dfrac{2(3 + 2)}{3 - 2} = 10 \neq 9.80$, so choice C is not the answer.

Choice D: $\dfrac{2\sqrt{3(2)}}{3 - 2} = 4.90 \neq 9.80$, so choice D is not the answer.

Choice E: $\dfrac{4\sqrt{3(2)}}{3 - 2} = 9.80$, so choice E **could be** the answer.

The answer is E.

9.   Answer: **D**
Coordinate Geometry (Easy)

By the direct application of the distance formula (which is just the Pythagorean Theorem), we find the perimeter of the triangle to be

$$\sqrt{(1-1)^2 + (7-4)^2} + \sqrt{(4-1)^2 + (4-7)^2} + \sqrt{(4-1)^2 + (4-4)^2} = 3 + \sqrt{18} + 3 = 6 + 3\sqrt{2}$$

The answer is D.

(For those who are not comfortable with square roots, you could find the answer by checking the values of the choices in the calculator directly.)

> Distance between two points (x_1, y_1) and (x_2, y_2) in the xy-plane
>
> $$\sqrt{(x_2 - x_1)^2 + (y_2 - y_1)^2}$$

10.   Answer: **C**
Trigonometry (Easy)

We can solve this equation directly as follows:

$$2\sin 2\theta = \sqrt{3} \Rightarrow \sin 2\theta = \frac{\sqrt{3}}{2} \Rightarrow 2\theta = \sin^{-1}\frac{\sqrt{3}}{2} \Rightarrow \theta = \frac{1}{2}\sin^{-1}\frac{\sqrt{3}}{2} = 30°$$

The answer is C.

Plugging-in Tips:

We can plug the numbers in the choices into the given equation to see whether the equality holds or not. Here, we may approximate $\sqrt{3}$ as 1.73.

Choice A: Plug $x = 0°$
$2\sin 2(0°) = 0 \neq 1.73$, so choice A is not the answer.

Choice B: Plug $x = 25.7°$
$2\sin 2(25.7°) = 1.56 \neq 1.73$, so choice B is not the answer.

Choice C: Plug $x = 30°$
$2\sin 2(30°) = 1.73$, so choice C **should be** the answer.

Choice D: Plug $x = 45°$
$2\sin 2(45°) = 2 \neq 1.73$, so choice D is not the answer.

Choice E: Plug $x = 90°$
$2\sin 2(90°) = 0 \neq 1.73$, so choice E is not the answer.

The answer is C.

11.   Answer: **C**
Functions (Easy)

Based on the formula for finding the vertex of a quadratic function, the minimum cost of producing one computer is achieved when $x = \dfrac{-(-400)}{2(5)} = 40$. Therefore, the minimum cost is $5(40)^2 - 400(4) + 12{,}000 = 4{,}000$.

The answer is C.

> Formulas for finding the vertex (maximum/minimum) of the quadratic function $y = f(x) = ax^2 + bx + c$
>
> $$x = \frac{-b}{2a},\quad y = f(\frac{-b}{2a})$$

Graphing Calculator Tips:

You can input the function $5x^2 - 400x + 12,000$ directly into the graphing calculator and find the minimum of the curve to be 4,000.
The answer is C.

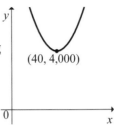

(40, 4,000)

12. Answer: **B**
Algebra (Medium)

We can express b as the subject directly as follows:

$$\frac{1}{a} + \frac{1}{b} + \frac{1}{c} = \frac{1}{d} \Rightarrow \frac{1}{b} = \frac{1}{d} - \frac{1}{a} - \frac{1}{c} \Rightarrow \frac{1}{b} = \frac{ac - cd - ad}{acd} \Rightarrow b = \frac{acd}{ac - cd - ad}$$

The answer is B.

Plugging-in Tips:

Taking arbitrary numbers as the values of a, b and c, we can plug them into the expressions in the choices and see which one is correct. Let's take $a = 2$, $b = 3$ and $c = 4$ here. Then

$$\frac{1}{2} + \frac{1}{3} + \frac{1}{4} = \frac{1}{d} \Rightarrow \frac{13}{12} = \frac{1}{d} \Rightarrow d = \frac{12}{13}.$$

Choice A: $\quad \dfrac{12}{13} - 2 - 4 = -\dfrac{66}{13} \neq 3$, so choice A is not the answer.

Choice B: $\quad \dfrac{2(4)(\frac{12}{13})}{2(4) - 2(\frac{12}{13}) - 4(\frac{12}{13})} = 3$, so choice B **could be** the answer.

Choice C: $\quad \dfrac{2(4)(\frac{12}{13})}{2(4) - 2(\frac{12}{13}) + 4(\frac{12}{13})} = \dfrac{3}{4} \neq 3$, so choice C is not the answer.

Choice D: $\quad \dfrac{2(4)(\frac{12}{13})}{2(\frac{12}{13}) - 2(4) - 4(\frac{12}{13})} = -\dfrac{3}{4} \neq 3$, so choice D is not the answer.

Choice E: $\quad \dfrac{2(4)(\frac{12}{13})}{4(\frac{12}{13}) - 2(4) - 2(\frac{12}{13})} = -\dfrac{6}{5} \neq 3$, so choice E is not the answer.

The answer is B.

13.   Answer: **B**

Trigonometry (Easy)

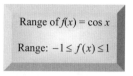

From the range of cos x, we have

$-1 \le \cos x \le 1 \Rightarrow 2 \ge -2 \cos x \ge -2 \Rightarrow 5 \ge 3 - 2 \cos x \ge 1$

The answer is B.

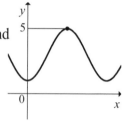

Graphing Calculator Tips:

You can input the function $3 - 2\cos x$ directly into the graphing calculator and find the maximum is 5.

The answer is B.

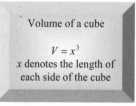

14.   Answer: A

Functions (Easy)

We can solve the question directly as follows:

$g(5) = \sqrt{5^2 + 2(5)} = \sqrt{35}$

$f(g(5)) = f(\sqrt{35}) = \dfrac{1}{(\sqrt{35})^2 + 1} = \dfrac{1}{36} = 0.03$

The answer is A.

15   Answer: **B**

Solid Geometry (Medium)

Letting s be the length of each side of the cube, let's try to express it in terms of x first: $36x^2 = 6s^2 \Rightarrow s^2 = 6x^2 \Rightarrow s = \sqrt{6}x$ feet.

(Here, we only take the positive root of s because the length of each side of the cube must be positive.)

Therefore, the volume of the cube is $(\sqrt{6}x)^3 = 6^{3/2} x^3 = 6\sqrt{6}x^3$ cubic feet.

(For those who are not comfortable with square roots, you could find the answer by checking the values of the choices in the calculator directly.)

The answer is B.

16.   Answer: **D**

Coordinate Geometry (Easy)

By letting the coordinates of B be (x, y), we have $(\dfrac{4+x}{2}, \dfrac{-3+y}{2}) = (6, 1)$.

Therefore, $\dfrac{4+x}{2} = 6 \Rightarrow 4+x = 12 \Rightarrow x = 8$ and

$\dfrac{-3+y}{2} = 1 \Rightarrow -3+y = 2 \Rightarrow y = 5$

The answer is D.

> Coordinates of the mid-point between two points (x_1, y_1) and (x_2, y_2) in the xy-plane
>
> $(\dfrac{x_1 + x_2}{2}, \dfrac{y_1 + y_2}{2})$

17.   Answer: **D**

Probability & Statistics (Easy)

> Definition of average (arithmetic mean)
>
> total sum of the numbers in the set divided by number of items in the set

By making x the smallest number of the 5 consecutive numbers, the other 4 numbers will then be $x+1, x+2, x+3$ and $x+4$.

Therefore, $\dfrac{x+(x+1)+(x+2)+(x+3)+(x+4)}{5} = 30 \Rightarrow 5x+10 = 150 \Rightarrow 5x = 140 \Rightarrow x = 28$

As a result, we know that the 5 consecutive numbers are 28, 29, 30, 31 and 32, the median of the set is 30.
The answer is D.

> Definition of median
>
> If the number of items is odd, the median is the middle number of the set in ascending order.
> OR
> If the number of items is even, the median is the average of the middle two numbers of the set in ascending order.

18.   Answer: **D**

Trigonometry (Medium)

By factoring the first two terms, we can get the answer as follows:
$\cos^2 \alpha \sin^2 \alpha + \cos^4 \alpha + \sin^2 \alpha = \cos^2 \alpha (\sin^2 \alpha + \cos^2 \alpha) + \sin^2 \alpha = \cos^2 \alpha (1) + \sin^2 \alpha$

$= \cos^2 \alpha + \sin^2 \alpha = 1$

The answer is D.

> Trigonometric identity for the sum of squares of sin and cos
>
> $\sin^2 \theta + \cos^2 \theta = 1$

Plugging-in Tips:

Taking an arbitrary number as the value of α, we can plug it into the expressions given in the question and find the answer directly. Let's take $\alpha = 40°$ here, then,
$\cos^2 40° \sin^2 40° + \cos^4 40° + \sin^2 40° = 1$.

Choice A: It is given as 0, so choice A is not the answer.

Choice B: $\sin^2 40° = 0.41 \neq 1$, so choice B is not the answer.

Choice C: $\cos^2 40° = 0.59 \neq 1$, so choice C is not the answer.

Choice D: It is given as 1, so choice D **could be** the answer.

Choice E: $\cos 40° = 0.77 \neq 1$, so choice E is not the answer.

The answer is D.

19.   Answer: **C**

Algebra (Medium)

For this question, if we check each inequality carefully, we can find that for choice C, the inequality does not hold. Since we have $a > b > c$, then $a > c$ and $b > c$. By summing the two inequalities, the result is $a + b > 2c$. This indicates that $2c > a + b$ cannot be true. For other choices, we can always find some values for the unknowns that satisfy the inequalities.

The answer is C.

Plugging-in Tips:

Taking arbitrary numbers as the values of a, b and c, we can plug them into the expressions in the choices and see which inequality does not hold. Let's take $a = 3$, $b = 2$ and $c = 1$ here. Then,

Choice A: LHS $= 1 + 2 = 3$, RHS $= 3$. The inequality does not hold, so choice A **could be** the answer.

Choice B: LHS $= 2(3) = 6$, RHS $= 2 + 1 = 3$. The inequality holds, so choice B is not the answer.

Choice C: LHS $= 2(1) = 2$, RHS $= 3 + 2 = 5$. The inequality does not hold, so choice C **could be** the answer.

Choice D: LHS $= 3(2) = 6$, RHS $= 2(1) = 2$. The inequality holds, so choice D is not the answer.

Choice E: LHS $= 3 + 1 = 4$, RHS $= 2(2) + 1 = 5$. The inequality holds, so choice E is not the answer.

Here, **we have two possible answers**. Therefore, we need to plug in **different** sets of values of a, b and c until only one answer is left. Let's take $a = -1$, $b = -2$ and $c = -3$ this time.

Choice A: LHS $= -2 + -3 = -5$, RHS $= -1$. The inequality holds, so choice A is not the answer.

Choice C: LHS $= 2(-3) = -6$, RHS $= -1 + (-2) = -3$. The inequality does not hold, so choice C **could be** the answer.

The answer is C.

20.   Answer: **D**

Functions (Easy)

$$f(-x) = \frac{1+(-x)}{-x} = \frac{1-x}{-x} = -\left(\frac{1-x}{x}\right) = \frac{x-1}{x}$$

The answer is D.

Plugging-in Tips:

Taking an arbitrary number as the value of x, we can plug it into the expressions in the choices and see which one is correct. Let's take $x = 3$ here. Then, $f(-3) = \frac{1-3}{-3} = \frac{2}{3}$.

Choice A: It is given as 0, so choice A is not the answer.

Choice B: $\frac{1-3}{3} = -\frac{2}{3} \neq \frac{2}{3}$, so choice B is not the answer.

Choice C: $\frac{3}{1+3} = \frac{3}{4} \neq \frac{2}{3}$, so choice C is not the answer.

Choice D: $\frac{3-1}{3} = \frac{2}{3}$, so choice D **could be** the answer.

Choice E: $\frac{3-1}{-3} = -\frac{2}{3} \neq \frac{2}{3}$, so choice E is not the answer.

The answer is D.

21.   Answer: **B**

Miscellaneous (Medium)

> Definition of direct variation
>
> If y varies directly as x, then $y = kx$ where k is a positive constant.

By the formulas for direct variation and inverse variation and the information given in the question, we have $x = ky$ and $y = \frac{m}{z}$ where k and m are positive constants.

> Definition of inverse variation
>
> If y varies inversely as x, then $y = \frac{k}{x}$ where k is a positive constant.

By directly substituting the second equation into the first one, we obtain $x = k(\frac{m}{z}) = \frac{km}{z}$. Since when $x = 3$, $z = 5$, we get $3 = \frac{km}{5} \Rightarrow km = 15$ and we have $x = \frac{15}{z}$. Therefore, when $x = 6$, $6 = \frac{15}{z} \Rightarrow z = \frac{15}{6} = 2\frac{1}{2}$.

The answer is B.

22.   Answer: **E**
Functions (Medium)

In the question, it is given that the initial amount is 1,000 grams and the final amount is 100 grams. So we have $a = 1,000$ and $A(t) = 100$. By using the given equation, we can find the corresponding t as follows:

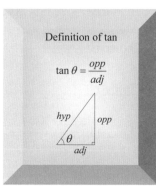

Definition of natural logarithmic (ln) function

$$y = e^x \Leftrightarrow \ln y = x$$

$$100 = 1,000e^{\frac{-t}{300}} \Rightarrow \frac{1}{10} = e^{\frac{-t}{300}} \Rightarrow \ln\frac{1}{10} = \frac{-t}{300} \Rightarrow t = -300\ln\frac{1}{10} = 690.7...$$

= 691 seconds (correct to the nearest second) = 11 minutes 31 seconds
The answer is E.

23.   Answer: **C**
Trigonometry (Medium)

For this question, we can find the value of x first as follows:

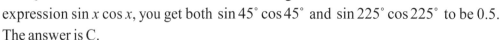

$$\sin x - \cos x = 0 \Rightarrow \sin x = \cos x \Rightarrow \frac{\sin x}{\cos x} = 1 \Rightarrow \tan x = 1 \Rightarrow x = 45°$$

Definition of tan

$$\tan\theta = \frac{opp}{adj}$$

By the "CAST" rule, we know that there should be another solution for x in Quadrant III: $x = 180° + 45° = 225°$. Putting them back into the expression $\sin x \cos x$, you get both $\sin 45° \cos 45°$ and $\sin 225° \cos 225°$ to be 0.5. The answer is C.

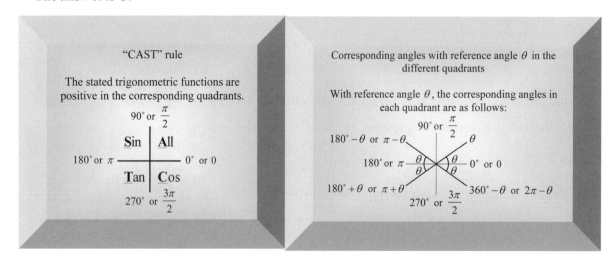

In this question, you can graph the function $y = \sin x - \cos x$ and trace when the function will be equal to 0. Then, you will find the value of x to be 0.785 or 3.93 (in radian measure). Putting them back into the expression $\sin x \cos x$, you get both $\sin 0.785 \cos 0.785$ and $\sin 3.93 \cos 3.93$ to be 0.5.

The answer is C.

24.   Answer: **A**

Functions (Medium)

For this question, we need to separate the function into the following two cases:

For $x < 0,\ -x > 0 \Rightarrow -x + 4 > 4 \Rightarrow f(x) > 4$

For $x \geq 0,\ x^{\frac{1}{4}} \geq 0 \Rightarrow x^{\frac{1}{4}} + 2 \geq 2 \Rightarrow f(x) \geq 2$

Combining the above cases, we have $f(x) \geq 2$.

The answer is A.

Graphing Calculator Tips:

You can input the expressions $-x + 4$ and $x^{\frac{1}{4}} + 2$ directly into the graphing

calculator, limiting their domains as stated in the question, to obtain this graph:

The range is $f(x) \geq 2$.

The answer is A.

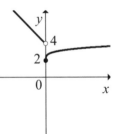

25.   Answer: **C**

Trigonometry (Medium)

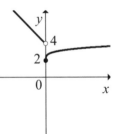

Trigonometric identity for $\sin x$

radian measure:

$\sin x = \cos(\dfrac{\pi}{2} - x)$

By applying the trigonometric identities to the equation, we have

$$\sin\theta + \sin(\frac{\pi}{2} - \theta) + \cos\theta + \cos(\frac{\pi}{2} - \theta) = \sin\theta + \cos\theta + \cos\theta + \sin\theta$$
$$= 2\sin\theta + 2\cos\theta = 2(\sin\theta + \cos\theta)$$

The answer is C.

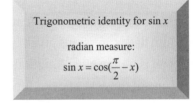

Trigonometric identity for $\cos x$

radian measure:

$\cos x = \sin(\dfrac{\pi}{2} - x)$

Plugging-in Tips:

Taking an arbitrary number as the value of θ, we can plug it into the expressions given in the question and find the answer directly. Let's take $= 1.1$ here, then,

$$\sin 1.1 + \sin(\frac{\pi}{2} - 1.1) + \cos 1.1 + \cos(\frac{\pi}{2} - 1.1) = 2.69$$

Choice A: $2\sin 1.1 = 1.78 \neq 2.69$, so choice A is not the answer.

Choice B: $2\cos 1.1 = 0.91 \neq 2.69$, so choice B is not the answer.

Choice C: $2(\sin 1.1 + \cos 1.1) = 2.69$, so choice C **could be** the answer.

Choice D: $2(\sin 1.1 - \cos 1.1) = 0.88 \neq 2.69$, so choice D is not the answer.

Choice E: $2(\cos 1.1 - \sin 1.1) = -0.88 \neq 2.69$, so choice E is not the answer.

The answer is C.

26.   Answer: **E**
Functions (Medium)

For this question, we need to check the expression in every choice to see which one is not an even function. It is given that $f(x)$ is an even function, so $f(-x) = f(x)$.

| Definition of Even Function |
| Even function: $f(-x) = f(x)$ |

Choice A: $f(-(-x)) = f(x) = f(-x)$. It's an even function, so choice A is not the answer.

Choice B: $-f(-x) = -f(x)$. It's an even function, so choice B is not the answer.

Choice C: $f(-x) + 3 = f(x) + 3$. It's an even function, so choice C is not the answer.

Choice D: $|f(-x)| = |f(x)|$. It's an even function, so choice D is not the answer.

Choice E: $f(-x - 4) = f(-(x + 4)) = f(x + 4)$, which does not return the original function $f(x - 4)$, so it may not be an even function. Choice E **could be** the answer.

The answer is E.

Plugging-in Tips:

| Identities for the squares $(a + b)^2$ and $(a - b)^2$ |
| $(a + b)^2 = a^2 + 2ab + b^2$ |
| $(a - b)^2 = a^2 - 2ab + b^2$ |

Taking an arbitrary even function as $f(x)$, we can plug it into the expressions given in the question and see which one is not an even function. Let's take $f(x) = x^2$ here (one of the easiest even functions that is known to us), then,

Choice A: $f(-x) = (-x)^2 = x^2$.
It's an even function, so choice A is not the answer.

Choice B: $-f(x) = -x^2$ and $-f(-x) = -(-x)^2 = -x^2$.
It's an even function, so choice B is not the answer.

Choice C: $f(x) + 3 = x^2 + 3$ and $f(-x) + 3 = (-x)^2 = x^2 + 3$.
It's an even function, so choice C is not the answer.

Choice D: $|f(x)|=|x^2|$ and $|f(-x)|=|(-x)^2|=|x^2|$.

It's an even function, so choice D is not the answer.

Choice E: $f(x-4)=(x-4)^2=x^2-8x+16$ but

$f(-x-4)=(-x-4)^2=x^2+8x+16$.

It's **not** an even function, so choice E **could be** the answer.

The answer is E.

Graphing Calculator Tips:

By taking $f(x)=x^2$, we can input all the functions given in the choices into the calculator to see which one is **NOT** symmetrical about the y-axis.

Choice A: $f(-x)=(-x)^2=x^2$. It's symmetrical about the y-axis, so choice A is not the answer.

Choice B $-f(x)=-x^2$. It's symmetrical about the y-axis, so choice B is not the answer.

Choice C: $f(x)+3=x^2+3$. It's symmetrical about the y-axis, so choice C is not the answer.

Choice D: $|f(x)|=|x^2|$. It's symmetrical about the y-axis, so choice D is not the answer.

Choice E: $f(x-4)=(x-4)^2=x^2-8x+16$. It's **not** symmetrical about the y-axis, so choice E **could be** the answer.

The answer is E.

Graphical representation of
an even function

Any even function is
symmetrical about the y-axis.

27.   Answer: **E**

Functions (Medium)

Rewrite $f(x)=\sqrt[5]{9-x^2}=(9-x^2)^{\frac{1}{5}}$. Since we know that the domain of the function $x^{\frac{1}{5}}$ is the set of all real numbers, there is no restriction for $9-x^2$, which implies that x can be any number here. Therefore, the domain of $f(x)$ is also the set of all real numbers.

The answer is E.

Domain of $f(x)=x^{\frac{1}{n}}$
(n is a positive integer)

If n is odd,
Domain: all real numbers

Graphing Calculator Tips:

You can plug the given function into your graphing calculator directly to get the following graph:

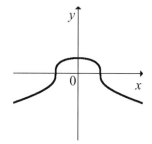

Observing the graph, we can see that for every x-value, there is a corresponding y-value, so the domain is the set of all real numbers.

The answer is E.

28.   Answer: **A**

Coordinate Geometry (Medium)

Let's denote the intersection of the altitude of C to the base AB and AB itself as D, as in the following sketch:

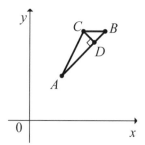

In order to find the answer to the question, we need to find the coordinates of D. Here, we have to find the equations of AB and CD first.

Since $m_{AB} = \dfrac{7-4}{6-3} = 1$, then the equation of AB is

$y - 4 = 1(x - 3) \Rightarrow y = x + 1$

Since $m_{CD} = \dfrac{-1}{m_{AB}} = -1$, then the equation of CD is

$y - 8 = -1(x - 5) \Rightarrow y = -x + 13$

Slope for the line passing through two points (x_1, y_1) and (x_2, y_2) in the xy-plane

$$\frac{y_2 - y_1}{x_2 - x_1}$$

Slopes of perpendicular lines

Let m_1 and m_2 be the slopes of the perpendicular lines, then

$$m_1 m_2 = -1 \Leftrightarrow m_1 = \frac{-1}{m_2}$$

OR

One of them is vertical and the other one is horizontal.

Equation of a straight line

$$y - y_1 = m(x - x_1)$$

m denotes the slope of the straight line
(x_1, y_1) denotes a point on the straight line

Therefore, we can solve the above two equations simultaneously to find the coordinates of D. By putting the second equation into the first one, we have

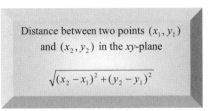

Distance between two points (x_1, y_1) and (x_2, y_2) in the xy-plane

$$\sqrt{(x_2 - x_1)^2 + (y_2 - y_1)^2}$$

$-x + 13 = x + 1 \Rightarrow 2x = 12 \Rightarrow x = 6$, so $y = 6 + 1 = 7$

(In fact, point D is just point B!)

Therefore, the required length is $\sqrt{(6-5)^2 + (7-8)^2} = \sqrt{2}$.

The answer is A.

29.   Answer: **D**

Functions (Medium)

Here, the absolute value function is applied to the x input. Therefore, for the positive values of x, there should be no effect to the graph. That is, for the right-hand side of the y-axis, the graph of $y = f(|x|)$ should be the same as the original graph.

Graph of $y = f(|x|)$ for the positive values of x:

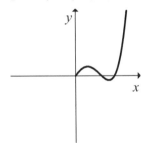

For the negative values of x, after applying the absolute value function to them, they will be all turned positive. Therefore, for the left-hand side of the y-axis, the graph $y = f(|x|)$ should be the reflection of the graph of $f(x)$ for positive x values in the y-axis.

Graph of $y = f(|x|)$ for the negative values of x:

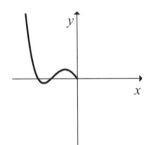

Combining the above results, we have the following graph:
The answer is D.

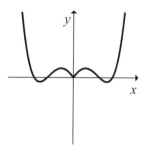

30   Answer: **E**
Coordinate Geometry (Medium)

The information given in the question can be represented by the following sketch:

Applying the Pythagorean Theorem directly, we have
$$5^2 + x^2 = 12^2 \Rightarrow 25 + x^2 = 144 \Rightarrow x^2 = 119 \Rightarrow x = \sqrt{119} = 10.9.$$
But this is not given in any of the choices.
The answer is E.

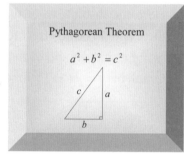

Pythagorean Theorem

$$a^2 + b^2 = c^2$$

31.   Answer: **E**
Functions (Medium)

Finding the solutions to the equation $f(x) + 4 = 0$ is equivalent to solving the equation $f(x) = -4$.
However, the information given in the question is only $f(4) = f(8) = 0$, so we don't have enough information to solve this problem.
The answer is E.

Graphical Method:

Since we are told that the solutions to the equation $f(x)$ are 4 and 8, we know that the graph will have x-intercepts at $x = 4$ and 8. Although the graph of $f(x) + 4$ can be obtained by moving up by 4 units, we don't have enough information to judge the shape of the curve. Therefore, it's impossible for us to judge the new x-intercepts after the transformation.
The answer is E.

Effect of $f(x) + k$ on the graph of $f(x)$
$(k > 0)$

Vertical shifting
$f(x) + k \Rightarrow$ Move $f(x)$ up by k units

32.   Answer: **A**
Algebra (Medium)

First of all, we solve the equation $(x-3)(x+2)(x-1) = 0$ and find x to be 3, –2 and 1. In order to judge the sign of the expression $(x-3)(x+2)(x-1)$, we let $f(x)$ be $(x-3)(x+2)(x-1)$ and take arbitrary values in the corresponding intervals between the above roots, as in the following table:

c	$x < -2$	$x = -2$	$-2 < x < 1$	$x = 1$	$1 < x < 3$	$x = 3$	$3 < x$
$f(x)$	negative	0	positive	0	negative	0	positive
	plug $x = -3$ $f(-3)$ $= (-3 - 3)$ $(-3 + 2)$ $(-3 - 1)$ $= -24$		plug $x = 0$ $f(0)$ $= (0 - 3)$ $(0 + 2)$ $(0 - 1)$ $= 6$		plug $x = 2$ $f(2)$ $=(2 - 3)$ $(2 + 2)$ $(2 - 1)$ $= -4$		plug $x = 4$ $f(4)$ $=(4 - 3)$ $(4 + 2)$ $(4 - 1)$ $= 18$

In order to have $(x-3)(x+2)(x-1) > 0$, we need to have $-2 < x < 1$ and $3 < x$.
The answer is A.

Graphing Calculator Tips:

You can plug the expression $(x-3)(x+2)(x-1)$ directly into the graphing calculator and then have the following graph:

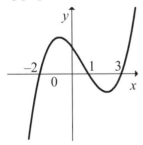

Obviously, in order to have $(x-3)(x+2)(x-1) > 0$, we need to have $-2 < x < 1$ and $3 < x$.
The answer is A.

33.   Answer: **B**

Functions (Medium)

Expanding $(1+x)^2$ into the general expression $ax^2 + bx + c$, we have $x^2 + 2x + 1$. With $a = 1 > 0$ in this expression, the graph is a parabola opening upward so the vertex is a minimum. Let's try to find the minimum of the equation to see whether it lies in the region defined by the question. The minimum of the function is achieved when $x = \dfrac{-2}{2(1)} = -1$ and its value is $(1+(-1))^2 = 0$.

Since $-2 \le -1 \le 2$, the minimum *is* included in the graph of $f(x)$ here. On the other hand, by testing the end points of the region provided, we have $(1+(-2))^2 = 1$ and $(1+2)^2 = 9$. Therefore, we know that the maximum value of the function is 9 when $x = 2$. Combining the above information, the range of the function can be found to be $0 \le f(x) \le 9$.

The answer is B.

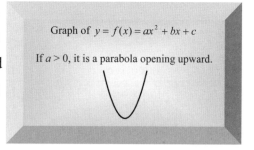

Identity for the square $(a+b)^2$

$$(a+b)^2 = a^2 + 2ab + b^2$$

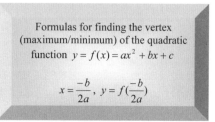

Graph of $y = f(x) = ax^2 + bx + c$

If $a > 0$, it is a parabola opening upward.

Formulas for finding the vertex (maximum/minimum) of the quadratic function $y = f(x) = ax^2 + bx + c$

$$x = \frac{-b}{2a},\quad y = f(\frac{-b}{2a})$$

Graphing Calculator Tips:

You can input the function $(1+x)^2$ directly into the calculator to find the minimum of the curve and trace the coordinates of the endpoints.

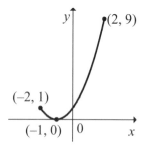

The answer is B.

34.   Answer: **B**

Miscellaneous (Medium)

$$(i+2)^3 = (i+2)^2(i+2) = (i^2 + 2(2)i + 4)(i+2)$$
$$= ((\sqrt{-1})^2 + 4i + 4)(i+2) = (-1 + 4i + 4)(i+2)$$
$$= (4i+3)(i+2) = 4i^2 + 3i + 4i(2) + 3(2)$$
$$= 4(\sqrt{-1})^2 + 11i + 6 = 4(-1) + 11i + 6 = 2 + 11i$$
The answer is B.

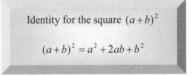

Identity for the square $(a+b)^2$

$(a+b)^2 = a^2 + 2ab + b^2$

Graphing Calculator Tips:

You can plug the expression $(i + 2)^3$ directly into the graphing calculator and find the answer is $2 + 11i$.
The answer is B.

35.   Answer: **C**

Trigonometry (Medium)

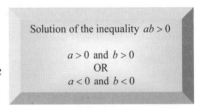

Solution of the inequality $ab > 0$

$a > 0$ and $b > 0$
OR
$a < 0$ and $b < 0$

Given that $\sin^2 \alpha \cos \alpha > 0$, $\sin^2 \alpha$ and $\cos \alpha$ must both be positive or negative at the same time. However, since $\sin^2 \alpha$ cannot be negative, it must be positive here. This implies that $\cos \alpha$ is positive also.
The answer is C.

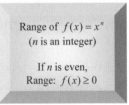

Range of $f(x) = x^n$
(n is an integer)

If n is even,
Range: $f(x) \geq 0$

36.   Answer: **B**

Probability & Statistics (Medium)

The sum of the numbers recorded is $1(6y) + 2(5y) + 3(4y) + 4(3y) + 5(2y) + 6(y) = 56y$.
The number of times the die has been thrown is $6y + 5y + 4y + 3y + 2y + y = 21y$.
Therefore, the average (arithmetic mean) of the result is
$$\frac{56y}{21y} = 2\frac{2}{3}$$
The answer is B.

Definition of average (arithmetic mean)

total sum of the numbers in the set divided by number of items in the set

Plugging-in Tips:

Taking an arbitrary value of y here, we can try to calculate the average (arithmetic mean) directly. Let's assume y to be 7, then, we have

Number thrown	Frequency
1	$6(7) = 42$
2	$5(7) = 35$
3	$4(7) = 28$
4	$3(7) = 21$
5	$2(7) = 14$
6	7

The sum of the numbers recorded is $1(42) + 2(35) + 3(28) + 4(21) + 5(14) + 6(7) = 392$.

The number of times the die has been thrown is $42 + 35 + 28 + 21 + 14 + 7 = 147$.

Therefore, the mean of the result is $\dfrac{392}{147} = 2\dfrac{2}{3}$.

The answer is B.

37.   Answer: **E**

Coordinate Geometry (Medium)

Since the x-axis is tangent to the graph of the equation $y = 2x^2 - Hx - 8$, there is only one intersection point between them; that is, there is only one real root to the equation $2x^2 - Hx - 8 = 0$. Here, a, b and c are 2, $-H$ and -8 respectively. Therefore,

$(-H)^2 - 4(2)(-8) = 0 \Rightarrow H^2 + 64 = 0 \Rightarrow H^2 = -64$

There is no solution for H.

The answer is E.

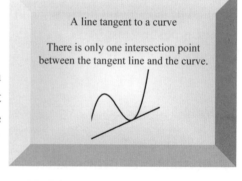

A line tangent to a curve

There is only one intersection point between the tangent line and the curve.

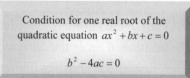

Condition for one real root of the quadratic equation $ax^2 + bx + c = 0$

$b^2 - 4ac = 0$

Plugging-in Tips:

We can plug in the numbers in each choice as H and then see whether the equality $b^2 - 4ac = 0$ holds for each corresponding quadratic equation.

Choice A: $(-(-4))^2 - 4(2)(-8) = 16 + 64 = 80 \neq 0$, so choice A is not the answer.

Choice B: From choice A, we know that -4 cannot be the value of H already, so choice B is not the answer.

Choice C: $(-(-8))^2 - 4(2)(-8) = 64 + 64 = 128 \neq 0$, so choice C is not the answer.

Choice D: $(8)^2 - 4(2)(-8) = 64 + 64 = 128 \neq 0$, so choice D is not the answer.

None of them can be the answer. Therefore, the answer is E.

Graphing Calculator Tips:

You can plug the numbers in each choice into the given equation and input them into the graphing calculator. You can see that the x-axis is tangent to none of the curves, so the answer is E.

38.   Answer: **C**

Algebra (Hard)

Method 1:

It is given that $\#a$ has different expressions for odd a's and even a's, so we can analyze the question in the following two cases:

If a is even, that is, a is 2, 4, ..., 100

a	2	4	....	100
$\#a$	$2+1 = 3$	$4+1 = 5$		$100+1 = 101$

If a is odd, that is, a is 1, 3, ..., 99

a	1	3	....	99
$\#a$	$-1+1 = 0$	$-3+1 = -2$		$-99+1 = -98$

Now, if we combine the above table, we have

a	1	2	3	4	.....	99	100
$\#a$	0	3	-2	5	......	-98	101
	$0+3 = 3$		$-2+5 = 3$			$-98+101 = 3$	

We can observe that for each pair above, the sum is 3. There are $\dfrac{100}{2} = 50$ pairs. Therefore, the required sum is $50(3) = 150$.

The answer is C.

Method 2:

By using the tables in Method 1, we can observe that #*a* can be divided into two arithmetic sequences.

If *a* is even, that is, *a* is 2, 4, ... , 100

a	2	4	....	100
#*a*	2+1 = 3	4+1 = 5		100+1 = 101

Here, the first term is 3, the common difference is 2, and there are 50 terms, so the sum of the #*a* terms here would be $\dfrac{(2 \times 3 + (50 - 1) \times 2) \times 50}{2} = 2{,}600$.

If *a* is odd, that is, *a* is 1, 3, ... , 99

a	1	3	....	99
#*a*	$-1+1=0$	$-3+1=-2$		$-99+1=-98$

Here, the first term is 0, the common difference is -2, and there are 50 terms, so the sum of the #*a* terms here would be

$\dfrac{(2 \times 0 + (50 - 1) \times (-2)) \times 50}{2} = -2{,}450$.

In order to get the required sum, we only need to add up the above sums; that is,

$2{,}600 + (-2{,}450) = 150$.

The answer is C.

> Sum of the first *n* terms of an arithmetic sequence
> $$S_n = \frac{(2a + (n-1)d)n}{2}$$
>
> *a* denotes the first term
> *d* denotes the common difference
> S_n denotes the sum of the first *n* terms

---

39.   Answer: **B**

Coordinate Geometry (Medium)

> Conversion between Cartesian coordinates and polar coordinates
>
> polar $\Rightarrow$ Cartesian :
> $x = r\cos\theta,\ y = r\sin\theta$

With the conversion formulas from polar coordinates to Cartesian coordinates, we can find the Cartesian coordinates of point *A*:

$x = -3\cos 60° = -3(\dfrac{1}{2}) = -\dfrac{3}{2}, y = r\sin\theta = -3\sin 60° = -3\dfrac{\sqrt{3}}{2} = \dfrac{-3\sqrt{3}}{2}$

Similarly, the Cartesian coordinates of point *B* can also be found:

$x = 3\cos(-60°) = 3(\dfrac{1}{2}) = \dfrac{3}{2}, y = r\sin\theta = 3\sin(-60°) = 3(-\dfrac{\sqrt{3}}{2}) = \dfrac{-3\sqrt{3}}{2}$

Since the *y*-coordinates of the two points are the same, the distance $|AB|$ is just the difference between their *x*-coordinates, that is, $\dfrac{3}{2} - (-\dfrac{3}{2}) = 3$.

The answer is B.

(Note: You could use the distance formula to find $|AB|$ but obviously the above method is simpler.)

40.   Answer: **D**
Miscellaneous (Medium)

Logarithmic identities

$$\log(ab) = \log a + \log b$$
$$\log a^p = p \log a$$

Decomposing 100 into prime factors gives us $100 = 2^2 \times 5^2$, so
$$\log 100 = \log(2^2 \times 5^2) = \log(2^2) + \log(5^2) = 2\log 2 + 2\log 5 = 2a + 2b$$
The answer is D.

Plugging-in Tips:

By finding the values of the expressions in the choices, we can see which one is correct. Since log $100 = 2$, then

Choice A: $\log 2 + \log 5 = 1 \neq 2$, so choice A is not the answer.
Choice B: $2\log 2 + \log 5 = 1.30 \neq 2$, so choice B is not the answer.
Choice C: $\log 2 + 2\log 5 = 1.70 \neq 2$, so choice C is not the answer.
Choice D: $2\log 2 + 2\log 5 = 2$, so choice D **should be** the answer.
Choice E: $(\log 2 + \log 5)^2 = 1 \neq 2$, so choice E is not the answer.
The answer is D.

41.   Answer: **B**
Solid Geometry (Medium)

By the following sketch, we know that after the rotation, we have a right circular cone with both radius and height of 3.

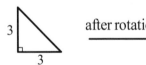
after rotation →

Volume of a cone

$$V = \frac{1}{3}\pi r^2 h$$

r denotes the radius of the base
h denotes the height of the cone

Therefore, the volume is $\dfrac{1}{3}\pi r^2 h = \dfrac{1}{3}\pi(3)^2(3) = 28.27$.
The answer is B.

42.   Answer: **B**
Trigonometry (Medium)

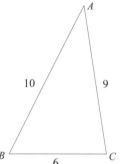

We need to use the cosine rule to solve this question. First of all, we know that the corresponding side of the angle with the smallest measure should be the shortest side, so we should put a to be 6 as in the diagram on the right:

Then, by directly applying the cosine rule, we have

$$6^2 = 9^2 + 10^2 - 2(9)(10)\cos A$$

$$\Rightarrow A = \cos^{-1}(\frac{9^2 + 10^2 - 6^2}{2(9)(10)}) = 36°$$

The answer is B.

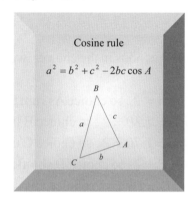

43.   Answer: **D**
Probability and Statistics (Medium)

Let's use S, T, U, V, W, X, Y and Z to denote the 8 people in the question, where S and T are the two shortest people. For the line, we have the following notations for different positions:

position 1 position 2 position 3 position 4 position 5 position 6 position 7 position 8

Since the two shortest people must stand one at either end of the line, S and T must stand at positions 1 and 8. Therefore, for position 1, we have 2 choices. There is no restriction for the remaining positions, so for position 2, we have 6 choices. After one of U, V, W, X, Y and Z has been chosen for position 2, we have 5 choices for position 3. We can carry out a similar analysis up to position 7. For position 8, since one of S and T has been chosen for position 1, so there is only one choice for it. The number of choices for each position is summarized as follows:

position 1	position 2	position 3	position 4	position 5	position 6	position 7	position 8
2 choices	6 choices	5 choices	4 choices	3 choices	2 choices	1 choice	1 choice

From the above information, the number of arrangements is: $2 \times 6 \times 5 \times 4 \times 3 \times 2 \times 1 \times 1 = 1,440$
The answer is D.

44.   Answer: **C**

Solid Geometry (Hard)

After folding the given sector into a right cone, we have the following:

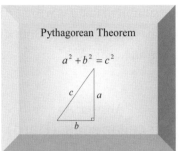

For the cone formed, the circumference of the base is 6π, the slant height is 7, r denotes the radius of the base and h denotes the height of the cone. In order to get the volume of the cone, we need to find r and h. The calculation is as follows:

$2\pi r = 6\pi \Rightarrow r = 3$

$r^2 + h^2 = 7^2 \Rightarrow 3^2 + h^2 = 49 \Rightarrow h^2 = 40 \Rightarrow h = \sqrt{40}$

(Here, only the positive root for h is needed since it denotes the height of the cone.)

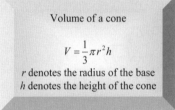

Therefore, the volume of the cone is $\dfrac{1}{3}\pi(3)^2\sqrt{40} = 59.61$

The answer is C.

45.   Answer: **D**

Miscellaneous (Medium)

For this question, x_1 and x_2 are given. Based on these two numbers, we can find x_3 directly by the given formula. Then, we can find the following terms recursively using the same method.

For $n = 2$, $x_{2+1} = x_2 + x_{2-1} = x_2 + x_1 = 2 + 1 = 3$, so we have $x_3 = 3$.

For $n = 3$, $x_{3+1} = x_3 + x_{3-1} = x_3 + x_2 = 3 + 2 = 5$, so we have $x_4 = 5$.

For $n = 4$, $x_{4+1} = x_4 + x_{4-1} = x_4 + x_3 = 5 + 3 = 8$, so we have $x_5 = 8$.

The answer is D.

46.   Answer: **D**

Functions (Medium)

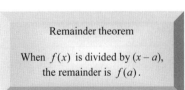

By the remainder theorem, the remainder required is

$f(2) = 2^3 - K(2)^2 - 6K(2) + K = 8 - 4K - 12K + K = 8 - 15K$

The answer is D.

47.   Answer: **A**
Miscellaneous (Hard)

In order to give an indirect proof of the statement "If p, then q", we need to begin with the assumption that q is wrong. Therefore, in this question, we need to have the negation of "Either a or b is zero", that is, "Both a and b are non-zero".
The answer is A.

48.   Answer: **A**
Miscellaneous (Hard)

First of all, we need to observe the following pattern of the powers of i:

$i^1 = i$

$i^2 = (\sqrt{-1})^2 = -1$

$i^3 = i^2 \times i = -1 \times i = -i$

$i^4 = i^3 \times i = -i \times i = -i^2 = -(-1) = 1$

Since $i^4 = 1$, the pattern repeats itself as follows:

$i^5 = i^4 \times i = 1 \times i = i$

$i^6 = i^4 \times i^2 = 1 \times -1 = -1$

$i^7 = i^4 \times i^3 = 1 \times -i = -i$

$i^8 = i^4 \times i^4 = 1 \times 1 = 1$

......

Therefore, we can group every four terms in the given expression as follows:
(Note: for the final group, there are only three terms as there are only 87 terms given here.)

$i + 2i^2 + 3i^3 + 4i^4 = i + 2(-1) + 3(-i) + 4(1) = 2 - 2i$

$5i^5 + 6i^6 + 7i^7 + 8i^8 = 5i + 6(-1) + 7(-i) + 8(1) = 2 - 2i$

$9i^9 + 10i^{10} + 11i^{11} + 12i^{12} = 9i + 10(-1) + 11(-i) + 12(1) = 2 - 2i$

......

$81i^{81} + 82i^{82} + 83i^{83} + 84i^{84} = 81i + 82(-1) + 83(-i) + 84(1) = 2 - 2i$

$85i^{85} + 86i^{86} + 87i^{87} = 85i + 86(-1) + 87(-i) = -86 - 2i$

Here, we have $\dfrac{84}{4} = 21$ groups of $2 - 2i$. Together with the final group, the required sum is

$21(2 - 2i) + (-86 - 2i) = -44 - 44i$.

The answer is A.

49.   Answer: **D**

Coordinate Geometry (Hard)

For this question, we need to sketch out the graph to determine the answer. $y = 0$ and $x = 0$ denote the x-axis and y-axis, respectively. $y = x + 1$ is a straight line going up, with slope 1 and y-intercept 1, while $y = -x + 5$ is a straight line going down with slope -1 and y-intercept 5.

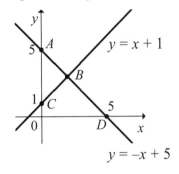

Equation of a straight line

$y = mx + b$
m denotes the slope of the straight line
b denotes the y-intercept of the straight line

Here, we use A, B, C and D to denote the intersection points. The coordinates of A, C and D are $(0, 5)$, $(0, 1)$ and $(5, 0)$, respectively. B is the intersection point of the lines $y = x + 1$ and $y = -x + 5$. We can find its coordinates by solving these two equations simultaneously: $x + 1 = -x + 5 \Rightarrow 2x = 4 \Rightarrow x = 2$. Putting this back into the first equation, we have $y = 2 + 1 = 3$. The coordinates of B are $(2, 3)$. The lengths of the sides can then be found: The required area is

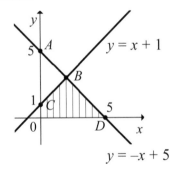

Area of $\triangle OAD$ – Area of $\triangle ABC = \dfrac{1}{2}(5)(5) - \dfrac{1}{2}(4)(2) = 8.5$

The answer is D.

50   Answer: **A**
Miscellaneous (Hard)

$n! = 4830(n-2)! \Rightarrow n \times (n-1) \times (n-2) \times ..... \times 2 \times 1$

$= 4830(n-2) \times ...... \times 2 \times 1 \Rightarrow n(n-1) = 4830$

Now, the original equation is reduced to a quadratic equation, so we can use the usual technique for quadratic equations to solve it.

> Definition of $n!$
> (n is a non-negative integer)
>
> When $n > 0$,
> $n! = n \times (n-1) \times (n-2) \times ..... \times 2 \times 1$
> When $n = 0$,
> $\quad\quad 0! = 1$

$n(n-1) = 4830 \Rightarrow n^2 - n = 4830 \Rightarrow n^2 - n - 4830 = 0 \Rightarrow (n+69)(n-70) = 0$
$\Rightarrow n = -69$ or 70

Since $n \geq 0$, n can only be 70.

The answer is A.

(You could use the quadratic formula to solve the above quadratic equation.)

> Formulas for the roots of the
> quadratic equation $ax^2 + bx + c = 0$
>
> $x = \dfrac{-b \pm \sqrt{b^2 - 4ac}}{2a}$

Here, $a = 1$, $b = -1$ and $c = -4830$.

$n = \dfrac{-b \pm \sqrt{b^2 - 4ac}}{2a} = \dfrac{-(-1) \pm \sqrt{(-1)^2 - 4(1)(-4830)}}{2(1)} = \dfrac{1 \pm 139}{2} = -69$ or 70.

Since $n \geq 0$, n can only be 70.

(Note: Many calculators are unable to deal with large factorials (they report an overflow error), so the plugging-in strategy will not work.)

Solutions To Sample Test 3

1.   Answer: **E**
Algebra (Easy)

For this question, you only need to input the values directly into the calculator to get the answer:

$$(-1)^{-2} - (-2)^{-3} + (-3)^{-1} = \frac{19}{24}.$$

The answer is E.

2.   Answer: **D**
Algebra (Easy)

$$\frac{a}{b} = 1 - \frac{1}{x} = \frac{x-1}{x} \Rightarrow \frac{b}{a} = \frac{x}{x-1}$$

The answer is D.

Plugging-in Tips:

Taking an arbitrary number as the value of x, we can plug it into the expressions in the choices and see which one is correct. Let's take $x = 3$, then $\dfrac{a}{b} = 1 - \dfrac{1}{3} = \dfrac{2}{3} \Rightarrow \dfrac{b}{a} = \dfrac{3}{2}$.

Choice A: $3 \neq \dfrac{3}{2}$, so choice A is not the answer.

Choice B: $3 - 1 = 2 \neq \dfrac{3}{2}$, so choice B is not the answer.

Choice C: $\dfrac{3-1}{3} = \dfrac{2}{3} \neq \dfrac{3}{2}$, so choice C is not the answer.

Choice D: $\dfrac{3}{3-1} = \dfrac{3}{2}$, so choice D **could be** the answer.

Choice E: $\dfrac{1}{3} - 1 = -\dfrac{2}{3} \neq \dfrac{3}{2}$, so choice E is not the answer.

The answer is D.

3.   Answer: **B**
Trigonometry (Easy)

We can obtain the graph of $y = f(x) = 2\sin x + 1$ from that of $y = \sin x$ by stretching it vertically by a factor of 2 and then moving it up by 1 unit. Since the maximum value of $y = \sin x$ is 1 where

$x = \dfrac{\pi}{2}$, the maximum value of $f(x) = 2\sin x + 1$ is $2(1) + 1 = 3$.

There is no change to the corresponding x-value; that is,

the coordinates of M are $\left(\dfrac{\pi}{2}, 3\right)$.

The answer is B.

Graph of $y = \sin x$

Effect of $kf(x)$ on the graph of $f(x)$
$(k > 0)$

If $k > 1$, there is a vertical stretch by a factor of k.

Plugging-in Tips:

Effect of $f(x) + k$ on the graph of $f(x)$
$(k > 0)$

Vertical shifting
$f(x) + k \Rightarrow$ Move $f(x)$ up by k units

We can plug the coordinates given in the choices into the original equation to see whether the equality holds or not. Since we want to find the coordinates of M, the maximum of , we should start by plugging in greatest y-value first, and stop once the equality holds. In the given choices, the maximum y-value is 3 in choices B and E.

Choice B: $2\sin(\dfrac{\pi}{2}) + 1 = 3$, so choice B **could be** the answer.

Choice E: $2\sin(\dfrac{3\pi}{2}) + 1 = -1 \neq 3$, so choice E is not the answer.

The answer is B.

4.   Answer: **D**
Solid Geometry (Easy)

In order to have the maximum number of rectangular blocks, we need to fit them into the box so that there is no space remaining on each side of the box. To achieve this, there is only one way to place the blocks:
match the 3-inch side of the blocks with the 27-inch side of the box
match the 8-inch side of the blocks with the 64-inch side of the box
match the 12-inch side of the blocks with the 60-inch side of the box

In this way, the number of blocks in the box is $\dfrac{27}{3} \times \dfrac{64}{8} \times \dfrac{60}{12} = 360$.

The answer is D.

5.   Answer: **D**

Algebra (Easy)

This question is about the rate of work. In order to finish a job in x days, $\dfrac{1}{x}$ of the job has to be finished per day. Therefore, by letting b be the number of days required for Oscar to finish the job, we can express the information in the question as follows:

	Time to finish the job (Days)	Proportion of job to be finished in one day
Andy	4	$\dfrac{1}{4}$
Oscar	b	$\dfrac{1}{b}$
Andy and Oscar together	3	$\dfrac{1}{3}$

Based on the above table we have $\dfrac{1}{4}+\dfrac{1}{b}=\dfrac{1}{3} \Rightarrow \dfrac{1}{b}=\dfrac{1}{12} \Rightarrow b=12$.

The answer is D.

6.   Answer: **A**

Trigonometry (Easy)

We can solve the given equation directly as follows:

$$\tan 2\theta - 2 = 0 \Rightarrow \tan 2\theta = 2 \Rightarrow 2\theta = \tan^{-1} 2 \Rightarrow \theta = \frac{\tan^{-1} 2}{2} = 31.7°$$

The answer is A.

Plugging-in Tips:

We can plug the numbers in the choices into the given equation to see whether the equality holds or not.

Choice A: $\tan 2(31.7°) - 2 = -0.00$, so choice A **should be** the answer.
Choice B: $\tan 2(45°) - 2$ is undefined, so choice B is not the answer.
Choice C: $\tan 2(63.4°) - 2 = -3.34 \neq 0$, so choice C is not the answer.
Choice D: $\tan 2(64.3°) - 2 = -3.25 \neq 0$, so choice D is not the answer.
Choice E: $\tan 2(73.4°) - 2 = -2.65$, so choice E is not the answer.
The answer is A.

7.   Answer: **B**
Functions (Easy)

Range of $f(x) = \sqrt{x}$

Range: $f(x) \geq 0$

By the range of $f(x) = \sqrt{x}$, we have $\sqrt{x+1} \geq 0 \Rightarrow \sqrt{x+1} - 2 \geq -2 \Rightarrow y \geq -2$.
The answer is B.

Graphing Calculator Tips:

You can input the expression $\sqrt{x+1} - 2$ directly into the graphing calculator to obtain the following graph:

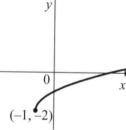

The minimum value of y is -2 and the graph is increasing to infinity, so the range is $y \geq -2$.
The answer is B.

8.   Answer: **B**
Algebra (Medium)

Method 1:

Since they travel the same distance, we can set up an equation for x and y as $xy = (y-1)(x+1)$.
We simplify the above equation as follows:

$$xy = (y-1)(x+1) \Rightarrow xy = xy - x + y - 1 \Rightarrow x - y = -1$$

Therefore, $\dfrac{1}{2x - 2y} = \dfrac{1}{2(x-y)} = \dfrac{1}{2(-1)} = -\dfrac{1}{2}$.
The answer is B.

Method 2:

After getting $x - y = -1$, we can express it as $x = y - 1$. By putting it back into $\dfrac{1}{2x - 2y}$, we have $\dfrac{1}{2(y-1) - 2y} = \dfrac{1}{2y - 2 - 2y} = \dfrac{1}{-2} = -\dfrac{1}{2}$.
The answer is B.

9.   Answer: **C**

Coordinate Geometry (Easy)

Conversion between Cartesian coordinates and polar coordinates

polar $\Rightarrow$ Cartesian :
$x = r\cos\theta, y = r\sin\theta$

With the conversion formulas from polar coordinates to Cartesian coordinates, we can find the Cartesian coordinates of the required point:

$$x = \sqrt{2}\cos(-\frac{3\pi}{4}) = \sqrt{2}(-\frac{1}{\sqrt{2}}) = -1, \; y = \sqrt{2}\sin(-\frac{3\pi}{4}) = \sqrt{2}(-\frac{1}{\sqrt{2}}) = -1$$

The answer is C.

10.   Answer: **A**

Trigonometry (Easy)

Trigonometric identities for $\cos x$

degree measure:
$\cos(180° + x) = -\cos x$
$\cos x = \sin(90° - x)$

By the trigonometric identities for $\cos x$,

we have $\dfrac{\cos(180° + \theta)}{\sin(90° - \theta)} = \dfrac{-\cos\theta}{\cos\theta} = -1$.

The answer is A.

Plugging-in Tips:

Taking an arbitrary number as the value of θ, we can plug it into the expressions given in the question and find the answer directly. Let's take $\theta = 42°$ here, then, $\dfrac{\cos(180° + 42°)}{\sin(90° - 42°)} = -1$.

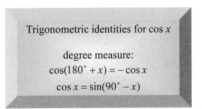

Definition of cot

$\cot\theta = \dfrac{1}{\tan\theta} = \dfrac{\cos\theta}{\sin\theta}$

Choice A: It is given as -1, so choice A **could be** the answer.

Choice B: It is given as 0, so choice B is not the answer.

Choice C: It is given as 1, so choice C is not the answer.

Choice D: $\tan 42° = 0.90 \neq -1$, so choice D is not the answer.

Choice E: $\cot 42° = \dfrac{1}{\tan 42°} = 1.11 \neq -1$, so choice E is not the answer.

The answer is A.

11.   Answer: **E**
Functions (Easy)

With $f(x) = 0$ when $x = -1, 2$ and 3, $f(x)$ should have the factors $(x + 1)(x - 2)(x - 3)$. All the choices have these three factors here, so we need something else to distinguish them. Next, we need to check which expression is not 12 when $x = 0$.

Choice A: $2(0 + 1)(0 - 2)(0 - 3) = 12$, so choice A is not the answer.

Choice B: $-(0 + 1)(0 - 2)^2(0 - 3) = 12$, so choice B is not the answer.

Choice C: $-(0 + 1)^2(0 - 2)^2(0 - 3) = 12$, so choice C is not the answer.

Choice D: $2(0 + 1)^2(0 - 2)(0 - 3) = 12$, so choice D is not the answer.

Choice E: $0.5(x + 1)(x - 2)(x - 3)^2 = -9 \neq 12$, so choice E **could be** the answer.

The answer is E.

12.   Answer: **A**
Algebra (Medium)

The information given in the question can be expressed mathematically as follows:

$$x(1 + a\%)(1 - b\%) = y \Rightarrow x(1 + \frac{a}{100})(1 - \frac{b}{100}) = y \Rightarrow x(\frac{100 + a}{100})(\frac{100 - b}{100}) = y$$

$$\Rightarrow \frac{x(100 + a)(100 - b)}{10,000} = y \Rightarrow x = \frac{10,000y}{(100 + a)(100 - b)}$$

The answer is A.

Plugging-in Tips:

Taking arbitrary numbers as the values of x, a and b, we can plug them into the expressions in the choices and see which one is correct. Let's take x, a and b, to be 1,000, 4 and 3 respectively, then, $y = 1000(1 + 4\%)(1 - 3\%) = 1008.8$

Choice A: $\dfrac{10,000(1,008.8)}{(100 + 4)(100 - 3)} = 1,000$, so choice A **could be** the answer.

Choice B: $(1 + \dfrac{4}{100})(1 - \dfrac{3}{100})(\dfrac{1}{1,008.8}) = 0.001 \neq 1,000$, so choice B is not the answer.

Choice C: $(1 + \dfrac{4}{100} - \dfrac{3}{100})(1,008.8) = 1,018.888 \neq 1,000$, so choice C is not the answer.

Choice D: $\dfrac{1,008.8}{(1+4)(1-3)} = -100.88 \neq 1,000$, so choice D is not the answer.

Choice E: $(1,008.8)(1 - \dfrac{3}{100} + \dfrac{4}{100} - \dfrac{3(4)}{100}) = 897.832 \neq 1,000$,

so choice E is not the answer.

The answer is A.

13.   Answer: **D**

Trigonometry (Medium)

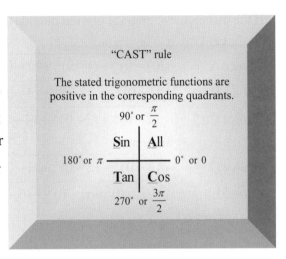

Given that $\sin x < 0$ and $\cos x < 0$, by the "CAST" rule, we know that x must be in Quadrant III; that is, $\tan x$ must be positive. Then, with the calculator we find $\tan(\sin^{-1} -\dfrac{15}{17}) = \dfrac{15}{8}$. We must have $\tan x$ to be positive, so this is our answer.

The answer is D.

14.   Answer: **A**

Functions (Easy)

We cannot solve this question directly because there are many possible answers for $g(x)$. We need to plug the choices into the given equation to see which one is our answer.

Choice A: $g(1) = 7(1) - 5 = 2 \Rightarrow f(g(1)) = f(2) = 3(2) + 4 = 10$,
so choice A **could be** the answer.

Choice B: $g(1) = 5(1) + 7 = 12 \Rightarrow f(g(1)) = f(12) = 3(12) + 4 = 40$,
so choice B is not the answer.

Choice C: $g(1) = 5(1) - 7 = -2 \Rightarrow f(g(1)) = f(-2) = 3(-2) + 4 = -2$,
so choice C is not the answer.

Choice D: $g(1) = 5(1) + 3 = 8 \Rightarrow f(g(1)) = f(8) = 3(8) + 4 = 28$,
so choice D is not the answer.

Choice E: $g(1) = -5(1) + 3 = -2 \Rightarrow f(g(1)) = f(-2) = 3(-2) + 4 = -2$,
so choice E is not the answer.

The answer is A.

15.   Answer: **C**
Solid Geometry (Medium)

Here, we only need to compare distances between the points given and the origin with the radius of the sphere, 4. If the distance < 4, then the point is <u>inside</u> the sphere. If the distance $= 4$, then the point is <u>on</u> the sphere. If the distance > 4, then the point is <u>outside</u> the sphere.

Distance between two points (x_1, y_1, z_1) and (x_2, y_2, z_2) in the *xyz*-space

$$\sqrt{(x_1 - x_2)^2 + (y_1 - y_2)^2 + (z_1 - z_2)^2}$$

We have:

Choice A: $\sqrt{(0-0)^2 + (1-0)^2 + (2-0)^2} = \sqrt{5} = 2.24 < 4$, so choice A is not the answer.

Choice B: $\sqrt{(1-0)^2 + (2-0)^2 + (3-0)^2} = \sqrt{14} = 3.74 < 4$, so choice B is not the answer.

Choice C: $\sqrt{(2-0)^2 + (3-0)^2 + (4-0)^2} = \sqrt{29} = 5.39 > 4$, so choice C **could be** the answer.

Choice D: $\sqrt{(3-0)^2 + (2-0)^2 + (1-0)^2} = \sqrt{14} = 3.74 < 4$, so choice D is not the answer.

Choice E: $\sqrt{(-2-0)^2 + (1-0)^2 + (0-0)^2} = \sqrt{5} = 2.24 < 4$, so choice E is not the answer.

The answer is C.

16.   Answer: **D**
Coordinate Geometry (Easy)

By the slope formula, we have

Slope for the line passing through two points (x_1, y_1) and (x_2, y_2) in the *xy*-plane

$$\frac{y_2 - y_1}{x_2 - x_1}$$

$$\frac{a-3}{3-b} = 2 \Rightarrow a - 3 = 2(3 - b)$$
$$\Rightarrow a - 3 = 6 - 2b \Rightarrow a = 9 - 2b$$

The answer is D.

17.   Answer: **B**
Probability & Statistics (Easy)

Since the first and last digits are fixed, we can only choose different numbers for the middle 5 digits. For each of the 5 digits, there are 10 different choices. Therefore, by the multiplication principle, we have $10^5 = 100,000$ different choices.

The answer is B.

18.   Answer: **A**
Trigonometry (Medium)

With the fact that $90° < \theta < 180°$, we know that θ lies in Quadrant II. In that quadrant, $\cos\theta$ and $\tan\theta$ must be negative by the "CAST" rule. From the question, $\sin\theta = \dfrac{3}{5} \Rightarrow \theta = \sin^{-1}\dfrac{3}{5}$, using the calculator we obtain $\cos(\sin^{-1}\dfrac{3}{5}) = \dfrac{4}{5}$ and $\tan(\sin^{-1}\dfrac{3}{5}) = \dfrac{3}{4}$. However, since $\cos\theta$ and $\tan\theta$ must be negative, we have $\cos\theta = -\dfrac{4}{5}$ and $\tan\theta = -\dfrac{3}{4}$. Then, $2\cos\theta + 3\tan\theta = 2(-\dfrac{4}{5}) + 3(-\dfrac{3}{4}) = \dfrac{-77}{20}$.

The answer is A.

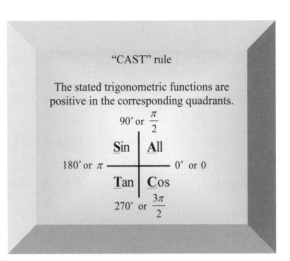

"CAST" rule

The stated trigonometric functions are positive in the corresponding quadrants.

19.   Answer: **E**
Algebra (Medium)

It is given that $a:b = 2:3$ and $b:c = 6:1$, therefore, $a:b:c = 4:6:1$. Combining this with $c:d = 4:5$, we have $a:b:c:d = 16:24:4:5$. Therefore,
$$(b^2 - 2a^2 - c^2):(3d^2 - c^2) = (24^2 - 2(16)^2 - (4)^2):(3(5)^2 - (5)^2) = 48:59$$
The answer is E.

Plugging-in Tips:

Taking arbitrary numbers as the values of a and b, we can get the corresponding values of c and d and plug them into the expressions in the question to find the answer directly. Let's take a and b to be 2 and 3, respectively, then

$$b:c = 6:1 \Rightarrow 3:c = 6:1 \Rightarrow \frac{3}{c} = \frac{6}{1} \Rightarrow 3 = 6c \Rightarrow c = 0.5$$

$$c:d = 6:1 \Rightarrow 0.5:d = 4:5 \Rightarrow \frac{0.5}{d} = \frac{4}{5} \Rightarrow 2.5 = 4d \Rightarrow d = 0.625$$

$$(b^2 - 2a^2 - c^2):(3d^2 - c^2) = (3^2 - 2(2)^2 - (0.5)^2):(3(0.625)^2 - (0.5)^2)$$
$$= 0.75:0.921875 = 0.81$$

Choice A: $56:59 = \dfrac{56}{59} = 0.95 \neq 0.81$, so choice A is not the answer.

Choice B: $54:59 = \dfrac{54}{59} = 0.92 \neq 0.81$, so choice B is not the answer.

Choice C: $52:59 = \dfrac{52}{59} = 0.88 \neq 0.81$, so choice C is not the answer.

Choice D: $50:59 = \dfrac{50}{59} = 0.85 \neq 0.81$, so choice D is not the answer.

Choice E: $48:59 = \dfrac{48}{59} = 0.81$, so choice E **could be** the answer.

The answer is E.

20.   Answer: **E**

Functions (Easy)

All the rectangles given in the question are of width 1. For each intersection point of the graph of $y = \sqrt{x}$ and the rectangles, the coordinates are given as follows:

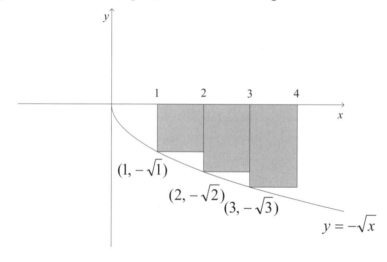

Therefore, the sum of the area of the rectangles is $\sqrt{1} \times 1 + \sqrt{2} \times 1 + \sqrt{3} \times 1 = 4.15$

The answer is E.

21.   Answer: **D**
Miscellaneous (Medium)

By the information given in the question, we have the first term, a, to be 10 and the equation $a_{10} = a + (10 - 1)d = a + 9d = 28$.

With $a = 10$, we have $10 + 9d = 28 \Rightarrow 9d = 18 \Rightarrow d = 2$.

Therefore, the sum of the first 20 terms of this sequence is $\dfrac{(2(10) + (20 - 1)2)20}{2} = 580$.

The answer is D.

> n^{th} term of an arithmetic sequence
>
> $$a_n = a + (n - 1)d$$
> a denotes the first term
> d denotes the common difference
> a_n denotes the nth term

> Sum of the first n terms of an arithmetic sequence
>
> $$S_n = \frac{(2a + (n-1)d)n}{2}$$
>
> a denotes the first term
> d denotes the common difference
> S_n denotes the sum of the first n terms

22.   Answer: **B**
Functions (Medium)

In this question, we need to plug $-x$ into each answer choice to see whether the stated equation is satisfied.

Choice A: $f(-x) = (-x)^4 = x^4$ but $-f(x) = -x^4$.
The equation is not satisfied, so choice A is not the answer.

Choice B: $f(-x) = \sin(-x - \pi) = \sin(-(x + \pi)) = -\sin(x + \pi) = -(-\sin(x)) = \sin x$ and
$-f(x) = -\sin(x - \pi) = -\sin(-(\pi - x)) = -(-\sin(\pi - x)) = \sin(\pi - x) = \sin x$
The equation is satisfied, so choice B **could be** the answer.

Choice C: $f(-x) = (-x - 3)^5 = -(x + 3)^5$ but $-f(x) = -(x - 3)^5$.
The equation is not satisfied, so choice C is not the answer.

Choice D: $f(-x) = (-x)^3 + 4 = -x^3 + 4$ but $-f(x) = -(x^3 + 4) = -x^3 - 4$.
The equation is not satisfied, so choice D is not the answer.

Choice E: $f(-x) = |-x| = |x|$ but $-f(x) = -|x|$.
The equation is not satisfied, so choice E is not the answer.

The answer is B.

Plugging-in Tips:

Taking an arbitrary number as the value of x, we can plug it into the expressions in the choices and see whether the equation $f(-x) = -f(x)$ is satisfied for each corresponding function. Let's take $x = 3$ here. Then,

Choice A: $f(-3) = (-3)^4 = 81, - f(3) = -3^4 = -81$.

The equation is not satisfied, so choice A is not the answer.

Choice B: $f(-3) = \sin(-3 - \pi) = 0.14, - f(3) = -\sin(3 - \pi) = -(-0.14) = 0.14$.

The equation is satisfied, so choice B **should be** the answer. (Note: Remember to use RADIAN mode on your calculator here.)

Choice C: $f(-3) = (-3 - 3)^5 = -7776, - f(3) = -(3 - 3)^5 = 0$.

The equation is not satisfied, so choice C is not the answer.

Choice D: $f(-3) = (-3)^3 + 4 = -23, - f(3) = -(3^3 + 4) = -31$.

The equation is not satisfied, so choice D is not the answer.

Choice E: $f(-3) = |-3| = 3, - f(3) = -|3| = -3$.

The equation is not satisfied, so choice E is not the answer.

The answer is B.

23.   Answer: **A**

Trigonometry (Medium)

In this question, let's examine each statement as follows:

I. $\sin A = \sin(B + C)$

Since the sum of angles in a triangle is $180°$, $B + C = 180° - A$.

Then, $\sin(B + C) = \sin(180° - A) = \sin A$.

Therefore, statement I is always correct.

II. $\sin A < \sin C < \sin B$

By the sine rule, we have

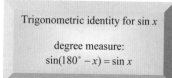

Trigonometric identity for $\sin x$

degree measure:
$\sin(180° - x) = \sin x$

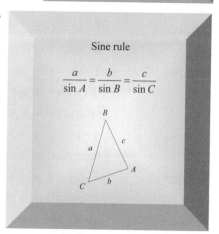

Sine rule

$$\frac{a}{\sin A} = \frac{b}{\sin B} = \frac{c}{\sin C}$$

$$\frac{a}{\sin A} = \frac{b}{\sin B} = \frac{c}{\sin C} \Rightarrow a:b:c = \sin A : \sin B : \sin C$$

Therefore, $a < c < b \Rightarrow \sin A < \sin C < \sin B$. Statement II is always correct.

III. $\cos(A + C) < \cos B$

Since the sum of angles in a triangle is $180°$, $A + C = 180° - B$.

Then, $\cos(A + C) = \cos(180° - B) = -\cos B$. Because we do not know which value of $\cos(A + C)$ and $\cos B$ is going to be negative, we cannot be sure which one is greater. Therefore, statement III is not always correct.

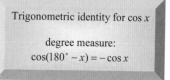

Trigonometric identity for $\cos x$

degree measure:
$\cos(180° - x) = -\cos x$

Therefore, only statements I and II are always true.

The answer is A.

24.   Answer: **D**

Functions (Medium)

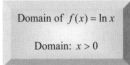

Domain of $f(x) = \ln x$

Domain: $x > 0$

Since the domain of $f(x) = \ln x$ is $x > 0$, for $f(x) = \ln \sqrt{x^2 - 1}$ we must

have $\sqrt{x^2 - 1} > 0 \Rightarrow x^2 - 1 > 0 \Rightarrow x^2 > 1^2 \Rightarrow x > 1$ or $x < -1$

The answer is D.

Solution of the quadratic
inequality $x^2 > k^2$ where $k > 0$

$x > k$ or $x < -k$

Graphing Calculator Tips:

You can input the expression $\ln \sqrt{x^2 - 1}$ directly into the graphing calculator and get the following
graph:

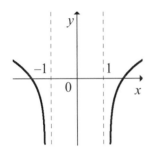

Observing the graph, we can see that x can only be in the intervals $x > 1$ or $x < -1$.
The answer is D.

25.   Answer: **D**

Trigonometry (Medium)

By the range of $\sin x$, we have
$$-1 \le \sin x \le 1 \Rightarrow -1 \le \sin 2x \le 1 \Rightarrow 2 \le 3 + \sin 2x \le 4$$

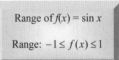

Range of $f(x) = \sin x$

Range: $-1 \le f(x) \le 1$

$$\Rightarrow \frac{1}{2} \ge \frac{1}{3 + \sin 2x} \ge \frac{1}{4} \Rightarrow \frac{3}{2} \ge \frac{3}{3 + \sin 2x} \ge \frac{3}{4}$$

Therefore, the minimum value of y is $\dfrac{3}{4}$. In order to attain the

minimum value of y, working backward from the above
inequality, we must have

$$\sin 2x = 1 \Rightarrow 2x = \sin^{-1} 1 = \frac{\pi}{2} \Rightarrow x = \frac{\pi}{4}.$$

The answer is D.

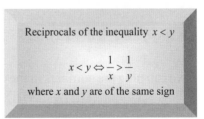

Reciprocals of the inequality $x < y$

$$x < y \Leftrightarrow \frac{1}{x} > \frac{1}{y}$$

where x and y are of the same sign

Plugging-in Tips:

We can plug the coordinates given in the choices into the original equation to see whether the equality holds or not. Since we want to find the coordinates of the minimum of y, we should start to plug in with the smallest y-value first, and stop once the equality holds. In the given choices, the minimum y-value is $\dfrac{3}{4}$ in choices C and D.

Choice C: $\dfrac{3}{3+\sin 2(\dfrac{\pi}{2})} = 1 \neq \dfrac{3}{4}$, so choice C is not the answer.

Choice D: $\dfrac{3}{3+\sin 2(\dfrac{\pi}{4})} = \dfrac{3}{4}$, so choice D **could be** the answer.

The answer is D.

Graphing Calculator Tips:

You can plug $\dfrac{3}{3+\sin 2x}$ directly into the calculator to find that the coordinates of the minimum

point are $\left(\dfrac{\pi}{4}, \dfrac{3}{4}\right)$.

The answer is D.

26.   Answer: **B**
Functions (Easy)

Finding $f^{-1}(4)$ is just the same as solving the equation $4 = x^3 + 1$.
$4 = x^3 + 1 \Rightarrow x^3 = 3 \Rightarrow x = 3^{\frac{1}{3}} = 1.44$
The answer is B.

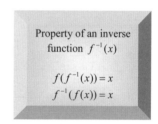

Property of an inverse
function $f^{-1}(x)$

$f(f^{-1}(x)) = x$
$f^{-1}(f(x)) = x$

Plugging-in Tips:

We can plug the numbers in the choices into the given equation to see whether the equality holds.
Choice A: $f(0.02) = 0.02^3 + 1 = 1.00 \neq 4$, so choice A is not the answer.
Choice B: $f(1.44) = 1.44^3 + 1 = 3.99 \approx 4$, so choice B **should be** the answer.
Choice C: $f(1.71) = 1.71^3 + 1 = 6.00 \neq 4$, so choice C is not the answer.

Choice D: $\quad f(27) = 27^3 + 1 = 19684 \neq 4$, so choice D is not the answer.

Choice E: $\quad f(65) = 65^3 + 1 = 274626 \neq 4$, so choice E is not the answer.

The answer is B.

27. Answer: **D**
Functions (Easy)

By the formulas for the transformation of graphs and the information given in the question, we have $f(x) \Rightarrow f(x+2) \Rightarrow f(x+2) - 1$. Therefore,

$$g(x) = f(x+2) - 1 = (x+2)^2 + 1 - 1 = x^2 + 4x + 4$$

$$\Rightarrow g(2) = 2^2 + 4(2) + 4 = 16$$

The answer is D.

Effect of $f(x+k)$ on the graph of $f(x)$
$(k > 0)$

Horizontal shifting
$f(x+k) \Leftrightarrow$ Move $f(x)$ left by k units

Effect of $f(x) - k$ on the graph of $f(x)$
$(k > 0)$

Vertical shifting
$f(x) - k \Leftrightarrow$ Move $f(x)$ down by k units

Identity for the square $(a+b)^2$

$$(a+b)^2 = a^2 + 2ab + b^2$$

28. Answer: **B**
Coordinate Geometry (Medium)

The set of points that are 4 units from the point $(2, -2)$ forms a circle of radius 4 units centered at $(2, -2)$. Therefore, the equation of the circle is

$$(x-2)^2 + (y-(-2))^2 = 4^2$$

$$\Rightarrow x^2 - 4x + 4 + y^2 + 4y + 4 = 16$$

$$\Rightarrow x^2 - 4x + y^2 + 4y - 8 = 0$$

The answer is B.

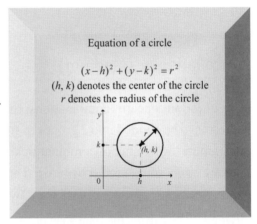

Equation of a circle

$$(x-h)^2 + (y-k)^2 = r^2$$
(h, k) denotes the center of the circle
r denotes the radius of the circle

Identities for the squares $(a+b)^2$ and $(a-b)^2$

$$(a+b)^2 = a^2 + 2ab + b^2$$
$$(a-b)^2 = a^2 - 2ab + b^2$$

29.   Answer: **E**

Functions (Medium)

In order to solve this problem, we need to consider two cases,
$x - 6 < 0$ and $x - 6 \geq 0$; that is, $x < 6$ and $x \geq 6$.
For $x < 6$, $|x - 6| = -(x - 6)$, so

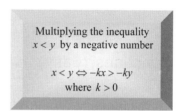

Multiplying the inequality
$x < y$ by a negative number

$x < y \Leftrightarrow -kx > -ky$
where $k > 0$

$|x - 6| < 4 \Rightarrow -(x - 6) < 4 - x + 6 < 4 \Rightarrow -x < -2 \Rightarrow x > 2$
For $x \geq 6$, $|x - 6| = x - 6$, so
$|x - 6| < 4 \Rightarrow x - 6 < 4 \Rightarrow x < 10$
Combining the above results, we have $2 < x < 10$.
The answer is E.

Graphing Calculator Tips:

You can input the functions $y = |x - 6|$ and $y = 4$ into the graphing calculator directly and then find
the intervals where the graph of the first equation is lower than the graph of the second. The
interval found is $2 < x < 10$.
The answer is E.

30.   Answer: **C**

Miscellaneous (Medium)

This question concerns combinations. But it has a twist at the end, so we need to be careful! For
12 teams to be divided into 2 groups of 6 teams, since order does not matter, we should use C_6^{12}
to compute the number of combinations. But, every time we choose a team of 6 people from 12,
we are also choosing another 6 (the 6 left behind). This means
when we use C_6^{12}, we count each team twice. So we need to

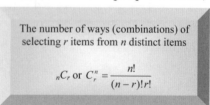

The number of ways (combinations) of
selecting r items from n distinct items

$_nC_r$ or $C_r^n = \dfrac{n!}{(n-r)!r!}$

divide C_6^{12} by 2 to get the final answer, that is $C_6^{12} \div 2 = 462$
The answer is C.

31.   Answer: **E**

Functions (Medium)

For $x > 2$, $f(x)$ is taken to be $x^{\frac{1}{3}}$; so $f(x) = x^{\frac{1}{3}} > 2^{\frac{1}{3}} = 1.26 \Rightarrow f(x) > 1.26$
For $x \leq 2$, $f(x)$ is taken to be $2x - 1$; $f(x) = 2x - 1 \leq 2(2) - 1 = 3 \Rightarrow f(x) \leq 3$
By combining these two inequalities, the range is the set of all real numbers.
The answer is E.

Graphing Calculator Tips:

You can input $f(x)$ into the graphing calculator directly by inputting the corresponding expressions for the intervals as defined in the question. You will see that for each *y*-value, there must be a corresponding *x*-value, so the range is the set of all real numbers.
The answer is E.

32.　Answer: **C**

Algebra (Medium)

The given expression is a cubic equation in $|x|$. Let $y = |x|$, then we can transform the original equation to $y^3 - 7y + 6 = 0$. It is difficult for us to factor a cubic equation, so we need to use trial and error to find the value of *y*. Remember that there are a maximum of three factors because it's a cubic equation. Let's test it with the factors of 6 first:

Plug $y = 1$, $1^3 - 7(1) + 6 = 0$; $y = 1$ is a solution.
Plug $y = -1$, $(-1)^3 - 7(-1) + 6 = 12 \neq 0$; $y = -1$ is not a solution.
Plug $y = 2$, $2^3 - 7(2) + 6 = 0$; $y = 2$ is a solution.
Plug $y = -2$, $(-2)^3 - 7(-2) + 6 = 12 \neq 0$; $y = -2$ is not a solution.
Plug $y = 3$, $3^3 - 7(3) + 6 = 12 \neq 0$; $y = 3$ is not a solution.
Plug $y = -3$, $(-3)^3 - 7(-3) + 6 = 0$; $y = -3$ is a solution.

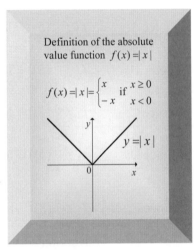

Definition of the absolute value function $f(x) = |x|$

$$f(x) = |x| = \begin{cases} x \\ -x \end{cases} \text{ if } \begin{matrix} x \geq 0 \\ x < 0 \end{matrix}$$

$y = |x|$

We can stop here because we have already found three factors. Now, we have $y = 1$, 2 or -3, that is $|x| = 1$, 2 or -3. Since $|x|$ must be positive, $|x|$ can only be 1 or 2. For each value here, there are two possible solutions of *x*. Therefore, we have four solutions to *x*.
The answer is C.

Graphing Calculator Tips:

You can input the expression $|x|^3 - 7|x| + 6$ directly into the graphing calculator to find four *x*-intercepts; so there are four solutions to *x* here.
The answer is C.

33.   Answer: **A**

Functions (Medium)

In order to find the inverse function $f^{-1}(x)$, we first take $y = f(x)$, then we swap the positions of x and y and try to express y as a function of x again. Now, we have $y = \log_2 x$. By swapping x and y, we have $x = \log_2 y$. Applying the definition of the logarithmic function directly, we get the following: $x = \log_2 y \Rightarrow 2^x = y$. Therefore, $f^{-1}(x) = 2^x$. The answer is A.

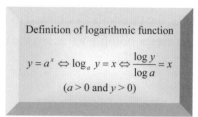

Definition of logarithmic function

$y = a^x \Leftrightarrow \log_a y = x \Leftrightarrow \dfrac{\log y}{\log a} = x$

$(a > 0$ and $y > 0)$

Property of an inverse function $f^{-1}(x)$

$f(f^{-1}(x)) = x$

Plugging-in Tips:

We can use the identity $f(f^{-1}(x)) = x$ to find the inverse function. Taking an arbitrary number as the value of x, we can plug it into the expressions in the choices and see whether the equality holds. Let's take $x = 5$, then

Choice A: $f(f^{-1}(5)) = \log_2 2^5 = \dfrac{\log 2^5}{\log 2} = 5$, so choice A **could be** our answer.

Choice B: $f(f^{-1}(5)) = \log_2 5^2 = \dfrac{\log 5^2}{\log 2} = 4.64 \neq 5$, so choice B is not our answer.

Choice C: $f(f^{-1}(5)) = \log_2 \dfrac{5}{2} = \dfrac{\log 2.5}{\log 2} = 1.32 \neq 5$, so choice C is not our answer.

Choice D: $f(f^{-1}(5)) = \log_2 \dfrac{2}{5} = \dfrac{\log 0.4}{\log 2} = -1.32 \neq 5$, so choice D is not our answer.

Choice E: $f(f^{-1}(5)) = \log_2 (\log_5 2) = \dfrac{\log(\log_5 2)}{\log 2} = \dfrac{\log(\dfrac{\log 2}{\log 5})}{\log 2} = -1.22 \neq 5$,

so choice E is not our answer.

The answer is A.

34.   Answer: **E**

Miscellaneous (Medium)

For $\dfrac{a}{b} - 1 > 0$, let's try to rearrange the terms in this inequality:

$\dfrac{a}{b} - 1 > 0 \Rightarrow \dfrac{a}{b} > 1$

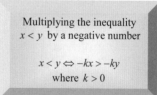

Multiplying the inequality $x < y$ by a negative number

$x < y \Leftrightarrow -kx > -ky$
where $k > 0$

Be careful! We cannot move b to the right-hand side because we have no way of knowing the sign of b. If b were negative, the ">" sign would flip to "<". Therefore, we can do nothing further. The answer is E.

Common Mistake:

Some of you may try to plug in numbers to find the answer. Let's try to take arbitrary numbers as the values of a and b satisfying $\dfrac{a}{b} - 1 > 0$, and try to plug them into the expressions in the choices to see which inequality does not hold. Let's take a and b to be 3 and 2, respectively, then

Choice A: the inequality holds, so choice A is not the answer.
Choice B: the inequality does not hold so choice B **could be** the answer.
Choice C: the inequality holds, so choice C is not the answer.
Choice D: the inequality holds, so choice D is not the answer.

You might conclude from this that the answer is B. However, the correct answer is E. The reason is that during the process of plugging-in, the case of negative numbers has been neglected. This is a drawback of the plugging-in method.

35.   Answer: **C**
Trigonometry (Medium)

In this question, let's examine each equation as follows:

I. $\sin^2\theta = -\dfrac{1}{3} \Leftrightarrow \sin\theta = \pm\sqrt{-\dfrac{1}{3}}$; however, the (real) square root of a negative number is undefined: there is no real solution here.

II. $\cos^2\theta = 3 \Leftrightarrow \cos\theta = \pm\sqrt{3} = \pm1.73$; however, the range of $\cos\theta$ is $-1 \leq \cos\theta \leq 1$ and ±1.73 is out of the range of $\cos\theta$: there is no real solution here.

> Range of $f(x) = \cos x$
> Range: $-1 \leq f(x) \leq 1$

III. $\tan^2\theta = 5 \Leftrightarrow \tan\theta = \pm\sqrt{5} = \pm2.24$; since the range of $\tan\theta$ is the set of all real numbers, we can find the real solutions to the equation here.

> Range of $f(x) = \tan x$
> Range: all real numbers

(Caution: **STOP** when you know that there is real solution to the equation. We only need to judge whether there is real solution, not find the exact values of the solutions. It would waste a lot of time to keep going and find the exact values of the solutions. Don't bother.)
Therefore, only equation III has real solutions.
The answer is C.

Graphing Calculator Tips:

We can use the graphing calculator to help us to solve this question as follows:

I $\sin^2 \theta = -\dfrac{1}{3}$

You can input the functions $y = \sin^2 \theta$ and $y = -\dfrac{1}{3}$ into the graphing calculatordirectly

to find there is no intersection between them. Therefore, there is no real solution.

II $\cos^2 \theta = 3$

You can input the functions $y = \cos^2 \theta$ and $y = 3$ into the graphing calculator directly

to find there is no intersection between them. Therefore, there is no real solution.

III $\tan^2 \theta = 5$

You can input the functions $y = \tan^2 \theta$ and $y = 5$ into the graphing calculator directly

to find there are intersections between them. Therefore, we can find real solutions to

the equation.

Therefore, only equation III has real solutions.

The answer is C.

36.   Answer: **C**

Probability & Statistics (Medium)

Since the probability of getting a head is 0.3, the probability of getting a tail is 0.7. Also,"getting no heads in 3 trials" is equivalent to "getting all tails in 3 trials". Therefore, to answer this question, we should try to find the probability of getting all tails in 3 trials, that is, $0.7^3 = 0.343$.

The answer is C.

37.   Answer: **E**

Coordinate Geometry (Medium)

Method 1:

Sketching the triangle out, it looks like this:

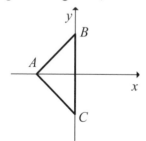

It may take a while for us to find all the lengths and angles of the triangle to verify which kind of triangle it is. Let's use intuition to judge. It looks like $AB = AC$ and the only possible right angle is $\angle BAC$. Therefore, we only need to compute the lengths and slopes of $\overline{AB}$ and $\overline{AC}$.

$$\overline{AB} = \sqrt{(-3-0)^2 + (0-3)^2} = \sqrt{18}$$
$$\overline{AC} = \sqrt{(-3-0)^2 + (0-(-3))^2} = \sqrt{18}$$

We have $AB = AC$, so it is an isosceles triangle.

Slope of $\overline{AB} = \dfrac{3-0}{0-(-3)} = 1$

Slope of $\overline{AC} = \dfrac{-3-0}{0-(-3)} = -1$

We have the product of the slopes of $\overline{AB}$ and $\overline{AC}$ as -1, so the lines are perpendicular to each other; that is, $\angle BAC$ is a right angle. Therefore, the triangle is isosceles and right angular. The answer is E.

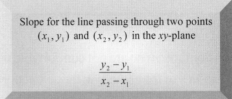

Distance between two points (x_1, y_1) and (x_2, y_2) in the xy-plane

$$\sqrt{(x_2 - x_1)^2 + (y_2 - y_1)^2}$$

Slope for the line passing through two points (x_1, y_1) and (x_2, y_2) in the xy-plane

$$\frac{y_2 - y_1}{x_2 - x_1}$$

Slopes of perpendicular lines

Let m_1 and m_2 be the slopes of the perpendicular lines, then

$$m_1 m_2 = -1 \Leftrightarrow m_1 = \frac{-1}{m_2}$$

OR

One of them is vertical and the other one is horizontal.

Method 2:

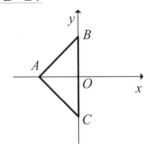

Sketching the triangle out, it looks like this:

Since the coordinates of A and B are $(-3, 0)$ and $(0, 3)$ respectively, $\triangle OAB$ must be an isosceles right-angled triangle. Similarly, the coordinates of A and C are $(-3, 0)$ and $(0, -3)$ respectively, so $\triangle OAC$ must also be an isosceles right-angled triangle which is congruent to $\triangle OAB$. Therefore, for $\triangle ABC$, we have $AB = AC$ and $\angle BAC = 45° + 45° = 90°$, that is, it is isosceles and right angular.

The answer is E.

38.   Answer: **A**

Algebra (Hard)

$(x^2 - 100)^{\frac{2}{3}} = 16 \Rightarrow (x^2 - 100)^2 = 16^3 \Rightarrow x^2 - 100 = \pm\sqrt{16^3} = \pm 64$

Therefore, we have two equations here:

$x^2 - 100 = 64 \Rightarrow x^2 = 164 \Rightarrow x = \pm\sqrt{164} = \pm 2\sqrt{41}$

$x^2 - 100 = -64 \Rightarrow x^2 = 36 \Rightarrow x = \pm\sqrt{36} = \pm 6$

The answer is A.

(For those who are not comfortable with square roots, you could find the answer by checking the values of the choices in the calculator directly.)

Plugging-in Tips:

We can plug the numbers given in the choices into the original equation to see whether the equality holds.

Choice A: $(6^2 - 100)^{\frac{2}{3}} = 16$, $((-6)^2 - 100)^{\frac{2}{3}} = 16$, $((2\sqrt{41})^2 - 100)^{\frac{2}{3}} = 16$, and

$((-2\sqrt{41})^2 - 100)^{\frac{2}{3}} = 16$. The equations **are** satisfied for all the numbers here; so choice A **should be** the answer.

Choice B: Although the numbers given satisfy the given equation, from the calculation in choice A, the roots $x = \pm 2\sqrt{41}$ are omitted here; so choice B is not the answer.

Choice C: Although the numbers given satisfy the given equation, from the calculation in choice A, the roots $x = \pm 6$ are omitted here; so choice C is not the answer.

Choice D: $(3^2 - 100)^{\frac{2}{3}} = 20.23 \neq 16$, so choice D is not the answer.

Choice E: $(12^2 - 100)^{\frac{2}{3}} = 12.46 \neq 16$, so choice E is not the answer.

The answer is A.

39.   Answer: **D**

Trigonometry (Hard)

First of all, let's sketch out the diagram described in the question.

From the diagram, we can observe that the angle of each triangle at the center is the same, that is, $\dfrac{360°}{3} = 120°$. Since it is given that the radius of the circle is 8, we can use the cosine rule to find x:

$$x^2 = 8^2 + 8^2 - 2(8)(8)\cos 120° \Rightarrow x^2 = 192 \Rightarrow x = \sqrt{192}$$

(Here, we only need to take the positive root of x because the length must be positive.)

Since each angle of an equilateral triangle is $60°$ and with the formula for the area of the triangle, we have

$$\dfrac{1}{2}(\sqrt{192})(\sqrt{192})\sin 60° = 96(\dfrac{\sqrt{3}}{2}) = 48\sqrt{3}.$$

The answer is D.

(For those who are not comfortable evaluating values for trigonometric functions and square roots, you could find the answer by checking the values of the choices in the calculator directly.)

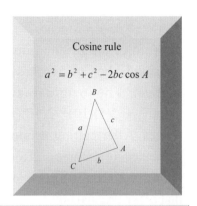

Cosine rule

$$a^2 = b^2 + c^2 - 2bc\cos A$$

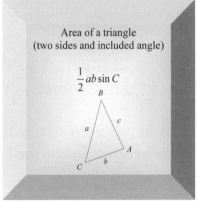

Area of a triangle
(two sides and included angle)

$$\dfrac{1}{2}ab\sin C$$

40.   Answer: **C**

Miscellaneous (Medium)

The integers described in the question are 9, 18, 27, ... , 99. Note that these numbers form an arithmetic sequence with both the first term and the common difference equal to 9. The number of terms n can be calculated as follows:

$$99 = 9 + 9(n-1) \Rightarrow 90 = 9(n-1) \Rightarrow 10 = n-1 \Rightarrow n = 11$$

Therefore, the sum of these numbers is

$$\dfrac{(2(9) + 9(11-1))11}{2} = 594.$$

The answer is C.

n^{th} term of an arithmetic sequence

$$a_n = a + (n-1)d$$
a denotes the first term
d denotes the common difference
a_n denotes the nth term

Sum of the first n terms of an arithmetic sequence

$$S_n = \dfrac{(2a + (n-1)d)n}{2}$$

a denotes the first term
d denotes the common difference
S_n denotes the sum of the first n terms

41.   Answer: **D**

Solid Geometry (Medium)

With the information given in the question, the volume of each cube is $\dfrac{250}{2} = 125$ cubic inches. Now we can calculate the length of each side of the cube as follows:

$125 = x^3 \Rightarrow x = 5$ inches.

Therefore, the original dimensions of the rectangular box are 5 inches by 5 inches by 10 inches. The original surface area is $2(5)(5) + 2(5)(10) + 2(10)(5) = 250$ square inches. After cutting it into two cubes, the combined surface area is $2(6)(5)^2 = 300$ square inches, which is 50 square inches greater than that of the original box.

The answer is D.

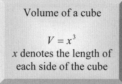

Volume of a cube

$V = x^3$

x denotes the length of each side of the cube

Surface area of a cube

$SA = 6x^2$

x denotes the length of each side of the cube

Surface area of a rectangular box

$SA = 2ab + 2bc + 2ca$

a, b & c denote the length, width & height of the rectangular box

42.   Answer: **E**
Coordinate Geometry (Hard)

With the conversion formulas between Cartesian coordinates and polar coordinates, the given formula can be transformed as follows:

$$r = \frac{1}{\sec\theta + \csc\theta}$$

$$r\sec\theta + r\csc\theta = 1$$

$$r\left(\frac{1}{\cos\theta}\right) + r\left(\frac{1}{\sin\theta}\right) = 1$$

$$r\sin\theta + r\cos\theta = \sin\theta\cos\theta$$

$$y + x = \frac{y}{r}\left(\frac{x}{r}\right)$$

$$r^2(x+y) = xy$$

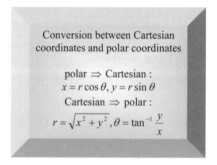

Conversion between Cartesian coordinates and polar coordinates

polar $\Rightarrow$ Cartesian :
$x = r\cos\theta, y = r\sin\theta$
Cartesian $\Rightarrow$ polar :
$r = \sqrt{x^2 + y^2}, \theta = \tan^{-1}\frac{y}{x}$

But since $r = \sqrt{x^2 + y^2}$, $r^2 = x^2 + y^2$. Therefore, the above equation becomes
$(x^2 + y^2)(x+y) = xy$

The answer is E.

43.   Answer: **C**
Probability & Statistics (Hard)

Based on the rule for the standard deviation of a set of numbers, the standard deviation will be doubled, that is, $2S$.

The answer is C.

Rule for the standard deviation of a set of numbers

If every term in the set is multiplied by k, then the standard deviation is also multiplied by k.

44.   Answer: **C**
Solid Geometry (Hard)

> **Equation of a straight line**
>
> $y = mx + b$
>
> m denotes the slope of the straight line
> b denotes the y-intercept of the straight line

$y = x + 1$ is a straight line going up with slope 1 and
y-intercept 1. Based on the information given in the question, we can make the following sketch:

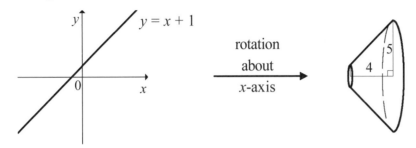

The solid obtained, called a frustum, is the remaining part of a larger cone after taking away a smaller cone from the top:

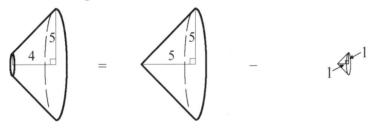

The larger cone has both radius and height of 5 units, while both the radius and height of the smaller cone are 1 unit. Therefore, the required volume is

$$\frac{1}{3}\pi(5)^2(5) - \frac{1}{3}\pi(1)^2(1) = \frac{125\pi}{3} - \frac{\pi}{3} = \frac{124\pi}{3}.$$

The answer is C.

> **Volume of a cone**
>
> $V = \frac{1}{3}\pi r^2 h$
>
> r denotes the radius of the base
> h denotes the height of the cone

45.   Answer: **C**
Miscellaneous (Medium)

First of all, when an integer is multiplied by 2, the product**must** be even. Therefore, we know that $2a$ must be even. In order for the sum to be odd, $3b$ must be odd; so obviously, b must be odd.

The answer is C.

Plugging-in Tips:

Taking arbitrary numbers as the values of a and b satisfying the conditions given in the choices, we can plug them into the expressions in the question and see which statement is correct.

Choice A: Take a and b to be 3 and 2, respectively. We have $2(3) + 3(2) = 12$, an even number, so choice A is not the answer.

Choice B: Take a and b to be 2 and 2, respectively. We have $2(2) + 3(2) = 12$, an even number, so choice B is not the answer.

Choice C: Take a and b to be 2 and 3, respectively. We have $2(2) + 3(3) = 13$, an **odd** number, so choice C **could be** the answer.

Choice D: Take a and b to be 2 and 2, respectively. We have $2(2) + 3(2) = 12$, an even number, so choice D is not the answer.

The answer is C.

46. Answer: **C**

Functions (Hard)

Identities for the squares $(a+b)^2$ and $(a-b)^2$

$$(a+b)^2 = a^2 + 2ab + b^2$$
$$(a-b)^2 = a^2 - 2ab + b^2$$

First of all let's try to express x^4 in terms of $x^2 + 1$ as follows:

$$x^4 = (x^2)^2 = (x^2 + 1 - 1)^2 = ((x^2 + 1) - 1)^2$$

By letting $z = x^2 + 1$, we have

$$f(z) = f(x^2 + 1) = x^4 + 1 = ((x^2 + 1) - 1)^2 + 1 = (z - 1)^2 + 1 = z^2 - 2z + 1 + 1 = z^2 - 2z + 2$$

Therefore, $f(x) = x^2 - 2x + 2$

The answer is C.

Plugging-in Tips:

We use the expressions in the choices directly and see whether we can go back to the given expression in the question:

Choice A: $f(x) = x^2 \Rightarrow f(x^2 + 1) = (x^2 + 1)^2 = x^4 + 2x^2 + 1 \neq x^4 + 1$,
so choice A is not the answer.

Choice B: $f(x) = x^2 + 1 \Rightarrow f(x^2 + 1) = (x^2 + 1)^2 + 1 = x^4 + 2x^2 + 2 \neq x^4 + 1$,
so choice B is not the answer.

Choice C: $f(x) = x^2 - 2x + 2 \Rightarrow f(x^2 + 1) = (x^2 + 1)^2 - 2(x^2 + 1) + 2 = x^4 + 1$,
so choice C **should be** the answer.

Choice D: $f(x) = x^2 + 2x - 2 \Rightarrow f(x^2 + 1) = (x^2 + 1)^2 + 2(x^2 + 1) - 2 = x^4 + 4x^2 + 1 \neq x^4 + 1$,
so choice D is not the answer.

Choice E: $f(x) = x^2 + 2x \Rightarrow f(x^2 + 1) = (x^2 + 1)^2 + 2(x^2 + 1) = x^4 + 4x^2 + 3 \neq x^4 + 1$,

so choice E is not the answer.

The answer is C.

47.　　Answer: **C**

Miscellaneous (Hard)

Below are the first few terms of an arithmetic sequence:

a, a + d, a + 2d, a + 3d ......

In order to be a geometric sequence at the same time, the ratio between each successive term must be the same, so we will have

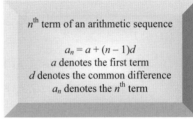

$$\frac{a+d}{a} = \frac{a+2d}{a+d} \Rightarrow (a+d)^2 = a(a+2d)$$

$$\Rightarrow a^2 + 2ad + d^2 = a^2 + 2ad \Rightarrow d^2 = 0 \Rightarrow d = 0$$

The answer is C.

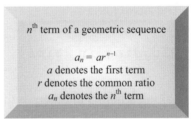

Plugging-in Tips:

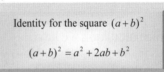

Taking an arbitrary number as the first term of an arithmetic sequence, we can use the numbers in the choices as the common difference and see whether it is a geometric sequence or not.

Let's take 3 to be our first term, then

Choice A:　Take the common difference as -2, then the arithmetic sequence will look like $3, 1, -1, -3, \ldots\ldots$ It is not a geometric sequence, so choice A is not the answer.

Choice B:　Take the common difference as -1, then the arithmetic sequence will look like $3, 2, 1, 0, \ldots\ldots$ It is not a geometric sequence, so choice B is not the answer.

Choice C:　Take the common difference as 0, then the arithmetic sequence will look like $3, 3, 3, 3, \ldots\ldots$ It **is** a geometric sequence, so choice C **could be** the answer.

Choice D:　Take the common difference as 1, then the arithmetic sequence will look like $3, 4, 5, 6, \ldots\ldots$ It is not a geometric sequence, so choice D is not the answer.

Choice A:　Take the common difference as 2, then the arithmetic sequence will look like $3, 5, 7, 9, \ldots\ldots$ It is not a geometric sequence, so choice E is not the answer.

The answer is C.

48. Answer: **B**

Miscellaneous (Hard)

With $P_r^n = \dfrac{n!}{(n-r)!}$ and $C_{r-1}^n = \dfrac{n!}{(n-(r-1))!(r-1)!} = \dfrac{n!}{(n-r+1)!(r-1)!}$, we have

$$\frac{P_r^n}{C_{r-1}^n} = \frac{n!}{(n-r)!} \div \frac{n!}{(n-r+1)!(r-1)!}$$

$$= \frac{n!}{(n-r)!} \times \frac{(n-r+1)!(r-1)!}{n!} = \frac{(n-r+1)!(r-1)!}{(n-r)!}$$

$$= \frac{(n-r+1)(n-r)(n-r)......(3)(2)(1)(r-1)!}{(n-r)(n-r)......(3)(2)(1)}$$

$$= (n-r+1)(r-1)!$$

The answer is B.

> The number of permutations of selecting r items from n distinct items
>
> $${}_nP_r \text{ or } P_r^n = \frac{n!}{(n-r)!}$$

> The number of ways (combinations) of selecting r items from n distinct items
>
> $${}_nC_r \text{ or } C_r^n = \frac{n!}{(n-r)!r!}$$

Plugging-in Tips:

Taking arbitrary numbers as the values of n and r, we can plug them into the expressions in the choices and see which one is correct. Let's take n and r to be 7 and 3, respectively; then using the calculator, we have $\dfrac{P_3^7}{C_{3-1}^7} = 10$.

Choice A: $(7-3-1)3! = 18 \neq 10$, so choice A is not the answer.

Choice B: $(7-3+1)(3-1)! = 10$, so choice B **could be** the answer.

Choice C: $(7+3-1)3! = 54 \neq 10$, so choice C is not the answer.

Choice D: $(7+3+1)(3-1)! = 22 \neq 10$, so choice D is not the answer.

Choice E: $(7-3-1)(3-1)! = 6 \neq 10$, so choice E is not the answer.

The answer is B.

49.   Answer: **D**

Coordinate Geometry (Hard)

With the length of the major axis equal to 8, we have $2a = 8 \Rightarrow a = 4$. Similarly, with the length of the minor axis equal to 4, we have $2b = 4 \Rightarrow b = 2$. Together with the center as $(2, -3)$, we have the equation of the ellipse:

$$\frac{(x-2)^2}{4^2} + \frac{(y-(-3))^2}{2^2} = 1 \Rightarrow \left(\frac{x-2}{4}\right)^2 + \left(\frac{y+3}{2}\right)^2 = 1$$

The answer is D.

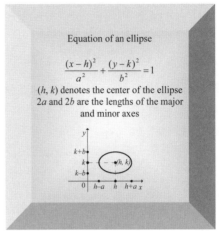

Equation of an ellipse

$$\frac{(x-h)^2}{a^2} + \frac{(y-k)^2}{b^2} = 1$$

(h, k) denotes the center of the ellipse
$2a$ and $2b$ are the lengths of the major and minor axes

50.   Answer: **E**

Algebra (Hard)

By expressing all the terms in the given expression with the same base of 2 and then carrying out the factorization (using the identity for the difference of squares), we have

$$\frac{2^{n+1} - 8^{3-n}}{2(2^n - 2^{4-n})} = \frac{2^{n+1} - 2^{3(3-n)}}{2^{n+1} - 2^{5-n}} = \frac{2^{n+1} - 2^{9-3n}}{2^{n+1} - 2^{5-n}} = \frac{2^{n+1}(1 - 2^{8-4n})}{2^{n+1}(1 - 2^{4-2n})} = \frac{1 - 2^{8-4n}}{1 - 2^{4-2n}} = \frac{1 - 2^{2(4-2n)}}{1 - 2^{4-2n}}$$

$$= \frac{(1 + 2^{4-2n})(1 - 2^{4-2n})}{1 - 2^{4-2n}} = 1 + 2^{4-2n}$$

The answer is E.

Identity for the square $(a - b)^2$

$$(a - b)^2 = a^2 - 2ab + b^2$$

Plugging-in Method:

Taking an arbitrary number as the value of n, we can plug it into the expressions in the choices and see which one is the answer. Let's take n to be 3, then, $\dfrac{2^{n+1} - 8^{3-n}}{2(2^n - 2^{4-n})} = \dfrac{2^{3+1} - 8^{3-3}}{2(2^3 - 2^{4-3})} = \dfrac{5}{4}$

Choice A: $\dfrac{1 - 2^{8-4(3)}}{2^{4-2(3)}} = \dfrac{15}{4} \neq \dfrac{5}{4}$, so choice A is not the answer.

Choice B: $2^{8-4(3)} = \dfrac{1}{16} \neq \dfrac{5}{4}$, so choice B is not the answer.

Choice C: $\dfrac{1 - 2^{3-2(3)}}{1 - 2^{4-2(3)}} = \dfrac{7}{6} \neq \dfrac{5}{4}$, so choice C is not the answer.

Choice D: $1 - 2^{4-2(3)} = \dfrac{3}{4} \neq \dfrac{5}{4}$, so choice D is not the answer.

Choice E: $1 + 2^{4-2(3)} = \dfrac{5}{4}$, so choice E **could be** the answer.

The answer is E.

Solutions To Sample Test 4

1.   Answer: **A**

Algebra (Easy)

$yz = 8 \Rightarrow y = \dfrac{8}{z}$, therefore, $\dfrac{x}{y} = \dfrac{4}{z} \div \dfrac{8}{z} = \dfrac{4}{z}\left(\dfrac{z}{8}\right) = 0.5$

The answer is A.

Plugging-in Tips:

Taking an arbitrary number as the value of z, we can get the values of x and y. Then, we can plug them into the given expression and find the answer directly. Let's take z to be 1 here, then $x = \dfrac{4}{1} = 4$

and $y(1) = 8 \Rightarrow y = 8$. Therefore, $\dfrac{x}{y} = \dfrac{4}{8} = 0.5$.

The answer is A.

2.   Answer: **C**

Algebra (Easy)

By letting $y = 8^x$, the original equation given in the question can be simplified as follows:

$8(8^x) - 6(8^x) - 1 = 0 \Rightarrow 8y - 6y - 1 = 0 \Rightarrow 2y - 1 = 0 \Rightarrow y = \dfrac{1}{2}$

By putting back $y = 8^x$, and using the definition of log, we

have $8^x = \dfrac{1}{2} \Rightarrow x = \dfrac{\log \frac{1}{2}}{\log 8} \Rightarrow x = -\dfrac{1}{3}$

The answer is C.

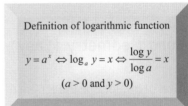

Definition of logarithmic function

$y = a^x \Leftrightarrow \log_a y = x \Leftrightarrow \dfrac{\log y}{\log a} = x$

($a > 0$ and $y > 0$)

Plugging-in Tips:

We can plug the numbers in the choices into the given equation to see whether the equality holds.

Choice A: Plug $x = -1$

$8(8^{-1}) - 6(8^{-1}) - 1 = -0.75 \neq 0$, so choice A is not the answer.

Choice B: Plug $x = -\dfrac{2}{3}$

$8(8^{-\frac{2}{3}}) - 6(8^{-\frac{2}{3}}) - 1 = -0.5 \neq 0$, so choice B is not the answer.

Choice C: Plug $x = -\dfrac{1}{3}$

$8(8^{\frac{-1}{3}}) - 6(8^{\frac{-1}{3}}) - 1 = 0$, so choice C **should be** the answer.

Choice D: Plug $x = \dfrac{1}{3}$

$8(8^{\frac{1}{3}}) - 6(8^{\frac{1}{3}}) - 1 = 3 \neq 0$, so choice D is not the answer.

Choice E: Plug $x = \dfrac{2}{3}$

$8(8^{\frac{2}{3}}) - 6(8^{\frac{2}{3}}) - 1 = 7 \neq 0$, so choice E is not the answer.

The answer is C.

Graphing Calculator Tips:

You can input $y = 8(8^x) - 6(8^x) - 1$ directly into the graphing calculator to find the x-intercept to be $-\dfrac{1}{3}$.

The answer is C.

3.   Answer: **C**
Trigonometry (Easy)

For this question you can use your calculator to find the answer directly: $4\tan(\sin^{-1} 0.6) = 3$
The answer is C.

4.   Answer: **E**
Solid Geometry (Easy)

First of all, let x be the length of the cube; then we can find the value of x as follows:

$96 = 6x^2 \Rightarrow x = 4$ inches

(Here, we only need to take the positive root of x because the length must be positive.)

Therefore, the volume of the cube is $4^3 = 64$ cubic inches.
The answer is E.

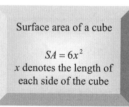

Surface area of a cube

$SA = 6x^2$
x denotes the length of each side of the cube

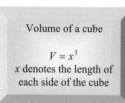

Volume of a cube

$V = x^3$
x denotes the length of each side of the cube

5.   Answer: **A**

Algebra (Medium)

The information given in the question can be expressed mathematically as follows:

$$\frac{648-150x}{150x} = 2x\% \Rightarrow \frac{648-150x}{150x} = \frac{2x}{100} \Rightarrow 648-150x = \frac{x}{50}(150x) \Rightarrow 648-150x = 3x^2$$

$$\Rightarrow 3x^2 +150x-648 = 0 \Rightarrow x^2 +50x-216 = 0 \Rightarrow (x+54)(x-4) = 0 \Rightarrow x = -54 \text{ or } 4.$$

Since x cannot be negative in this question (or the cost of the car will also be negative!), x can only be 4.

The answer is A.

(You could use the quadratic formula to solve the above quadratic equation.)

Here, $a = 1$, $b = 50$ and $c = -216$.

$$x = \frac{-b \pm \sqrt{b^2 - 4ac}}{2a} = \frac{-(50) \pm \sqrt{(50)^2 - 4(1)(-216)}}{2(1)} = \frac{-50 \pm 58}{2} = -54 \text{ or } 4.$$

Since x cannot be negative in this question, x can only be 4.

The answer is A.

> Formulas for the roots of the
> quadratic equation $ax^2 + bx + c = 0$
>
> $$x = \frac{-b \pm \sqrt{b^2 - 4ac}}{2a}$$

Plugging-in Tips:

We can plug the numbers in the choices given for x to see which one satisfies the given condition.

Choice A: Plug $x = 4$

Cost $= \$150(4) = \$600$. Therefore, $\frac{648 - 600}{600} = 0.08 = 8\% = 2(4)\%$, so choice

A **should be** the answer.

Choice B: Plug $x = 4.5$

Cost $= \$150(4.5) = \$675$. Therefore, $\frac{648 - 675}{675} = -0.04 = -4\% \neq 2(4.5)\%$,

so choice B is not the answer.

Here, we observe that, for the remaining choices, the numbers given <u>are getting bigger</u>, which leads to greater values for the cost. Since from choice B a negative return is obtained, obviously negative returns will also be recorded for choices C to E, which violates the given condition. Therefore, choices C to E cannot be the answers.

The answer is A.

6.　　Answer: **A**

Trigonometry (Medium)

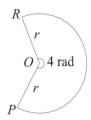

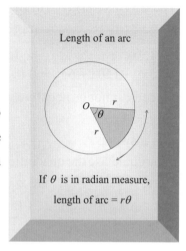

Length of an arc

In this question, be careful that the perimeter of the sector also includes the radii $\overline{OP}$ and $\overline{OR}$. In order to find the length of the arc PR, we need to find the radius first. Let r be the radius. Given that $\theta = 4$, we have

$r + r + r\theta = 18 \Rightarrow 2r + 4r = 18 \Rightarrow 6r = 18 \Rightarrow r = 3$

Therefore, the length of the arc PR is $r\theta = 3(4) = 12$

The answer is A.

If θ is in radian measure,

length of arc $= r\theta$

7.　　Answer: **D**

Functions (Easy)

$f(2.5) = 2.5 + \sqrt{2.5} \Rightarrow g(2.5) = f(f(2.5)))$

$= f(2.5 + \sqrt{2.5}) = 2.5 + \sqrt{2.5} + \sqrt{2.5 + \sqrt{2.5}} = 6.10$

The answer is D.

8.　　Answer: **E**

Algebra (Medium)

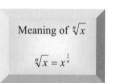

Meaning of $\sqrt[n]{x}$

$\sqrt[n]{x} = x^{\frac{1}{n}}$

First of all, we need to find the prime factorizations for 20, 90 and 60. We have $20 = 2^2 \times 5$, $90 = 2 \times 3^2 \times 5$ and $60 = 2^2 \times 3 \times 5$. Then,

$\log \sqrt[3]{20} + \log \sqrt[5]{90} - \log \sqrt[4]{60} = \log(20^{\frac{1}{3}}) + \log(90^{\frac{1}{5}}) - \log(60^{\frac{1}{4}})$

$= \log((2^2 \times 5)^{\frac{1}{3}}) + \log((2 \times 3^2 \times 5)^{\frac{1}{5}}) - \log((2^2 \times 3 \times 5)^{\frac{1}{4}})$

$= \log(2^{\frac{2}{3}} \times 5^{\frac{1}{3}}) + \log(2^{\frac{1}{5}} \times 3^{\frac{2}{5}} \times 5^{\frac{1}{5}}) - \log(2^{\frac{1}{2}} \times 3^{\frac{1}{4}} \times 5^{\frac{1}{4}})$

$= \log 2^{\frac{2}{3}} + \log 5^{\frac{1}{3}} + \log 2^{\frac{1}{5}} + \log 3^{\frac{2}{5}} + \log 5^{\frac{1}{5}} - (\log 2^{\frac{1}{2}} + \log 3^{\frac{1}{4}} + \log 5^{\frac{1}{4}})$

$= \frac{2}{3}\log 2 + \frac{1}{3}\log 5 + \frac{1}{5}\log 2 + \frac{2}{5}\log 3 + \frac{1}{5}\log 5 - \frac{1}{2}\log 2 - \frac{1}{4}\log 3 - \frac{1}{4}\log 5$

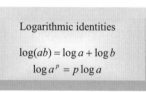

Logarithmic identities

$\log(ab) = \log a + \log b$

$\log a^p = p \log a$

$$= \frac{2}{3}a + \frac{1}{3}c + \frac{1}{5}a + \frac{2}{5}b + \frac{1}{5}c - \frac{1}{2}a - \frac{1}{4}b - \frac{1}{4}c = \frac{11}{30}a + \frac{3}{20}b + \frac{17}{60}c$$

The answer is E.

Plugging-in Tips:

We can plug the given numbers for *a, b* and *c* into the choices to find the answer directly. The value of the given expression is $\log \sqrt[3]{20} + \log \sqrt[5]{90} - \log \sqrt[4]{60} = 0.38$.

Choice A: $\frac{19}{30}\log 2 + \frac{7}{20}\log 3 + \frac{13}{60}\log 5 = 0.51 \neq 0.38$, so choice A is not the answer.

Choice B: $\frac{19}{30}\log 2 + \frac{13}{20}\log 3 + \frac{11}{60}\log 5 = 0.63 \neq 0.38$, so choice B is not the answer.

Choice C: $\frac{11}{60}\log 2 + \frac{13}{20}\log 3 + \frac{17}{30}\log 5 = 0.76 \neq 0.38$, so choice C is not the answer.

Choice D: $\frac{13}{30}\log 2 + \frac{17}{20}\log 3 + \frac{23}{60}\log 5 = 0.81 \neq 0.38$, so choice D is not the answer.

Choice E: $\frac{11}{30}\log 2 + \frac{3}{20}\log 3 + \frac{17}{60}\log 5 = 0.38$, so choice E **should be** the answer.

The answer is E.

9.   Answer: **E**
Coordinate Geometry (Easy)

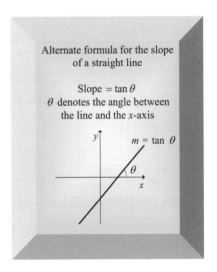

Alternate formula for the slope of a straight line

Slope $= \tan \theta$
θ denotes the angle between the line and the *x*-axis

$m = \tan \theta$

The slope for the line given here is $\tan 45° = 1$. Therefore, the equation of the line is

$$y - (-3) = 1(x - 2) \Rightarrow y + 3 = x - 2 \Rightarrow x - y - 5 = 0$$

The answer is E.

Equation of a straight line

$$y - y_1 = m(x - x_1)$$
m denotes the slope of the straight line
(x_1, y_1) denotes a point on the straight line

10.　　Answer: **C**

Trigonometry (Medium)

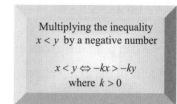

By the ranges of $\cos x$ and x^2, we have

$$-1 \leq \cos x \leq 1 \Rightarrow 0 \leq \cos^2 x \leq 1 \Rightarrow 0 \geq -3\cos^2 x \geq -3$$

$$\Rightarrow 4 \geq 4 - 3\cos^2 x \geq 1$$

Therefore, the greatest value of $4 - 3\cos^2 x$ is 4.

The answer is C.

Graphing Calculator Tips:

You can graph $y = 4 - 3\cos^2 x$ directly using a graphing calculator to find that the greatest value of the function is 4.

The answer is C.

11.　　Answer: **E**

Functions (Easy)

Given that $f(0) = 1$ and $f(\frac{\pi}{2}) = 2$, we have

$$a\sin 0 - b\cos 0 = 1 \Rightarrow -b = 1 \Rightarrow b = -1$$

$$a\sin\frac{\pi}{2} - b\cos\frac{\pi}{2} = 2 \Rightarrow a = 2$$

Therefore, $a - b = 2 - (-1) = 3$.

The answer is E.

12.　　Answer: **C**

Algebra (Medium)

Let $\$x$ and $\$y$ be the amount of money that John and Mary originally have. Because the ratio of John's amount of money to Mary's amount of money is 3 : 7, we have

$$x : y = 3 : 7 \Rightarrow \frac{x}{y} = \frac{3}{7} \Rightarrow x = \frac{3}{7}y\,.$$

We also know that if Mary gives $\$224$ to John, then the ratio of Mary's amount of money to John's amount of money will be 3 : 7, we have

$y - 224 : x + 224 = 3 : 7 \Rightarrow \dfrac{y - 224}{x + 224} = \dfrac{3}{7}$

$\Rightarrow 7(y - 224) = 3(x + 224) \Rightarrow 7y - 1568 = 3x + 672$

By putting $x = \dfrac{3}{7} y$ into the above equation, it becomes

$7y - 1568 = 3x + 672 \Rightarrow 7y = 3(\dfrac{3y}{7}) + 2240 \Rightarrow \dfrac{40y}{7} = 2240 \Rightarrow y = 392$

Then, $x = \dfrac{3}{7}(392) = 168$

Therefore, the amount of money they have altogether is $\$(392 + 168) = \$560$.

The answer is C.

13.   Answer: **D**

Trigonometry (Medium)

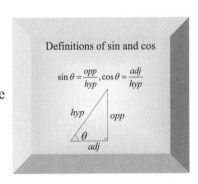

Definitions of sin and cos

$\sin\theta = \dfrac{opp}{hyp}, \cos\theta = \dfrac{adj}{hyp}$

Based on the information given in the diagram, we have

$\sin\theta = \dfrac{-c}{a}$ and $\cos\theta = \dfrac{b}{a}$. Therefore,

$\sin\theta + \cos\theta = \dfrac{-c}{a} + \dfrac{b}{a} = \dfrac{b - c}{a}$.

The answer is D.

Plugging-in Tips:

Since the given triangle is a right triangle, the lengths of its sides must satisfy the equation in the Pythagorean Theorem.

(Note: The a, b and c here have **no relationship** with those defined in the equation for Pythagorean Theorem. We have to take a as the hypotenuse here. **Don't** mix them up!)

Taking arbitrary numbers as the values of a, b and c where they satisfy the identity $b^2 + c^2 = a^2$, we can find α in the following diagram:

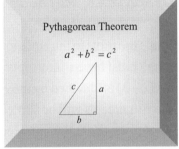

Pythagorean Theorem

$a^2 + b^2 = c^2$

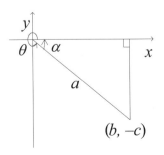

Then, we can find θ and plug it into the given expression, and find the answer directly. Let's take a, b and c to be 5, 4 and 3, respectively. Then,

$$\cos \alpha = \frac{b}{a} = \frac{4}{5} \Rightarrow \alpha = \cos^{-1} 0.8 = 36.87° \Rightarrow \theta = 360 - 36.87° = 323.13°.$$

Therefore, the given expression is $\sin 323.13° + \cos 323.13° = 0.2$.

Choice A: $4 + 3 = 7 \neq 0.2$, so choice A is not the answer.

Choice B: $4 - 3 = 1 \neq 0.2$, so choice B is not the answer.

Choice C: $\dfrac{4+3}{5} = 1.4 \neq 0.2$, so choice C is not the answer.

Choice D: $\dfrac{4-3}{5} = 0.2$, so choice D **should be** the answer.

Choice E: $3 - 4 = -1 \neq 0.2$, so choice E is not the answer.

The answer is D.

14.   Answer: **D**
Functions (Easy)

Algebraic Method:

Since we know that the roots to the equation $f(x) = 0$ are 5 and 8, $f(x)$ must have the factors $(x - 5)(x - 8)$. Then, $f(x - 3)$ will have the factors $((x - 3) - 5)((x - 3) - 8)$, which are $(x - 8)(x - 11)$. Therefore, 8 and 11 must be the roots to the equation $f(x - 3) = 0$.
The answer is D.

Graphical Method:

Since the roots to the equation $f(x) = 0$ are 5 and 8, the graph must have x-intercepts at $x = 5$ and 8. Furthermore, as $f(x - 3)$ is obtained by moving $f(x)$ 3 units to the right, the x-intercepts will be shifted to the right by 3 units also. Therefore, the new x-intercepts are 8 and 11.
The answer is D.

> Effect of $f(x-k)$ on the graph of $f(x)$
> $(k > 0)$
>
> Horizontal shifting
> $f(x-k) \Leftrightarrow$ Move $f(x)$ right by k units

15.   Answer: **B**

Solid Geometry (Medium)

If the diameter of the base of the cone is increased by 50 %, then its radius is also increased by 50%. By letting r be the radius of the base and h be the height of the cone, the new radius of the base becomes $1.5r$ and the new height becomes $0.5h$. Therefore, the new volume is $\frac{1}{3}\pi(1.5r)^2(0.5)h = 1.125(\frac{1}{3}\pi r^2h)$, which indicates an increase of 12.5%.

The answer is B.

> **Volume of a cone**
>
> $$V = \frac{1}{3}\pi r^2 h$$
>
> r denotes the radius of the base
> h denotes the height of the cone

Plugging-in Tips:

First of all, we know that if the diameter of the base of the cone is increased by 50 %, then its radius is also increased by 50%. Taking arbitrary numbers as the values of r and h, we can find the original and new volumes of the cone. Then, we can compare them to find the answer directly. Let's take r and h to be 2 and 3, respectively. So we have

the original volume $= \frac{1}{3}\pi(2)^2(3) = 12.57$ and the new volume $= \frac{1}{3}\pi(2 \times 1.5)^2(3 \times 0.5) = 14.14$.

Therefore, the percentage change is $\dfrac{14.14 - 12.57}{12.57} = 0.125 = 12.5\%$. That is, there is an increase of 12.5%.

The answer is B.

16.   Answer: **D**

Coordinate Geometry (Easy)

For l_1, the slope is $\dfrac{6-0}{0-4} = \dfrac{-3}{2}$. Since l_1 is parallel

to l_2, the slope of l_2 is also $\dfrac{-3}{2}$. Then, the equation

of l_2 is $y - 0 = \dfrac{-3}{2}(x-6) \Rightarrow y = \dfrac{-3}{2}x + 9$.

The y-intercept of l_2 is therefore 9.

The answer is D.

> **Slope for the line passing through two points** (x_1, y_1) and (x_2, y_2) in the xy-plane
>
> $$\frac{y_2 - y_1}{x_2 - x_1}$$

> **Equation of a straight line**
>
> $$y = mx + b$$
> m denotes the slope of the straight line
> b denotes the y-intercept of the straight line
> OR
> $$y - y_1 = m(x - x_1)$$
> m denotes the slope of the straight line
> (x_1, y_1) denotes a point on the straight line

> **Slopes of parallel lines**
>
> Let m_1 and m_2 be the slopes of the parallel lines, then $m_1 = m_2$

Common Mistake:

Some of you may have thought that the difference between the *x*-intercepts is the same as that between the *y*-intercepts and then got the required answer by just adding 2 to 6 to get 8. **Be careful!** Generally, the difference between the *x*-intercepts of two lines is **DIFFERENT** from the distance between their *y*-intercepts.

17.   Answer: **D**

Probability & Statistics (Easy)

There is no restriction for combinations; therefore, using the multiplication principle, the number of different combinations is $5 \times 3 \times 2 = 30$.
The answer is D.

18.   Answer: **E**

Trigonometry (Medium)

$\cos^4 \alpha - \sin^4 \alpha = (\cos^2 \alpha)^2 - (\sin^2 \alpha)^2$
$= (\cos^2 \alpha - \sin^2 \alpha)(\cos^2 \alpha + \sin^2 \alpha)$
$= (\cos^2 \alpha - \sin^2 \alpha)(1) = \cos^2 \alpha - \sin^2 \alpha$

The answer is E.

Identity for the difference of squares $a^2 - b^2$
$a^2 - b^2 = (a+b)(a-b)$

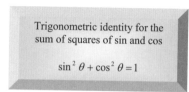

Trigonometric identity for the sum of squares of sin and cos
$\sin^2 \theta + \cos^2 \theta = 1$

Plugging-in Tips:

We can plug any arbitrary value into α in the expression above and then see which one is the answer. Let's plug $\alpha = 40°$, then we have $\cos^4 40° - \sin^4 40° = 0.17$.

Choice A: It is given as 0, so choice A is not the answer.
Choice B: It is given as 1, so choice B is not the answer.
Choice C: $\cos^2 40° = 0.59 \neq 0.17$, so choice C is not the answer.
Choice D: $\sin^2 40° = 0.41 \neq 0.17$, so choice D is not the answer.
Choice E: $\cos^2 40° - \sin^2 40° = 0.17$, so choice E **could be** the answer.
The answer is E.

19.   Answer: **B**

Algebra (Medium)

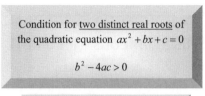

Condition for two distinct real roots of the quadratic equation $ax^2 + bx + c = 0$

$$b^2 - 4ac > 0$$

Using the given information that $a = c$ and $a > 0$, we have

$b^2 - 4ac > 0 \Rightarrow b^2 - 4a^2 > 0 \Rightarrow b^2 > 4a^2$
$\Rightarrow b^2 > (2a)^2 \Rightarrow b > 2a$ or $b < -2a$

The answer is B.

Solution of the quadratic inequality $x^2 > k^2$ where $k > 0$

$$x > k \text{ or } x < -k$$

20.   Answer: **D**

Functions (Medium)

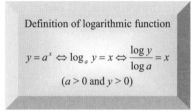

Definition of logarithmic function

$$y = a^x \Leftrightarrow \log_a y = x \Leftrightarrow \frac{\log y}{\log a} = x$$

$$(a > 0 \text{ and } y > 0)$$

In order to find the inverse function, we first need to take y to be $f(x)$, and then swap the positions of x and y, and finally express y in terms of x as follows:

Swapping the positions of x and y: $y = 3^{x+2} \Rightarrow x = 3^{y+2}$

Expressing y in terms of x:

$x = 3^{y+2} \Rightarrow \log_3 x = y + 2 \Rightarrow y = \log_3 x - 2 \Rightarrow f^{-1}(x) = \log_3 x - 2$

The answer is D.

Plugging-in Tips:

Taking an arbitrary value for x, we can plug it into the expressions in the choices and see whether the equation $f(f^{-1}(x)) = x$ is satisfied. Let's take x to be 7 here.

Choice A: $3^{\frac{1}{2}\log_3 7 + 2} = 23.8 \neq 7$, so choice A is not the answer.

Choice B: $3^{2\log_3 7 + 2} = 441 \neq 7$, so choice B is not the answer.

Choice C: $3^{\log_3 7 + 2 + 2} = 567 \neq 7$, so choice C is not the answer.

Choice D: $3^{\log_3 7 - 2 + 2} = 7$, so choice D **could be** the answer.

Choice E: $3^{\log_3 2(7) + 2} = 126 \neq 7$, so choice E is not the answer.

The answer is B.

Property of an inverse function $f^{-1}(x)$

$$f(f^{-1}(x)) = x$$

21.   Answer: **A**
Miscellaneous (Medium)

Using the following diagram, we can figure out the maximum and the minimum magnitude of $u + v$.

$$\underset{5}{\underset{u}{\bullet\!\!\longrightarrow}\underset{12}{v\longrightarrow}}$$

$$\underset{5}{\underset{u}{\bullet}\;\underset{7}{u+v}}$$

$$\underset{17}{\underset{u+v}{\bullet\longrightarrow}}$$

$$\underset{12}{\underset{v}{\bullet\longrightarrow}}$$

Meaning of the magnitude of a vector

Magnitude of a vector = Length of a vector

In the choices, 5 is out of the range 7 to 17.
The answer is A.

22.   Answer: **C**
Functions (Medium)

In order to find the domain of $f(x)$, we need to have $x^2 - 3x + 2$ to be non-zero. Since $x^2 - 3x + 2 = (x-1)(x-2)$, x cannot be 1 or 2.
The answer is C.

Domain of $f(x) = \dfrac{1}{x}$

Domain: $x \neq 0$

(You could use the quadratic formula to solve the above quadratic equation.)
If $x^2 - 3x + 2 = 0$, then, $a = 1$, $b = -3$ and $c = 2$.

$$x = \frac{-b \pm \sqrt{b^2 - 4ac}}{2a} = \frac{-(-3) \pm \sqrt{(-3)^2 - 4(1)(2)}}{2(1)} = \frac{3 \pm 1}{2} = 2 \text{ or } 1.$$

However, $x^2 - 3x + 2$ must be non-zero, so x cannot be 1 or 2.
The answer is C.

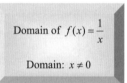

Formulas for the roots of the quadratic equation $ax^2 + bx + c = 0$

$$x = \frac{-b \pm \sqrt{b^2 - 4ac}}{2a}$$

Graphing Calculator Tips:

You can input the expression $\dfrac{1}{x^2 - 3x + 2}$ directly into the graphing calculator to find that the function is undefined when x is 1 or 2; so the domain is the set of all real numbers x such that $x \neq 1, 2$.
The answer is C.

23.   Answer: **B**

Trigonometry (Medium)

We can solve this equation directly as follows:

$$2\cos 3\theta = \sqrt{3} \Rightarrow \cos 3\theta = \frac{\sqrt{3}}{2}$$

Since we have $\cos^{-1} \dfrac{\sqrt{3}}{2} = 30°$, by the "CAST"

rule and the corresponding angles in different

quadrants, we have the following diagram:

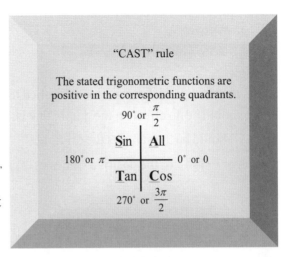

"CAST" rule

The stated trigonometric functions are positive in the corresponding quadrants.

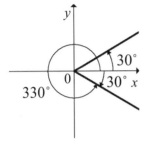

Therefore, $3\theta = 30°$ or $330°$, that is,

$\theta = 10°$ or $110°$

The answer is B.

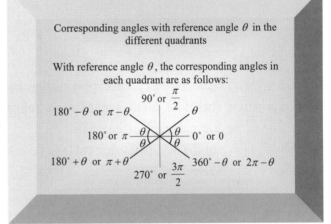

Corresponding angles with reference angle θ in the different quadrants

With reference angle θ, the corresponding angles in each quadrant are as follows:

Plugging-in Tips:

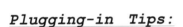

We can plug the numbers given in the choices into the equation to see whether the equality holds.
Here, we can approximate $\sqrt{3}$ as 1.73.

Choice A: $2\cos 3(10°) = 1.73$ but $2\cos 3(90°) = 0 \neq 1.73$, so choice A is not the answer.

Choice B: We do not need to check for $\theta = 10°$ here because it is checked in choice A already. $2\cos 3(110°) = 1.73$, so choice B **should be** the answer.

Choice C: We do not need to check for $\theta = 10°$ here because it is checked in choice A already. But $2\cos 3(120°) = 2 \neq 1.73$, so choice C is not the answer.

Choice D: $2\cos 3(20°) = 1 \neq 1.73$, so choice D is not the answer.

Choice E: Since $125.7°$ is out of the domain defined, choice E is not the answer.

The answer is B.

24.   Answer: **A**

Functions (Medium)

Here, the absolute value function is applied to $f(x)$. Therefore, for the positive values of $f(x)$ there should be no effect on the graph; that is, for the part of $f(x)$ <u>above</u> the x-axis, the graph of $|f(x)|$ should be the same as the original.

Graph of $|f(x)|$ for the positive values of $f(x)$:

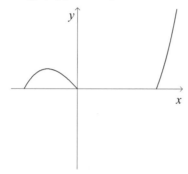

For the <u>negative</u> values of $f(x)$, after applying the absolute value function to them, they will be all <u>turned positive</u>. Therefore, for the part of $f(x)$ below the x-axis, the graph $|f(x)|$ should be the <u>reflection</u> of the original graph in the x-axis.

Graph of $|f(x)|$ for the negative values of $f(x)$:

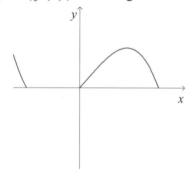

Combining the above results, we have the following graph:

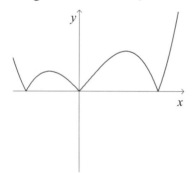

The answer is A.

25.   Answer: **D**
Trigonometry (Hard)

Let the length of XY be x. Based on the figure given, we have the following information:

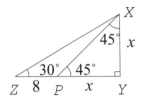

In $\triangle XYZ$, we have

$$\tan 30^\circ = \frac{x}{x+8} \Rightarrow \tan 30^\circ (x+8) = x \Rightarrow x \tan 30^\circ + 8 \tan 30^\circ = x$$

$$\Rightarrow x - x \tan 30^\circ = 8 \tan 30^\circ \Rightarrow x(1 - \tan 30^\circ) = 8 \tan 30^\circ$$

$$\Rightarrow x = \frac{8 \tan 30^\circ}{1 - \tan 30^\circ} = \frac{\frac{8}{\sqrt{3}}}{1 - \frac{1}{\sqrt{3}}} = 4\sqrt{3} + 4$$

(For those who are not comfortable evaluating values for trigonometric functions and square roots, you could find the answer by checking the values of the choices in the calculator directly.)

The answer is D.

26.   Answer: **E**
Functions (Hard)

After expanding and regrouping the terms, we will have the following:

$$(x-2)(x-3) = (a-2)(a-3)$$
$$x^2 - 5x + 6 = a^2 - 5a + 6$$
$$x^2 - 5x + 5a - a^2 = 0$$

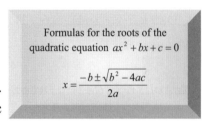

(Note: Here, we should treat x as a variable and a as a constant. The a here has **no relationship** with the a defined in the quadratic formula on the right. **Don't** mix them up!)

In the above quadratic equation, we have a, b and c as 1, -5 and $5a - a^2$, respectively.

Therefore, the solutions to the equation are

$$x = \frac{-(-5) \pm \sqrt{(-5)^2 - 4(1)(5a - a^2)}}{2} = \frac{5 \pm \sqrt{4a^2 - 20a + 25}}{2}$$

$$= \frac{5 \pm \sqrt{(2a)^2 - 2(2a)(5) + 5^2}}{2} = \frac{5 \pm \sqrt{(2a-5)^2}}{2} = \frac{5 \pm (2a-5)}{2}$$

> Identity for the square $(a-b)^2$
>
> $(a-b)^2 = a^2 - 2ab + b^2$

Therefore, $x = a$ or $5 - a$.

The answer is E.

Plugging-in Tips:

We can plug the values provided in the choices into the original equation to see whether the equality holds. Here, it is quite obvious that choices A to D cannot be our answer because there is at least 1 answer in each choice independent of a. By putting a constant value into x, the equality can never hold since the right hand-side of the equation is always in terms of a. Therefore, the answer is E.

27.   Answer: **D**

Functions (Medium)

In order to have $f(x) = g(x)$, we have $x^3 - x = 6x^2 - 30 \Rightarrow x^3 - 6x^2 - x + 30 = 0$. Then we can plug the numbers given in the choices into the above equation to see whether the equality holds.

Choice A: $1^3 - 6(1)^2 - (1) + 30 = 24 \neq 0$, so choice A is not the answer.

Choice B: $(-3)^3 - 6(-3)^2 - (-3) + 30 = -48 \neq 0$, so choice B is not the answer.

Choice C: From choice A, we know that 1 is not the solution of the equation, so choice C is not the answer.

Choice D: $(-2)^3 - 6(-2)^2 - (-2) + 30 = 0$, $3^3 - 6(3)^2 - 3 + 30 = 0$ and $5^3 - 6(5)^2 - 5 + 30 = 0$, so choice D **could be** the answer.

Choice E: $(-1)^3 - 6(-1)^2 - (-1) + 30 = 24 \neq 0$, so choice E is not the answer.

The answer is D.

Graphing Calculator Tips:

By plugging in the expressions of $f(x)$ and $g(x)$ into the graphing calculator, we find that they intersect when x equals to -2, 3 and 5.

The answer is D.

28.   Answer: **E**

Coordinate Geometry (Medium)

In this question, we investigate the three straight lines independently first.

$y = x$ is a straight line with slope 1 and y-intercept 0. To find the corresponding inequality for the two regions separated by this line, we can pick an arbitrary point on one region and check the inequality as follows:

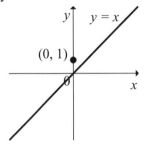

Taking $(0, 1)$ from the upper part of $y = x$, it is obvious that $1 > 0$ so we have $y > x$. Therefore, $y > x$ is the corresponding inequality for the upper region of $y > x$ while $y < x$ represents the lower region.

Let's use the similar approach for the two remaining lines.

$y = 2x$ is a straight line with slope 2 and y-intercept 0.

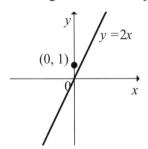

Taking $(0, 1)$ from the upper part of $y = 2x$, it is obvious that $1 > 2(0)$ so we have $y > 2x$. Therefore, $y > 2x$ is the corresponding inequality for the upper region of $y = 2x$, while $y < 2x$ represents the lower region.

Since $3x + 4y = 12 \Rightarrow 4y = -3x + 12 \Leftrightarrow y = \dfrac{-3}{4}x + 3$, it's a straight line going down with slope $\dfrac{-3}{4}x$ and y-intercept 3.

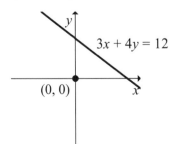

Taking $(0, 0)$ from the lower part of $3x + 4y = 12$, it is obvious that $3(0) + 4(0) < 12$ so we have $3x + 4y < 12$. Therefore, $3x + 4y < 12$ is the corresponding inequality for the lower region of $3x + 4y = 12$, while $3x + 4y > 12$ represents the upper region.

In the diagram given in the question, the region required is the intersection of the upper region of $y = x$, the lower region of $y = 2x$ and the lower region of $3x + 4y = 12$. Therefore, the corresponding inequalities are $y > x$, $y < 2x$ and $3x + 4y < 12$.

The answer is E.

29.　Answer: **C**
Functions (Medium)

By the definition of the absolute value function, we have the following:

$$|x-1| = \begin{cases} x-1 \\ -(x-1) = -x+1 \end{cases} \text{ if } \begin{array}{l} x-1 \geq 0 \Leftrightarrow x \geq 1 \\ x-1 < 0 \Leftrightarrow x < 1 \end{array}$$

Therefore, $y = \dfrac{|x-1|}{x} = \begin{cases} \dfrac{x-1}{x} = 1 - \dfrac{1}{x} & x \geq 1 \\[2mm] \dfrac{-x+1}{x} = -1 + \dfrac{1}{x} & x < 1 \end{cases}$ if

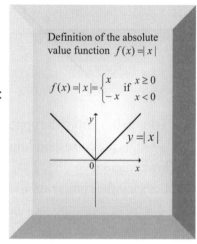

Definition of the absolute value function $f(x) = |x|$

$$f(x) = |x| = \begin{cases} x \\ -x \end{cases} \text{ if } \begin{array}{l} x \geq 0 \\ x < 0 \end{array}$$

$y = |x|$

In order to find the range of y, we need to consider the cases for $x \geq 1$ and $x < 1$ separately. For $x \geq 1$:

$$x \geq 1 \Rightarrow 0 < \frac{1}{x} \leq 1 \Rightarrow 0 > -\frac{1}{x} \geq -1 \Rightarrow 1 > 1 - \frac{1}{x} \geq 0 \Rightarrow 1 > y \geq 0$$

For $x < 1$, we need to check the following two cases:

$$0 < x < 1 \Rightarrow \frac{1}{x} > 1 \Rightarrow -1 + \frac{1}{x} > 0 \Rightarrow y > 0$$

$$x < 0 \Rightarrow \frac{1}{x} < 0 \Rightarrow -1 + \frac{1}{x} < -1 \Rightarrow y < -1$$

(Note: $x = 0$ is not included here because it is not in the domain.)

Combining the results above, the range of y is $y < -1$ or $y \geq 0$.

The answer is C.

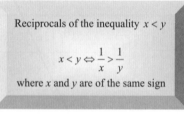

Reciprocals of the inequality $x < y$

$$x < y \Leftrightarrow \frac{1}{x} > \frac{1}{y}$$

where x and y are of the same sign

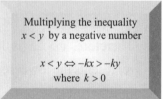

Multiplying the inequality $x < y$ by a negative number

$$x < y \Leftrightarrow -kx > -ky$$

where $k > 0$

Graphing Calculator Tips:

You can input the given function into your graphing calculator directly and find the range of y is $y < -1$ or $y \geq 0$.

The answer is C.

---

30.   Answer: **A**

Functions (Medium)

Since $a > 0$, $f(x) = ax^2 + bx + c$ is a parabola opening upward; that is, the vertex is its minimum value. By the formula for finding the vertex (maximum/minimum) of a quadratic function, the

minimum is $f\left(-\dfrac{b}{2a}\right)$.

The answer is A.

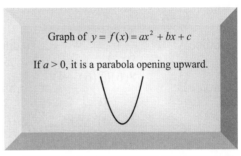

Graph of $y = f(x) = ax^2 + bx + c$

If $a > 0$, it is a parabola opening upward.

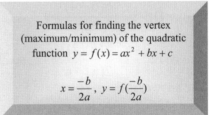

Formulas for finding the vertex (maximum/minimum) of the quadratic function $y = f(x) = ax^2 + bx + c$

$$x = \frac{-b}{2a}, \ y = f(\frac{-b}{2a})$$

---

31.   Answer: **A**

Coordinate Geometry (Medium)

With r equal to 0, it means that the distance between the origin and the points on the graph is always 0. Only the origin satisfies this condition, so the graph of $r = 0$ is just a single point.

The answer is A.

---

32.   Answer: **E**

Algebra (Medium)

For the away trip, the time used is $\dfrac{l}{x}$ hours.

For the return trip, the time used is $\dfrac{l}{x - 4}$ hours.

Since it is given that the total time used is t hours, we have

$$\frac{l}{x} + \frac{l}{x-4} = t \Rightarrow l(\frac{1}{x} + \frac{1}{x-4}) = t \Rightarrow l(\frac{x-4+x}{x(x-4)}) = t \Rightarrow l(\frac{2x-4}{x(x-4)}) = t \Rightarrow l = \frac{tx(x-4)}{2x-4}$$

The answer is E.

435

Plugging-in Tips:

Taking arbitrary numbers as the values of l and x, we can find the value of t. Then we can plug the values into the given expression and find the answer directly. Let's take l and x to be 12 and 6, respectively. Then, the time used for the away trip is $\dfrac{12}{6} = 2$ hours, and the time used for the return trip is $\dfrac{12}{6-4} = 6$ hours. Therefore, $t = 2 + 6 = 8$.

Choice A: $\dfrac{8(6)}{6-4} = 24 \neq 12$, so choice A is not the answer.

Choice B: $\dfrac{8(6)(2(6)-4)}{6-1} = 76.8 \neq 12$, so choice B is not the answer.

Choice C: $\dfrac{8(2(6)-4)}{6} = 10.67 \neq 12$, so choice C is not the answer.

Choice D: $\dfrac{6(6-4)}{8} = 1.5 \neq 12$, so choice D is not the answer.

Choice E: $\dfrac{8(6)(2)}{2(6)-4} = 12$, so choice E **could be** the answer.

The answer is E.

33. Answer: **E**

Functions (Medium)

If $f(x, y) = (x, y)$, then we have

$$(x+y, x-y) = (x, y) \Rightarrow \begin{cases} x+y = x \\ x-y = y \end{cases} \Rightarrow \begin{cases} y = 0 \\ x = 2y \end{cases} \Rightarrow x = y = 0$$

Therefore, the only point satisfying the equation is $(0, 0)$.

The answer is E.

34. Answer: **E**

Miscellaneous (Medium)

Given that p and q are even integers, let's check the expressions in the choices directly to see which one must be odd.

Choice A: The sum of two even integers must be even, so choice A is not the answer.

Choice B: The difference of two even integers must be even, so choice B is not the answer.

Choice C: The product of two even integers must be even, so choice C is not the answer.

Choice D: The quotient of a general even integer divided by another general even integer cannot be determined to be odd or even, so choice D is not the answer.

Choice E: Since $p+1$ and $q-1$ are odd and the product of odd integers must be odd, we know choice E **could be** the answer.

The answer is E.

Plugging-in Tips:

Taking arbitrary even numbers as the values of p and q, we can plug them into the expressions given in the choices and find the answer directly. Let's take p and q to be 12 and 16, respectively.

Choice A: $12+16 = 28$ is even, so choice A is not the answer.

Choice B: $12-16 = -4$ is even, so choice B is not the answer.

Choice C: $12 \times 16 = 192$ is even, so choice C is not the answer.

Choice D: $\dfrac{12}{16} = \dfrac{3}{4}$ is not an integer, so choice D is not the answer.

Choice E: $(12+1)(16-1) = 195$ is odd, so choice E **could be** the answer.

The answer is E.

35.   Answer: **B**
Trigonometry (Medium)

The shaded area is

(the area of the sector) – (the area of the triangle) $= \dfrac{1^2\theta}{2} - \dfrac{1}{2}(1)(1)\sin\theta = \dfrac{\theta}{2} - \dfrac{\sin\theta}{2} = \dfrac{1}{2}(\theta - \sin\theta)$

The answer is B.

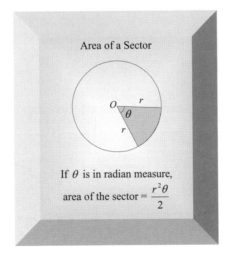

Area of a Sector

If θ is in radian measure,

area of the sector $= \dfrac{r^2\theta}{2}$

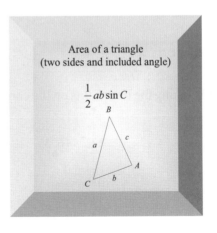

Area of a triangle
(two sides and included angle)

$\dfrac{1}{2}ab\sin C$

36.   Answer: **C**
Probability & Statistics (Medium)

After the addition of the new players, there are a total of 16 players. In order to get the new average height of the whole team, we need to divide the new sum of the heights by the new total number of players, that is, $\dfrac{190 \times 12 + 185 \times 4}{16} = 188.75$.

The answer is C.

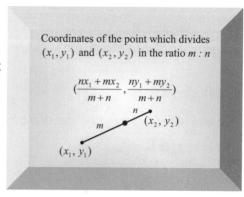

Definition of average (arithmetic mean)

total sum of the numbers in the set divided by number of items in the set

Common Mistake:

Some of you may try to get the new average height by just doing $\dfrac{190 + 185}{2} = 187.5$. **Be careful!**

What we need is to divide the new sum of heights by the new **TOTAL** number of players. Here, we have the total number of players as 16 instead of 2!

37.   Answer: **B**
Coordinate Geometry (Medium)

Method 1:

By the formula for finding the coordinates of the point which divides (x_1, y_1) and (x_2, y_2) in the ratio $m : n$, the required coordinates are

$(\dfrac{1(6) + 3(6)}{3 + 1}, \dfrac{1(-9) + 3(3)}{3 + 1}) = (6, 0)$.

The answer is B.

Coordinates of the point which divides (x_1, y_1) and (x_2, y_2) in the ratio $m : n$

$(\dfrac{nx_1 + mx_2}{m + n}, \dfrac{ny_1 + my_2}{m + n})$

Method 2:

Sketching the two points on the coordinate plane, we have the following:

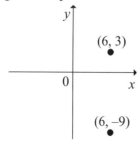

It is obvious that the two points lie on a vertical line where they are 12 units apart. In order to find the point that divides the segment in the ratio 3 : 1, we first need to divide the line into 4 equal parts; that is, 3 units per part. Then, we can have the following:

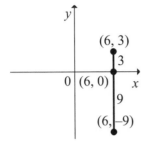

Therefore, the coordinates of the required point are $(6, 0)$.

The answer is B.

38.   Answer: **D**

Algebra (Medium)

For this question, if we check each inequality carefully, we will find that the inequality must hold for choice D. Since we have $a < b$ and $b < c$, then $a < b < c$, that is, we have $a < c$ and $b < c$. By adding up the two inequalities, we set $a + b < 2c$, which is exactly the same as choice D. For the other choices, we can always find some values for the unknowns that do not satisfy the inequality. The answer is D.

Plugging-in Tips:

Taking arbitrary numbers as the values of a, b and c, we can plug them into the expressions in the choices and see which inequality does not hold. Let's take $a = 1$, $b = 2$ and $c = 3$ here. Then,

Choice A: LHS = $2 + 3 = 5$, RHS = $2(1) = 2$.
            The inequality does not hold, so choice A is not the answer.
Choice B: LHS = $1 + 2 = 3$, RHS = 3.
            The inequality does not hold, so choice B is not the answer.
Choice C: LHS = $2 - 1 = 1$, RHS = $3 - 2 = 1$.
            The inequality does not hold, so choice C is not the answer.
Choice D: LHS = $1 + 2 = 3$, RHS = $2(3) = 6$.
            The inequality holds, so choice D **could be** the answer.
Choice E: LHS = $1 + 3 = 4$, RHS = $2(2) = 4$.
            The inequality does not hold, so choice E is not the answer.

The answer is D.

39.   Answer: **A**
Trigonometry (Medium)

Given that $\sin x > 0$ and $\cos x < 0$, by the "CAST" rule, we know that x must be in Quadrant II; that is, $\tan x$ must be negative. Then, by the calculator we have $\tan(\sin^{-1}\frac{12}{13}) = \frac{12}{5}$. But we $\tan x$ must be negative; therefore, $\tan x$ has to be $-\frac{12}{5}$. The answer is A.

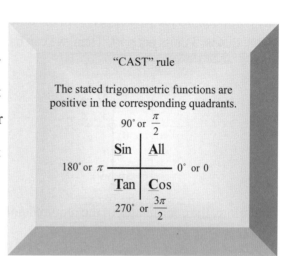

"CAST" rule

The stated trigonometric functions are positive in the corresponding quadrants.

40.   Answer: **C**
Miscellaneous (Easy)

Since there is a constant difference between consecutive terms, the given sequence is an arithmetic sequence. Here, the first term is 50 and the common difference is -3. Therefore, the 20th term is $50 + (20 - 1)(-3) = -7$.
The answer is C.

n^{th} term of an arithmetic sequence

$$a_n = a + (n - 1)d$$
a denotes the first term
d denotes the common difference
a_n denotes the nth term

41.   Answer: **B**
Solid Geometry (Medium)

We can calculate the distance between points as follows:
$$AB = \sqrt{(-1-1)^2 + (2-(-2))^2 + (-3-3)^2} = \sqrt{56} = 7.48...$$
$$AC = \sqrt{(-1-(-1))^2 + (2-(-2))^2 + (-3-3)^2} = \sqrt{52} = 7.21...$$
$$BC = \sqrt{(1-(-1))^2 + (-2-(-2))^2 + (3-3)^2} = 2$$
The shortest distance is BC and its length is 2.
The answer is B.

Distance between two points (x_1, y_1, z_1) and (x_2, y_2, z_2) in the xyz-space

$$\sqrt{(x_1 - x_2)^2 + (y_1 - y_2)^2 + (z_1 - z_2)^2}$$

42.   Answer: **C**
Trigonometry (Medium)

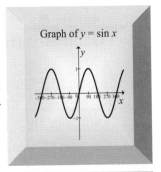

Graph of $y = \sin x$

From the graphs of the trigonometric functions, we can see that in the given range of x, only the graphs of $\cos x$ and $\tan x$ are increasing. Only statements I and III are true.

The answer is C.

Plugging-in Tips:

Let's plug $200°$ and $220°$ into a and b to see which of the statements given is/are true.

I $\cos 200° = -0.93...$, $\cos 220° = -0.76...$, so we have
$\cos 200° < \cos 220°$, statement I is true.

II $\sin 200° = -0.34...$, $\sin 220° = -0.64...$, so we have
$\sin 200° > \sin 220°$, statement II is not true.

III $\tan 200° = 0.36...$, $\tan 220° = 0.83...$, so we have
$\tan 200° < \tan 220°$, statement III is true.

Only statements I and III are true.

The answer is C.

Graph of $y = \cos x$

Graph of $y = \tan x$

43.   Answer: **D**
Probability & Statistics (Hard)

We want to have 3 heads and 2 tails from 5 coins, so the number of combinations would be C_3^5 (or you can say that it is C_2^5, it is the same number, as you can check!). The probability of getting a head is 0.3, so the probability of getting a tail is $1 - 0.3 = 0.7$; therefore, the probability of each combination of 3 heads and 2 tails is $(0.3)^3 (0.7)^2$. So, the overall probability would be $C_3^5 (0.3)^3 (0.7)^2 = 0.1323$

The answer is D.

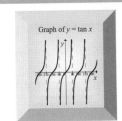

The number of ways (combinations) of selecting r items from n distinct items

$$_nC_r \text{ or } C_r^n = \frac{n!}{(n-r)!\,r!}$$

44. Answer: **B**
Solid Geometry (Hard)

In order to find the volume of the space between the sphere and the cube, we need to find the volumes of the sphere and the cube and then take the difference between them.

Given that the radius of the sphere is 6, its diameter is 12. Knowing that the cube is inscribed in the sphere, we know that the longest distance measured in the cube will also be 12. Since, in a cube, each side is the same, by using the formula of the longest distance measured in a box, we have

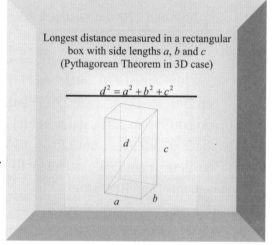

Relationship between a cube and a sphere where the cube is inscribed in the sphere

Diameter of the sphere
= Longest distance (diagonal) measured in the cube
= Diagonal of the cube

Longest distance measured in a rectangular box with side lengths a, b and c
(Pythagorean Theorem in 3D case)

$$d^2 = a^2 + b^2 + c^2$$

$$12 = \sqrt{a^2 + a^2 + a^2} \Rightarrow 144 = 3a^2 \Rightarrow a = \sqrt{48}$$

(Here, we only need to take the positive root of a because length must be positive.)

So, the volume of the cube is $(\sqrt{48})^3$. On the other hand, the volume of the sphere is $\frac{4}{3}\pi r^3 = \frac{4}{3}\pi 6^3 = 288\pi$. Therefore, the volume of the space between the sphere and the cube is

$$288\pi - (\sqrt{48})^3 = 572.224... = 572.22 \text{ (correct to}$$
2 decimal places.)

The answer is B.

45. Answer: **C**
Miscellaneous (Medium)

In this question, we can express $f(x)$ as follows:

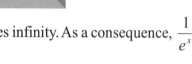

Meaning of x^{-n}

$$x^{-n} = \frac{1}{x^n}$$

$$f(x) = e^{-x} = \frac{1}{e^x}$$

We know that when x approaches infinity, e^x also approaches infinity. As a consequence, $\frac{1}{e^x}$ approaches 0.

The answer is C.

Calculator Tips:

From the question, we know that x approaches infinity, so we can pick x to be 10, 100, 1,000,......
and substitute the values into $f(x)$ to get

$f(10) = 4.54 \times 10^{-5}$

$f(100) = 3.72 \times 10^{-44}$

$f(1,000) = 0$ (that is, the answer is less than 10^{-99}, the accuracy level of the calculator)

From the above calculation, we can see that $f(x)$ approaches 0 when x approaches infinity.

The answer is C.

46.   Answer: **C**

Functions (Medium)

The graph of the function has the x-intercepts at $\dfrac{1}{2}$ and 2, so $h(x)$ must have the factors

$(x - \dfrac{1}{2})(x - 2)$ or $(2x - 1)(x - 2)$. All the choices here have these two factors, so this information
does not help us. So we next focus on the y-intercept; it is 4. Therefore, we should have $f(0) = 4$.

By putting 0 into the given choices, we get

Choice A: $-0.5(2(0) - 1)(0 - 2)^2 = 2 \neq 4$, so choice A is not the answer.

Choice B: $-0.5(2(0) - 1)(0 - 2)^3 = -4 \neq 4$, so choice B is not the answer.

Choice C: $0.5(2(0) - 1)(0 - 2)^3 = 4$, so choice C **could be** the answer.

Choice D: $0.5(2(0) - 1)^2(0 - 2)^3 = -4 \neq 4$, so choice D is not the answer.

Choice E: $(2(0) - 1)^2(0 - 2)^2 = 4$, so choice E **could be** the answer.

Now we have two possible choices, C and E. If we observe carefully, choice E can be expressed
as $[(2x - 1)(x - 2)]^2$. It can never be negative, which would violate the conditions of the given
graph, so choice E cannot be the answer.

The answer is C.

Graphing Calculator Tips:

You can input the expressions given in each of the choices into the graphing calculator to find that
the expression in choice C generates the same graph as given in the question.

The answer is C.

47.   Answer: **E**
Miscellaneous (Hard)

$$\frac{(a-2)!-(a-3)!}{(a-1)!} = \frac{[(a-2)\times(a-3)\times(a-4)\times....\times2\times1]-[(a-3)\times(a-4)\times....\times2\times1]}{(a-1)\times(a-2)\times(a-3)\times(a-4)\times....\times2\times1}$$

$$= \frac{[(a-3)\times(a-4)\times....\times2\times1]\times(a-2-1)}{(a-1)\times(a-2)\times[(a-3)\times(a-4)\times....\times2\times1]}$$

$$= \frac{a-3}{(a-1)(a-2)} = \frac{a-3}{a^2-3a+2}$$

The answer is E.

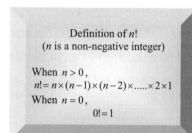

Definition of $n!$
(n is a non-negative integer)

When $n>0$,
$n! = n\times(n-1)\times(n-2)\times.....\times2\times1$
When $n=0$,
$$0!=1$$

Plugging-in Tips:

Taking an arbitrary number as the value of a, we can plug it into the given expression and find

the answer directly. Let's take a to be 7. Then, $\dfrac{(7-2)!-(7-3)!}{(7-1)!} = 0.133$.

Choice A: $\dfrac{7-3}{7^2-2(7)} = 0.114 \neq 0.133$, so choice A is not the answer.

Choice B: $\dfrac{7-2}{7^2-2(7)-1} = 0.147 \neq 0.133$, so choice B is not the answer.

Choice C: $\dfrac{7-2}{7^2-2(7)-3} = 0.156 \neq 0.133$, so choice C is not the answer.

Choice D: $\dfrac{7-3}{7^2-2(7)-3} = 0.125 \neq 0.133$, so choice D is not the answer.

Choice E: $\dfrac{7-3}{7^2-3(7)+2} = 0.133$, so choice E **could be** the answer.

The answer is E.

48.   Answer: **A**
Probability & Statistics (Medium)

It is given that $\dfrac{4}{7}$ of the students took the easy mathematics test, so $1-\dfrac{4}{7}=\dfrac{3}{7}$ of the students

took the hard one. Therefore, the percent of the students in the group who did not pass the test is

$$\frac{4}{7}\times(1-80\%)+\frac{3}{7}(1-33\frac{1}{3}\%) = 40\%$$

The answer is A.

49. Answer: **D**
Coordinate Geometry (Hard)

The equation of the circle centered at $(-3, 4)$ with radius 5 is

$(x-(-3))^2+(y-4)^2=5^2 \Rightarrow (x+3)^2+(y-4)^2=25$

Using the conversion formulas between Cartesian coordinates and polar coordinates, the above equation can be transformed as follows:

$$(x+3)^2+(y-4)^2=25$$
$$(r\cos\theta+3)^2+(r\sin\theta-4)^2=25$$
$$r^2\cos^2\theta+6r\cos\theta+9+r^2\sin^2\theta-8r\cos\theta+16=25$$
$$r^2(\cos^2\theta+\sin^2\theta)+6r\cos\theta-8r\sin\theta=0$$
$$r^2(1)+6r\cos\theta-8r\sin\theta=0$$
$$r(r+6\cos\theta-8\sin\theta)=0$$
$$r+6\cos\theta-8\sin\theta=0$$

The answer is D.

Identities for the squares $(a+b)^2$ and $(a-b)^2$

$$(a+b)^2=a^2+2ab+b^2$$
$$(a-b)^2=a^2-2ab+b^2$$

Conversion between Cartesian coordinates and polar coordinates

polar $\Rightarrow$ Cartesian :
$x=r\cos\theta, y=r\sin\theta$
Cartesian $\Rightarrow$ polar :
$r=\sqrt{x^2+y^2}, \theta=\tan^{-1}\dfrac{y}{x}$

Trigonometric identity for the sum of squares of sin and cos

$$\sin^2\theta+\cos^2\theta=1$$

50. Answer: **A**
Algebra (Hard)

By the definition of absolute value function $|x|$, we have

$|2-x|=\begin{cases}2-x\\-2+x\end{cases}$ if $\begin{matrix}2-x\geq0\Leftrightarrow x\leq2\\2-x<0\Leftrightarrow x>2\end{matrix}$

$|2x-1|=\begin{cases}2x-1\\-2x+1\end{cases}$ if $\begin{matrix}2x-1\geq0\Leftrightarrow x\geq\frac{1}{2}\\2x-1<0\Leftrightarrow x<\frac{1}{2}\end{matrix}$

Therefore, we need to separate the real numbers into the following intervals to analyze the given inequality:

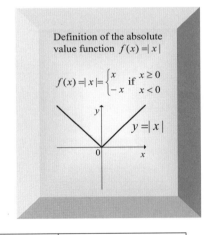

Definition of the absolute value function $f(x)=|x|$

$$f(x)=|x|=\begin{cases}x & \text{if } x\geq0\\-x & x<0\end{cases}$$

$y=|x|$

Separation of Intervals	$x<\dfrac{1}{2}$	$\dfrac{1}{2}\leq x\leq2$	$2<x$
Calculation	$\begin{matrix}\|2-x\|>\|2x-1\|\\\Leftrightarrow 2-x>-2x+1\\\Leftrightarrow x>-1\end{matrix}$	$\begin{matrix}\|2-x\|>\|2x-1\|\\\Leftrightarrow 2-x>2x-1\\\Leftrightarrow 1>x\end{matrix}$	$\begin{matrix}\|2-x\|>\|2x-1\|\\\Leftrightarrow -2+x>2x-1\\\Leftrightarrow -1>x\end{matrix}$
Result	$-1<x<\dfrac{1}{2}$	$\dfrac{1}{2}\leq x<1$	No solution

Combining the above results, we have $-1 < x < 1$.
The answer is A.

Graphing Calculator Tips:

You can input the two given absolute value functions directly into the graphing calculator to get the following graphs:

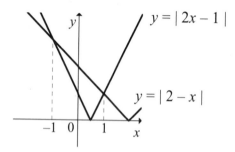

In order to have $|2 - x| > |2x - 1|$, we must have $-1 < x < 1$.
The answer is A.